Factbook
on Man

FACTBOOK on MAN

From Birth
to Death

Second Edition

Louis I. Dublin, Ph.D.

Second Vice-President and Statistician (Retired)
Metropolitan Life Insurance Company, New York

The Macmillan Company, New York
Collier-Macmillan Limited, London

Preface to
the Second Edition

The favorable reception given the first edition of this book, and, more especially, the marked changes which have taken place in the United States in the 15 years since its publication, have provided the author with adequate reasons for undertaking a revision of the volume. Particularly encouraging have been the many urgent inquiries from demographers, sociologists, public health administrators, statisticians, educators, social workers, and newspapermen as to when a new edition would be available. Fortunately, the completion of the 1960 census and the early publication of the results, together with the steady flow of reports from other governmental agencies, have facilitated this many-sided operation. It is hoped that this new compilation will serve, like its predecessor, the growing number of students and workers who are concerned with the basic facts of human life.

The organization of this second edition is similar to that of its predecessor, in that the data are presented in question-and-answer form. Experience has proved the value of this approach. The questions and answers are brief and specific, and bear on some essential item for the understanding of the subject matter of the chapter, whether it be population, the family, births, deaths, illness and its care, the problems of infancy and childhood, longevity, or the effects of war. Most readers, it has been found, have some particular question in mind when they use the volume; thus, the detailed index makes it easy to turn directly to the answer.

The aim, however, has been to do more than answer the 1,001 questions which have been asked. In fact, the questions were so chosen and arranged as to give the reader who has the courage to plow through a whole chapter a coherent outline and summary of the main theme under discussion. In this way many who use the book as an introduction to the subject may be led to more intensive study at a later date. Thus, the author's goal has been to serve two purposes: namely, to answer immediate questions as well as to supply an overall review of those areas of interest in the life of man with which sociologists are concerned, and with those special fields of health and welfare covered by government (those areas which, in the last analysis, are the concern of all educated and progressive citizens). According to many readers, the major value of the book has been the comprehensive view it presents of the many-sided activities of man in a complex society; the problems he encounters in his individual, family, and group life; how these problems have been solved, in whole or in part; the main trends; and what still remains for active consideration—whether these be in the areas of medical care, social security legislation, or control of the major diseases of mankind.

As might be expected, a number of difficulties have been encountered in the process of revising at this time. It has not been easy to keep pace with the steady flow of data from the official sources; no sooner have some chapters been rewritten than the figures for a later year have come to hand, necessitating continued revisions even during the period of proofreading. In addition, unlike its predecessor, which was a joint project with the author's many skillful associates in the Statistical Bureau of the Metropolitan Life Insurance Company, this revision has been a one-man operation to a large extent. This has necessitated delay in the completion of the task. But in one sense such delay has also had its advantages, for this has extended the period covered and permitted the study of trends in the data over a longer period of years. It is hoped that this will add to the value of the information presented.

The very fact of the author's retirement from the Metropolitan Life has made it necessary to turn more and more to friends and co-workers in the various governmental bureaus and in the many voluntary health and welfare associations. They are experts in the material which is the very essence of this book. Not only has the author asked them for specific information that is difficult to find in printed sources, but, even more important, he has looked to them to review whole chapters in their fields of special competence.

It would be impossible to do justice to all who have helped make this revision a reality. There are just too many to list individually. The author is grateful to all of them, but he must first acknowledge his debt to his old colleagues in the Metropolitan, who have left their mark on this work as well as on its predecessor. In addition, the following persons are singled out for acknowledgment:

Dr. Theodore S. Woolsey, Deputy Director, National Center for Health Statistics, U.S. Public Health Service

Dr. Edward T. Blomquist, Chief, Tuberculosis Program, U.S. Public Health Service

Dr. Harold S. Diehl, Senior Vice-President for Research, American Cancer Society

Mr. Richard Connelly, Executive Director, American Diabetes Association

Dr. Dean E. Krueger, Statistician, National Heart Institute, U.S. Public Health Service

Dr. Perry A. Lambird, School Health Section, Bureau of State Services, U.S. Public Health Service

Dr. Nathan W. Shock, Chief, Gerontology Branch, U.S. Public Health Service

Mr. R. L. Forney and Mr. H. Gene Miller, National Safety Council

Dr. Ewan Clague, Commissioner, and Mr. R. J. Myers, Bureau of Labor Statistics

Mr. Harry Milt, Director of Public Relations, National Association for Mental Health

Dr. Paul Q. Peterson, Assistant Surgeon General, U.S. Public Health Service

Miss Lenore A. Epstein, Deputy Director, Division of Research, Social Security Administration

Dr. Stanhope Bayne-Jones, formerly Chairman, Editorial Board, U.S. Army Medical History Program

These leaders in their respective fields have added greatly to the value of the book. They have helped the author detect errors; they have supplied the latest figures and have often suggested more constructive lines of approach. Nevertheless, in a work of this size and scope many slips will turn up to plague the author. For these and other limitations of the book he alone must be held responsible; for what is worthwhile, he gladly shares the credit with the small army of collaborators who have made these last years a rich and rewarding experience.

Louis I. Dublin

February, 1965

Preface to
the First Edition

A lifetime in the field of human biology, over forty years of which have been in the service of life insurance, has brought rich opportunities to observe and study a wide range of facts relating to man's health and welfare. It has been my good fortune during this long period to direct a staff of skilled workers with whose help a wealth of data has been compiled and analyzed. A large life insurance company like the Metropolitan, which is intimately concerned with the well-being of its policyholders and the communities in which they live, has use for such information in the conduct of its business. It has, moreover, as a public service, made such data generally available. The modes of dissemination have been many. Several hundred articles have been published in both the scientific and popular press. Many addresses have been made before scientific societies, and a number of books have been written that have brought together special areas of knowledge. A popular summary of our current studies is presented in our monthly *Statistical Bulletin,* now in its thirty-second year.

Our publications have been favored with a wide circle of readers representing both the general public and the technical world. Over the years we have received a great number of inquiries from individuals, business and industry, and various public agencies. There is a perennial interest in the facts that touch human life closely. The questions have been on such a variety of topics as population, birth, marriage, health, longevity, and the factors influencing them. This volume has been suggested by this far-flung correspondence. Many of the questions are taken directly from our files. It is hoped that this compilation of questions and answers will meet the needs of the large number who seek information on the topics covered.

The question-and-answer technique adopted here has the obvious advantage of quick and ready reference for the occasional inquirer. The detailed and comprehensive index will facilitate finding the answers to specific queries. At the same time, the requirements of those who may wish a more rounded exposition of the main topics have not been overlooked. The questions and answers for each chapter have been so selected and arranged as to cover the ground fairly broadly. Those who read through a whole chapter should find themselves well informed on the main points, at least. For readers whose appetites are whetted to study further, a list of selected references is given at the end of the volume. The book, in short, should be of interest to those who read to satisfy their curiosity as well as for those professionally concerned with the health and welfare of the American people. It is hoped that physicians, health and social workers, teachers and students of sociology and biology will find the volume useful.

Obviously a book of this type cannot hope to embrace the entire field of human biology; it does attempt, however, to cover a broad range of topics of current general interest. In the nature of the case, too, it is not the product of one mind. It represents rather the coordinated effort of the staff of the Statistical Bureau of the Metropolitan Life Insurance Company. It is a pleasure to acknowledge my indebtedness to a group of devoted colleagues and particularly to Mr. Mortimer Spiegelman, my collaborator, Mr. Herbert Marks,

Mr. Robert Vane, Mr. Henry Klein, Mr. Paul Jacobson, Miss Elizabeth Steele, and Mrs. Alice Beckwith. I acknowledge also my obligation to many friends and co-workers outside the office who have helped in reading and checking particular chapters. They are too many to name individually, but all of them have my heartfelt thanks.

Louis I. Dublin

October 1, 1951

Contents

Chapter 1

Who We Are—
The Population

1. What is the population of the world?

There are nearly, 3,300,000,000 persons living in the world today In the two centuries from 1650 to 1850 the population had doubled; and in the last 100 years it has doubled again. It is probable that it will double a second time by the year 2000. In some regions, particularly Northwestern Europe, the rate of population growth has fallen off materially. On the other hand, in other regions such as South America and Asia the rate of population growth is very high.

2. What part of the world population lives in the United States?

About 6 percent of the people in the world live in the United States. This country had a population of about 192,000,000 in mid-

1964. The United States is the fourth ranking nation in the world with respect to population, being outnumbered by mainland China with about 730,000,000; by India with about 460,000,000; and the USSR, which had about 225,000,000 inhabitants in mid-1963. Asia is by far the most populous continent; it is the home of more than half the world's people. Europe, including Soviet Russia, has 21 percent; North America about 9 percent; Africa close to 8 percent; South America about 5 percent; and Oceania, including Australia and New Zealand, about one-half of 1 percent.

3. How fast is the United States growing?

The increase in the number of people in the United States has been greater in recent years than in any comparable period of our history, although the rate of growth is much less than a century ago. When the United States was a new country, the population grew with phenomenal speed—as much as 3.5 percent a year. Now, with the total more than 47 times as large as in the first census in 1790, the rate of increase is down to about 1.7 percent a year. During the Depression years of the 1930's it averaged only about 0.7 percent per annum, a rate which, if continued, foreshadowed a stationary or even a declining population.

The decline in the rate of growth has been due in part to the cut in immigration and to the long-term decline in the birth rate. With our present population, immigration would have to reach nearly 2,000,000 a year, or about 12 times the total annual quota, to assume the relative importance it had 60 years ago. The birth rate, which had fallen to the lowest point in our history during the 1930's, rose sharply after World War II to a high of 25.8 per 1,000 per annum in 1947 but declined gradually to 21.6 in 1963.

4. How big is our population likely to be by the close of the century?

The current growth of the population largely reflects the fairly high birth rate of recent years, coupled with low mortality. In the 10-year period 1951 to 1960, nearly 41,000,000 babies were born, or an average in excess of 4,000,000 per year. This high figure is being maintained and will probably be continued for some time in the future, though the birth rate itself may decline somewhat further. If present trends continue, the best indications are that our population will rise to approximately 350,000,000 by the end of this century.

5. Has America's population grown faster than Europe's?

In the last 160 years the United States has grown at a more rapid rate than most countries of the world. The majority of nations in Northwestern and North Central Europe have been headed for a stationary, or even a declining population. France, for example, from the middle of the nineteenth century has increased only from about 35,000,000 to about 45,400,000 in 1960. During the five-year period from 1936 to 1940, the number of deaths in France exceeded the number of births. In more recent years, however, the population has been rising slowly. Ireland shows a current decline, and even Spain and Italy show rates of increase from only one-half to one percent per annum. The United States and the USSR are both growing at about the same as the world's rate.

6. What region of the world has the greatest prospect of population increase?

Asia has the potentiality for the largest increase in population. Most countries in that area still have some of the highest birth rates in the world; and if improved sanitary and health conditions bring reductions in mortality, while fertility remains at high levels, the population will certainly rise sharply. It is estimated that in such circumstances the population of China could reach about 1.6 billion and that of India one billion in the next 40 years, or double their present figures. This is entirely possible since these two huge countries are increasing their productivity, improving their health conditions, and making every effort to raise the standard of living of their people. The only question is whether they will be able to encourage their enormous numbers to control their reproductivity— usually a slow and difficult task.

On the other hand, South American and Middle American countries, though smaller in numbers, have prospects of even greater increase in the rate of population growth. These countries have already benefited greatly in recent decades from improvement in their sanitary conditions, bringing their death rates to very low levels. At the same time birth rates have remained high, with the result that the rate of natural increase in many of these Latin American countries has risen to close to the highest in the world. Thus Costa Rica, with a birth rate in excess of 50 per 1,000 and a death rate of 8.5, has a rate of increase in excess of 4 percent per annum. In South

America, Brazil, Ecuador, and Venezuela likewise show annual rates of increase in excess of 3 percent.

It is entirely possible that if present conditions of natural increase continue, the population of the Latin American countries will double in the course of the next generation, or before the year 2000, and rise to a level of about 500 million people.

7. What country has been losing population for 100 years?

Ireland has been diminishing in numbers for a century. There were more than six and a half million inhabitants in Southern Ireland in 1840 and under three million in 1960. Poverty and food shortages forced large numbers of Irish to leave their homes, most of them coming to North America. Emigration accounted for part of the population decline, the fall in the birth rate contributing as well. Both these factors reflected difficult economic conditions. Recent reports, however, show increased industrialization and other improvements in economic and social conditions. These may well result in a change of trend with a good prospect for population increases in the future.

8. Has the United States grown more from immigration or natural increase?

In all, about 42 million immigrants have come into this country since 1820, but in no year have the net additions to population from immigration equaled those from births. Immigration played its largest role in the country's growth in the 1880's, when about two-fifths of the growth resulted from this source.

Only in a limited sense can it be said that natural increase has been more important than immigration in a country where almost all the inhabitants have ancestors of foreign origin. Shortly after the Revolution, this country had already built up a population of close to four million (3,929,000 in 1790). Since then it has been able to absorb a large flow of immigrants, who have contributed their share to the building of our country and who have left their imprint on our customs and idiom.

9. Is there a large foreign-born element in the United States today?

At present, only about 5 percent of the people of the United States were born in other countries. Within the last century the proportion of foreign-born in our population has never been higher than 15 percent. In other words, the native element of the population has never been less than 85 percent of the total. The number of foreign-born residents reached a peak of 14,204,149 in 1930, although their proportion had already dropped to 11.6 percent of the population. Since the 1930's the number of foreign-born has fallen rapidly, while the total population has greatly increased.

10. Is the foreign-born population older than the native population?

One reason why the foreign-born population is decreasing rapidly is that their age level is much higher than that of the general population. During the periods of peak immigration, the bulk of those who came in were adults. Because of the subsequent restrictions on immigration, the foreign-born today are largely the survivors of pre-World War I immigrants and are well along in years. In 1960, while the median age of the native population was 27.9 years, that of the foreign-born was 57.3, with corresponding differences in the death rates of the two groups.

11. From what countries have most immigrants come?

Though the United States is often considered an offspring of Great Britain, the fact is that for more than a century the majority of our immigrants have not come from Britain, but from the continent of Europe. Relatively few are from other American nations, from Asia, or from Africa.

According to the census of 1860, 39 percent of the foreign-born were from Ireland, 31 percent from Germany, 14 percent from Great Britain, and 7 percent from the Scandinavian and other Northwestern European countries. Since then, the whole center of immigration has moved toward Southern and Eastern Europe. At the time of the 1940 census, Italy was the leading country of origin of our foreign-born, followed, in order of numbers, by Russia, Germany, Canada and Newfoundland (largely of British, Irish, and French descent), Poland, Great Britain, Scandinavia, Ireland, and the countries of Central Europe. At the time of the 1960 census, Italy was the leading country of origin of our foreign-born, followed, in order of numbers, by Germany, Canada, United Kingdom, Poland, Russia, Scandinavia, South Ireland, and the countries of Central Europe.

12. What have been the chief restrictions on immigration?

Originally, the control of immigration was exercised by individual states. Since great differences in policy developed, in 1875 Congress took the power of regulation for the federal government by passing a law to exclude prostitutes and alien convicts. By now there is a long list of excluded classes, including those with various mental or physical defects or diseases, contract laborers, illiterates, and those undesirable for political reasons.

The quota system was not started until after World War I. Originally, the number allowed to come in was 358,000, but this figure was later reduced. Today the total is 156,487. The numerical barriers were designed not only to keep the totals low but also to favor the nations which had formerly been important sources of immigration. Britain was given by far the largest quota, Germany the second largest, and Ireland the third.

13. What are nonquota immigrants?

There are many classes of aliens admissible without regard to quotas, including natives of independent nations of the Western Hemisphere and practicing professors and ministers, all of whom may bring their spouses and minor children. The wives or husbands and unmarried minor children of American citizens married before January 1, 1948, are also admitted, provided they do not belong to the excluded Asiatic races. In recent years nonquota immigration, particularly from the Western Hemisphere, has been increasingly important, at times amounting to more than half of the total.

14. How many "war brides" were there?

Under a special law, the wives or husbands of members of the armed services and the children resulting from marriages overseas were admitted without respect to quotas and transported to this country by the government. A total of 119,693 persons came in under this act; 114,691 of them were war brides, 333 were husbands, and 4,669 children. About three-quarters of the admissions were from Europe, 35,415 of them from Great Britain. From Germany there were 13,983; from Italy, 9,551; France, 8,692; Australia, 6,829; China, 5,687; and Japan, 757. Canada contributed 7,523.

15. Are immigrants different now from 40 years ago?

The general character of our immigration has changed a great deal. Currently, many more women than men are coming to our shores, whereas a generation or two ago the sex ratio was the other way round. As in the past, the immigrants were concentrated in the younger adult ages.

Sizable numbers under 16 years suggest that many children come in as members of family groups. To a greater degree than in the past, we are now receiving professionals, skilled workmen, clerical workers, farmers, and farm managers, while relatively fewer aliens are domestics and unskilled laborers. Formerly many had farm backgrounds, but few went into farming here. At present special efforts are being made to bring in farmers and farm workers.

16. Are the foreign-born more prolific than American women?

This used to be true, largely because the foreign-born came from places where large families were part of the accepted tradition. In recent years, however, they are at the same level as native white women in regard to the number of children.

17. In what regions have the foreign-born settled?

Most foreign-born have remained in the coastal states, although isolated national groups have settled in central areas (the Scandinavians in Minnesota and Wisconsin, for instance). Many immigrants were attracted to the industrial sections of Michigan, Ohio, Indiana, and Illinois. According to the census of 1960, New England and the Middle Atlantic states have the highest percentages of foreign-born in their white populations. Altogether, they accounted for 47.6 percent of all the foreign-born. The North Central states have 24.0 percent of the foreign-born, and the Pacific Coast states 15.8 percent. The East South Central states (Kentucky, Tennessee, Mississippi, and Alabama) had the lowest proportion of foreign-born.

18. Are the foreign-born primarily city dwellers?

The United States has been in the process of urbanization for more than a century, and the foreign-born have accelerated the trend. Cities, of course, offered a wide variety of employment and also enabled the new immigrants to live among their own countrymen. In addition, immigrants landed in large cities and inertia may have been an important factor in holding them there. New York, for example, the nation's leading port of entry, still had in 1960 more than one and one-half million foreign-born residents, amounting to 20 percent of the city's population.

19. Has there been much emigration from the United States?

Most migrants from Europe have made America their home, but many have gone back to their homelands. During the heavy immigration years from 1910 to 1914, inclusive, when 5,175,000 immigrants were admitted, more than 1,440,000 persons, or slightly less than one for every three coming in, emigrated from this country. Immigration exceeded emigration every year except during the Depression period from 1932 through 1935.

20. What have been the major trends in internal migration?

Americans have traditionally been a mobile people. Between one-fifth and one-quarter of the native population recorded in every census for the last 100 years had been born in some state other than the one of residence at the time of the census. In 1960, almost 43 million persons in this country had moved away from the states where they were born. In that year, almost half of those aged five and older were living in houses different from the homes they had occupied five years before. The migration characteristically has been from East to West, from South to North, and from rural areas to cities. All kinds of movement are still continuing. More recently, there has been a great migration to the suburban fringes of cities.

21. What proportion of the nation now lives in cities?

In 1790, 19 out of every 20 Americans were rural residents; the United States was largely a nation of farmers. At present, only 30 out of every 100 Americans live in rural areas, and of those only one-quarter are farm residents. Instead of 1 out of 20, now 14 out of every 20 Americans are city folk. Over half of them live in communities of at least 100,000 inhabitants, and the rest in places with populations ranging from 2,500 to 100,000.

22. Have the large cities grown as fast as the country as a whole?

The large cities have grown faster. New York, which has had the largest population in the country ever since the Revolution, went from 49,401 inhabitants in 1790 to 7,781,984 in 1960, a growth nearly four times as fast as that of the nation as a whole. Philadelphia, second largest city in 1790 with 28,522 persons, had 2,002,512 in 1960. The first census listed only 24 communities having more than 2,500 residents; in 1960 there were 5,400 such places. Until the census of 1840, New York was the only city which had more than 100,000 inhabitants. The 1960 census showed that 132 cities had more than 100,000 inhabitants, and 633 more had between 25,000 and 100,000.

23. Was the rural-to-urban trend ever reversed?

One-third of the largest cities of the country lost population during the Depression of the 1930's. There was a slight reversal of the trend toward urbanization in the New England, Middle Atlantic, East North Central, and Pacific Coast states. These industrial sections were the hardest hit by the drop in business activity. Over the nation as a whole the movement from rural to urban areas continued during the decade of the 1930's although at a much diminished pace. In both 1930 and 1940, 56 percent of the population was recorded as urban. World War II again accelerated the migration toward cities, especially in the South and the Far West. Currently, as we have seen, about 70 percent of the population is urban.

24. What area gained the most population in recent years?

The three Pacific Coast states—California, Oregon, and Washington—showed the largest population increase; 43.2 percent from 1950 to 1960, while the nation as a whole gained only 18.5 percent. Before World War II the Far West had been primarily an agricultural, lumbering, and fishing area. During the 1940's, however, industrial plants, shipyards and aircraft factories were set up, and workers of every kind were drawn from other sections of the country, particularly from the Central areas and the South. The boom in the Far West did not stop with the end of the war. The Coast states are still growing at a faster rate than the other regions.

25. What area lost the most by migration?

The South has had the largest net loss from migration recently. Both the Mountain and West North Central states have also had more persons move out than move in.

Despite its loss of migrants, the South as a whole grew by 16.5 percent from 1950 to 1960. Over the decade a few scattered states showed declines in number; the decrease was 7.2 percent in West Virginia; 6.5 percent in Arkansas; and less than 1 percent in Mississippi.

26. What is the racial composition of the American population?

In 1960, 88.5 percent of the population was white; the rest (11.5 percent) nonwhite. Negroes, with 10.5 percent of the total of all races, constituted the largest group among the nonwhites. Most of the other nonwhites were Indians; the Chinese and Japanese are also important in this group, which includes a scattering of Filipinos, Hindus, Koreans, Hawaiians, and Malays.

27. Has there been much internal migration of Negroes?

Negroes in recent years have been migrating in increasing numbers. The long-term Negro movement has been from the South to the North, and in the last decades also to the West. This has accounted for a large part of the migration loss of the Southern states since 1940. Even in the Depression decade from 1930 through 1939 the South experienced a net loss from migration of nearly one and a half million colored persons. In addition to the intersectional movement there has also been a heavy migration of the colored population from farms to cities. In the South most Negroes now live in urban areas. Increasing industrialization, especially during the war and postwar period has been bringing more of them into urban districts. Postwar surveys reveal that a large number of Negro veterans (about three-quarters of whom were Southern) did not wish to return to their former homes.

28. Where is the center of our Negro population?

Despite the heavy out-migration from the South, five states from this region—North Carolina, Georgia, Alabama, Louisiana and Texas—still have about one million or more Negro inhabitants each; in addition, New York and Illinois now have that many Negro inhabitants. In no state does the Negro population equal the white. The closest to a one to one ratio was found in 1940 in Mississippi when there were 1,074,578 Negroes to 1,106,327 whites. The largest single Negro community is in New York City, where three-quarters of a million Negroes now live.

29. Has the Negro population been increasing as fast as the white?

Until recently, the Negro population of this country was not growing as fast as the white. In 1850, Negroes were around 16 percent of all the people of the United States; in 1940 the proportion was only 9.8 percent. One of the most important factors in this decline was the large influx of whites from European countries. During the Depression decade, however, Negroes increased slightly faster than whites; in the next decade increased further to 9.9 percent in

1950. Currently, Negroes have birth rates 50 percent higher than whites and have brought their death rate down close to the white level.

30. What is the ratio of men to women in this country?

In 1945, for the first time in American history, women outnumbered men. The ratio then was 996 men to 1,000 women. The ratio of males to females has been falling steadily for many years, and in the census of 1960 it was down to 978 men to 1,000 women.

31. Does the ratio of males to females in the population remain the same throughout life?

At birth there is about a 6 percent excess of males over females. However, males suffer a higher mortality at every age, so that the excess of males is gradually reduced. In any generation followed from birth, the males outnumber females up to about age 19. Beyond that age, females show an increasing excess.

32. Does the sex ratio vary with geographic region?

In general, the newer sections of the country, which grew largely from migration, had more males than females. In the West, for example, in 1910, there were 1,289 males to 1,000 females; in the Northeastern states, however, the ratio was only 1,023. In 1960, on the other hand, only the West had an excess of males over females, and by a bare margin.

33. How do the sex ratios of the white and colored populations compare?

There is considerable difference in the sex ratio between the white and nonwhite populations; among the former, there were 1,027 females for every 1,000 males in 1960, compared with 1,060 females for every 1,000 males among the latter. This results from the relatively higher mortality among nonwhite males than among nonwhite females.

34. What is the median age of the American population?

In 1820 the median age in the United States—the age level dividing the entire population in two equal-sized groups, one older and one younger than the median—was 16.7 years. In 1960 it was up to 29.5. There has been little change in the median age of the population in the last two decades.

35. What is meant by the expression "the aging population"?

That expression refers to the gradual concentration of persons in the older age groups of the population. In 1850, about 2.6 percent of the population was 65 years old or more; in 1940, about 6.8 percent, or approximately nine million persons, were in the old-age group. Even though there was a record increase in young children from 1940 to 1960, the proportion of the population aged 65 or more rose still further, to 9.0 percent or to a total of 16,560,000. (See Chart 1.) The number who are 65 years and over is increasing by more than 400,000 a year.

The aging of our population is a result of three factors. Improved health conditions are bringing more survivors to midlife and later. The long-term downward trend of the birth rate has brought a decrease in the proportion of young children over the years. Finally, young immigrants are no longer coming to us in great numbers as in decades ago.

36. What proportion of the population is old enough to vote?

With the aging of the population, the proportion old enough to vote has also increased. In 1910, about 51,555,000 persons (56 percent of the nation) were at least 21 years old; this included women

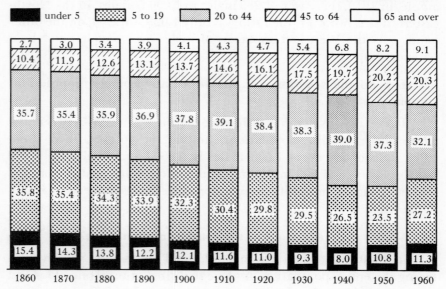

Chart 1. Percent distribution of total population by age, United States, 1860–1960.

who had not yet the right to vote. By the Presidential election year of 1960, the population old enough to vote had increased to more than 108,000,000, or over three-fifths of the country. Not all of them, however, had voting rights. About two million were adult aliens; others excluded were inmates of prisons and mental institutions.

37. What proportion of the population is in the school ages?

The school population has been declining in relative importance. In 1850, the proportion of the population at ages 5 to 19 was 37.4 percent; by 1940 it was only 26.4 percent. By 1950, when the war babies began to enter school, the school population began a proportional increase. The over-all change, however, for the period from 1940 to 1960 was a slight increase to 27.1 percent. In actual numbers, however, children of school age have increased to more than 48 million.

38. What are school enrollments likely to be in the next decade?

As the wave of war babies increased in age and passed through school, enrollments have risen. Since the birth rate has remained high for a number of years, this wave will be fairly long-drawn-out. By 1970, the population eligible for elementary, junior high, and high school is expected to reach close to 60 million. Elementary schools, the first to be affected, have already been hit by the increase in pupils and are suffering severe shortages in facilities and teachers. The high schools, likewise, are already overcrowded, and the wave of students is now reaching the colleges. We are now experiencing the second postwar crowding in secondary and higher educational institutions. The first was the rush of veterans to complete their education.

39. Have most adults in the United States had a high-school education?

In 1960, out of the population aged 25 or more, only 8.4 percent had had less than five years of schooling, but most of them could read and write. At the other end of the educational scale, 7.7 percent of the same age category had completed four years or more of college. About one-fourth of the adult population had finished high school.

The sexes differ in educational attainment. A greater proportion of men than women are found among those with limited schooling and also among those with college degrees. On the other hand, relatively more women than men complete high school.

40. What is the outlook for college attendance in the near future?

Recent surveys indicate that enrollment in our colleges and universities will continue to increase for some time in the future. The large numbers of boys and girls born in the immediate postwar years are now rapidly entering the college entrance ages. The uncertain question is whether the academic resources, physical and financial, necessary to absorb this large number of applicants, will be available.

41. What has been the trend of literacy in the United States?

Illiteracy has diminished until it is a small and localized problem in this country. In 1890, about one-seventh of the population aged 20 or more was unable to read and write. By 1930, the proportion had been reduced to around one-twentieth. In 1940, the Bureau of the Census gathered data on years of schooling instead of literacy. That year only a little over 3 percent of the population 20 or over had had no schooling at all. By 1959, the proportion of illiterate persons had been reduced to 2.2 percent, somewhat higher among males than among females. The problem is largely concentrated among the nonwhite people living in rural areas.

42. What states have the best records for schooling?

The Pacific Coast and Mountain states have the best record for schooling. In these two areas the median number of years of school completed by persons 14 years and over was 12.0 in 1960, compared with a national figure of 10.6. New England came next with 11.2 years. In the Pacific Coast states, 96.7 percent of the pupils enrolled attended daily as against 90.0 percent for the country.

School attendance has been rising steadily with the increasing urbanization of the country and the improvements in school transportation. The number of years of schooling per individual is highest in urban areas, almost as high among rural nonfarm residents, and lowest among farm residents. The need for a long education may seem less pressing on the farm since farm children begin to work at a much younger age than the children of city families.

43. What is the outlook for the size of the population of the United States?

The outlook is an optimistic one. But already our population experts are sounding a note of caution. The indications are that the population of the United States will reach 250 million by 1980 and 350 million by the end of this century. Fortunately, our material resources are such as to make possible a continuance of our high living standards. Nevertheless, there is a limit to population growth even in the most favored country, and the question will soon be asked whether we are wise enough as a nation to institute the necessary checks on our expansion in numbers before we begin seriously to threaten the well-being of our people.

Chapter 2

The Pattern
of Reproduction

1. What is the normal reproductive life of women?

On rare occasions, one reads of a girl who became a mother before reaching her teens, or of a woman who gave birth when she was nearing her sixties. Such happenings are curiosities, for the reproductive span of women usually begins about age 13 and ends around age 46 or 47. The beginning age of reproduction (age at menarche) has a rather narrow range of variation. On the other hand, the termination of the reproductive period (age at menopause) has a somewhat wider range of variation since the accompanying changes at this stage of life are not as sharply defined as at menarche. In the average case, the reproductive span of a woman's life is somewhat over 30 years. There is lacking good evidence of differences in the ages at menarche or at menopause between the various races of the world or the place of residence.

2. What is the normal reproductive life of men?

The reproductive life of men, especially toward the end, is much less sharply defined than for women. The birth records for the United States contain some pertinent figures in this connection. In 1960, there were only 82 fathers under 15 years of age, but about 6,780 such young mothers. In other words, the male reproductive period, as with females, begins near age 15; the difference in numbers reflects the fact that men are generally older than their wives. At the other end of the reproductive period, we find only 140 mothers of age 50 and over, but nearly 14,600 fathers at ages 55 and over. The much higher figure for older fathers than mothers indicates that there is no sudden or marked change in the reproductive capacity in the human male, but rather a long-term lessening of procreative power.

3. How many babies are born in the world each year?

We really have no precise answer to this question, since adequate birth records are not kept for most of the world. This is especially the case in underdeveloped countries, where we know, from indirect evidence, that birth rates are very high. Moreover, birth rates in such areas may fluctuate widely from year to year, depending upon epidemics, famines, and economic factors. A rough estimate would place the annual number of births in the world between 100 and 115 million. This means three births every second of the day. About three-fifths of the births are in Asia, one-eighth each in Europe and the Americas; and one-tenth in Africa.

4. How many babies are born annually in the United States and what is the birth rate?

The total number of live births in the United States during 1963, including both those recorded and not recorded, was about 4,081,000. With a midyear population of 189,300,000 for 1963, the crude birth rate comes to 21.6 per 1,000 population. The number of births reached a peak of 4,268,000 in 1961; this was over 80 percent higher than the low point of 2,307,000 births in 1933.

5. What is the average age of mothers at the birth of their children and how does the birth rate vary with age?

The average age of women at the birth of their children is 25.5 years, according to records for white mothers of the United States in 1960. For those becoming mothers for the first time, the average age is 21.5 years. One-third of the babies in 1960 were born to women at ages 20 to 24 and more than one-quarter to mothers 25 to 29 years. About half of the babies are born to fathers 20 to 29 years old. The ages of parents at the time their children are born are somewhat lower today than at the early part of this century, largely because the ages at marriage are lower and the size of families smaller.

In 1960 the birth rate among married women under age 20 was 54 per 100; at ages 20 to 24, the rate was 35 per 100; and at ages 25 to 29, it was 22. At 35 to 39 years, however, the rate was only 6 per 100.

6. What are the chances of twins, triplets, or quadruplets?

Of the confinements in the United States during 1960 in which at least one child was born alive, there were one set of twins for every 99 deliveries, one set of triplets for every 10,200 deliveries, and one set of quadruplets for every 900,000 deliveries. In 1960 alone, there were 42,720 sets of twins, 415 sets of triplets, and 14 sets of quadruplets. The chances of plural births rise with advance in age of the mother until ages 35 to 39; in fact, the chances of twinning are over twice as great at these ages than at 15 to 19.

7. What are identical twins?

Identical twins develop from the same ovum or egg and resemble each other so closely that they are hardly distinguishable. On the other hand, fraternal twins develop from two separate ova or eggs, and resemble each other no more than other brothers and sisters. Identical twins are always of the same sex, while fraternal twins may be of the same or of the opposite sex. Just about one-third of all sets of twins are identical, and the other two-thirds fraternal. Studies of twins are of scientific interest, for they provide an opportunity to examine the relative importance of environment and of heredity in shaping the life of the individual.

8. Are more boys than girls born each year?

Counting live births alone, in 1960 there were 105 boys born to every 100 girls in the white population of the United States, and 102 boys to every 100 girls in the colored population. The ratio of boys to girls tends to fall off slightly with advance in age of the mother at their birth. In twin births, the sex ratio is 101 boys to every 100 girls, while in triplet confinements there tends to be a slight excess of girls. In the case of quadruplets, there are about 150 girls for every 100 boys.

9. What proportion of married women remain childless?

Childlessness may either be voluntary or involuntary. According to census data, which do not distinguish between the two, about one-fifth of the married women in 1960 who had passed the reproductive period of life had not borne any children. This is more than double the proportion of the childless a generation earlier, in 1910. Childlessness among married women is much more common in cities than in rural areas. It is also more common for those whose schooling has extended to high school or beyond than for those with less schooling.

According to a survey conducted among a group of women in Indianapolis married from 12 to 15 years, more than one-tenth were not able to bear a child, even though desired.

10. What proportion of pregnancies fail to end in a live birth?

There are no data to indicate the situation in the country as a whole. In a survey conducted among a group of women in New York City, Raymond Pearl found that 13 percent had their pregnancy end in a miscarriage, abortion, or stillbirth. In another survey by Pearl, this time in Chicago, the failures in pregnancy came to 10.9 percent for white women and 15.9 percent for Negro women. Somewhat over 10 percent of a group of white women observed in Indianapolis reported such failure. Among this group, 1 percent of the pregnancies ended in a stillbirth, 7.5 percent in unintentional abortion, 1 percent in illegal abortion, and .5 percent in therapeutic abortion.

As a rough estimate, it may be said that somewhat over one-tenth, perhaps as much as one-eighth, of the pregnancies fail to end in a live birth.

11. What is meant by a live birth?

There is an official agreement that a live birth is one where a child shows any evidence of life after its complete delivery, such as action of the heart, breathing, or movement of voluntary muscle. Birth is said to be complete when the head, trunk, and limbs of the child are entirely outside the body of the mother, even if the cord is uncut and the placenta still attached. A fetus showing no evidence of life after separation from the mother, without regard to duration of pregnancy, constitutes a fetal death (stillbirth).

12. What proportion of babies are born in hospitals?

In 1960, 97 percent of the live births in the United States occurred in hospitals; 1 percent were attended by a physician elsewhere, and 2 percent by a midwife or other attendant. This is in marked contrast with the situation in 1937, when only 45 percent of the births were in hospitals, 45 percent were attended by a physician outside a hospital, and the rest were delivered by a midwife or someone else. The recent situation varies widely within the country. New England and the Pacific Coast states lead in the proportion of births occurring in hospitals; the South has the smallest proportion. In our cities, over 98 percent of the births are in hospitals, against 94 percent for the rural areas.

13. What is the cost of being born?

The cost of being born varies widely depending upon the location, the economic status of the family, whether the physician is a general practitioner or a specialist, and other factors. The following figures cover average costs in an Eastern city for a family in the middle income class. They provide for care by an obstetrician, a semi-private room for about five days in a hospital, and such other items as a layette, a family helper for a short period, and for incidentals:

Obstetrician	—	$300
Hospital	—	240
Layette	—	50
Maid	—	80
Incidentals	—	30
Total		$700

The actual cost will be less in smaller towns and in rural areas and especially so if the physician is a general practitioner. As many families now are covered by Blue Cross, Blue Shield, and by other forms of insurance, they will not feel the full impact of the above figures. Furthermore, families whose income is not sufficient to provide for the cost of a private physician can usually obtain the necessary services from their community hospital at a much lower figure.

14. At what season of the year are most babies born?

For many years prior to World War II, the seasonal pattern for births in the United States was very stable. There was a minor peak in February or March, a major peak in July and August, and a low point in December. This pattern was obscured during the rising birth rates of the war and immediate postwar years; for example, October was the peak month in 1946. In 1960, the peak months were July, August, and September, with the low point in June.

15. How many births in the United States are illegitimate?

It is estimated that there were about 240,200 illegitimate births in the United States during 1961, the peak year in total number of births. This is at a rate of 22.6 per 1,000 unmarried (single, widowed, or divorced) women at ages 15 to 44 years. There has been a steady rise in the rate of illegitimacy from the prewar level of 7.0 per 1,000 unmarried women in 1938–40. Nearly 6 percent of all births in 1961 were illegitimate; for white births, the figure was about 2 percent, but for the nonwhite, it was 22 percent. Over 40 percent of the illegitimate births were to girls under 20 years of age.

16. What has been the trend of the birth rate in the United States?

In the early days of the country, up to about 1830, our birth rate was over 50 per 1,000 population. However, even during that period the rate was declining, first gradually and later more rapidly, until a level of 32 per 1,000 was reached by 1900. The rate fell to 28.5 at the outbreak of World War I, during which it dropped very sharply, but temporarily. A postwar upsurge in 1920 gave way to a continuation of the downward trend which reached a low of 18.4 per 1,000 in 1933, when the Depression reached bottom. The recovery since then was at first slow, but it was greatly stimulated later by conditions arising out of World War II. A postwar peak was reached in 1947, with a birth rate of 27 per 1,000, the highest in a generation. Since then, the recorded birth rate has been tapering off, and was 21.6 in 1963.

17. Has there been any difference in the trend of birth rates among younger mothers as compared with older mothers?

From 1920 until the Depression year 1933, the birth rate declined at all ages of women within the reproductive period. For young mothers, under age 30, the year 1933 marked a turning point, the rates rising thereafter. This rise was gradual at first, and then rapid in the early war years. A late war recession in these birth rates under age 30 was followed by a postwar upsurge, which is still in evidence. For women at ages 30 to 34, the low point in birth rates came in 1936, later than for their younger sisters; for the age group 35 to 39 the low point was even later, about 1941, while that for ages 40 to 44 came in 1942. Birth rates for women 30 years and over have been stabilized during the last decade.

18. What has been the trend in the average number of children borne by American women?

The decline in the birth rate has brought with it a continuous and marked reduction in the average number of children borne by American women. In the period near 1800, the average American woman bore eight children. By 1910, women at ages 50 to 54, that is, at the close of their reproductive period, had had an average of five children. A generation later, in 1940, the average was only 3.2 children ever borne per married woman. In 1957–59 the number was still further reduced to 2.8 per married woman.

19. How is childlessness and size of family related to age at marriage?

Much of our recent information regarding the personal factors bearing upon the size of urban families comes from a survey conducted in Indianapolis during the summer of 1941. The purpose of this study was to gather and have available the essential facts in case, at any time, legislation be considered for encouraging larger families. In order to reduce the number of elements that might affect the results, most of the study was limited to couples where both husband and wife were Protestant and native white, married for the first time, and with the wife under 30 and husband under 40 at marriage; there were a few other qualifications. From this survey, it was found that the chances that a couple will remain childless rise rapidly with advance in the age of the wife at marriage. There is also, quite naturally, a rapid falling off in the chances of a large family. It was further observed that two-child families were most frequent among those marrying under 23 years of age; among those marrying later, one-child families were most frequent. Equally instructive are the data for Eire where the postponed age of marriage accounts for the low birth rate of recent years and the relatively small size of families.

20. What indication is there of the extent to which contraception is practiced, and of its success?

Data for the United States as a whole are lacking, but the situation undoubtedly varies widely within the country. In the selected group of native white Protestant couples included in the Indianapolis survey, it was found that about nine-tenths used contraception to control not only the number of their children, but also their spacing. Success in either prevention or postponement of a first or second pregnancy was reported by about half of the couples. After the third pregnancy about nine-tenths of the couples succeeded in the attempts to prevent another pregnancy.

21. Does the effective practice of contraception vary with the social-economic status of the family?

It has been frequently noted that the fertility of families in the higher social-economic classes is less than that of families lower in the scale. According to the findings among the selected Protestant families in the Indianapolis survey, a large part of such differences reflects the greater success of the more favored classes in planning their family size. However, among those families that planned both the number and spacing of their children, there was a tendency for the size of the family to increase with rise in the social-economic scale.

22. What proportion of couples succeed in having just the size family they wanted?

About three-quarters of the Protestant families in the Indianapolis survey reported that they had just the number of children they wanted, while one-quarter had more than they wanted. If these proportions are any indication at all for the country, it is apparent that the course of the birth rate is influenced largely by factors that bear upon the desires of the family.

23. What is the time interval desired between the birth of children into the family?

Almost three-quarters of the couples in the Indianapolis survey thought the first child should come within two or three years following marriage. The same interval was considered desirable by about five-sixths of the couples for the spacing between successive children.

However, these expressions of opinion did not conform to the actual happenings in families. Those stating that they planned both the number and spacing of their children reported greater intervals than the expressed opinion; the others reported shorter intervals.

24. To what extent is the birth rate among nonwhite women greater than that for white women?

The common impression that nonwhite women have birth rates well above those for white women is correct. Actually, the difference in 1960 was considerable. The nonwhite rate was 154 per 1,000 women aged 15 to 44 years, compared with 113 per 1,000 for white women of the same ages. Within this broad age range, there are some differences in the birth rates of the two races. Under age 20, the nonwhite have birth rates almost double those of the white. At all ages 20 and over the birth rate among nonwhite is appreciably higher than among white women.

25. Do foreign-born women still have higher birth rates than native-born women?

In 1920, the birth rate among foreign-born women was about 50 percent higher than that for the native-born. This margin was reduced to 17 percent by 1930. A decade later the difference was eliminated. This means that the birth rates of the foreign-born fell, over those two decades, much more rapidly than those of the native-born.[1]

26. What is the effect of war upon the birth rate?

Countries involved in a war have generally experienced a fall in the birth rate during the war period, and a rise after the close of hostilities. However, there have been striking variations from this pattern which have been introduced by such factors as the duration and intensity of the conflict.

The birth rate of the United States was barely affected by World War I, in which it participated for only one and one-half years—from April 1917 to November 1918. There was a decline in the rate for 1919, but this was followed by a high point in 1921. World War II presented a different picture. In the short period from 1940 to 1943, the birth rate in the United States rose by 18 percent. Two

---

[1] See answer to Question 16 of Chapter 1, page 7.

factors contributed to this rise, namely, war-induced prosperity and the sharp upswing in marriages in anticipation of active service in the armed forces. In the next two years, 1944 and 1945, the birth rate declined with the large transfer of men overseas. After the end of the war, with the release of men to civilian life, there was a resurgence in the birth rate (after allowance for unrecorded births) to a level of 27.0 per 1,000 in 1947, the highest since 1921. The birth rate has declined since then fairly gradually to 21.6 in 1963.

27. Does war affect the ratio of the sexes at birth?

There is no evidence that the normal excess of boy babies is increased significantly during periods of war or in the years immediately afterward. During and after World War II, the ratio of boys to girls in the United States averaged 106 to 100 in the white population, almost the same ratio that prevailed in the five years immediately before the war.

28. What is the prospect for the birth rate in the near future?

In the years immediately ahead, it is likely that the birth rate among young women having their first child will fall somewhat. Second and third births are expected to decrease also, but only slightly. Families of moderate size will in all probability continue to be popular, with large families definitely a thing of the past.

29. How does the birth rate vary geographically within the United States?

The highest birth rates are found in the Mountain and Southern states, and the lowest in the New England and Middle Atlantic states. For example, in 1960, the Mountain states had a birth rate of more than 27 per 1,000, while the Middle Atlantic states averaged a little more than 21 per 1,000.

30. How do the birth rates in the different parts of the world compare?

Birth rates are lowest in the English-speaking countries and in the countries of North, West, and Central Europe. They tend to be somewhat higher in Southern Europe and still higher in Eastern Europe. The rates are highest in Latin America, Africa, and Asia. For example, in 1960, the United States had an annual birth rate of

23.7 per 1,000, and England and Wales 17.2. On the other hand, the rate for Mexico was 46.0, that for Venezuela 45.2, and for Ceylon 36.6.

31. How does the age distribution of the population affect the birth rate?

Obviously, a community with a very small proportion of its population at the reproductive ages of life will have a low birth rate. On the other hand, where the proportion of population at these ages is high, the birth rate will be relatively high. This is why it is necessary to supplement crude birth rates (which are based on the total population) with the rates based on the number of females at the reproductive ages in order to get a picture of the true birth rate of the state or a nation. The birth rates of two communities are thus not strictly comparable without making allowance for differences in the age structure of their populations.

32. What population characteristics, other than its age distribution, affect the birth rate?

For one thing, a population in which women greatly outnumber men at the reproductive ages will have a relatively low proportion of the women married; this, of course, has an adverse effect upon the birth rate. On the other hand, the birth rate will be relatively high in a population in which a large proportion of the couples have been recently married. The occupational distribution of its wage-earning population is also reflected in the birth rate of a community. Rates tend to be relatively high in areas where most of the people are self-sufficient farmers, and low where clerical wage-earners predominate. If a large element of the community is made up of rather recent immigrants from areas of high fertility, its birth rate will also tend to be high. Rates are also likely to be high where a sizable fraction of the population is colored; for, as we have seen, the latter race usually have higher birth rates than whites.

33. What is meant by the crude rate of natural increase?

The crude rate of natural increase is the difference between the crude birth rate (Question 4) and the crude death rate. It measures the annual rate of increment, or decrement, of the population without taking into account the changes by immigration or emigration. For example, the crude birth rate in the United States in 1963 was 21.6 per 1,000, and the crude death rate 9.6 per 1,000, so that the crude rate of natural increase was 12.0 per 1,000 population.

34. What is meant by "gross reproduction rate"?

Since the birth rate of a community is influenced by its population characteristics, a valid comparison of the experience of two communities cannot be made without allowing for differences in these characteristics. One method used to allow for differences in age distribution is to compute the "gross reproduction rate." This will be clarified by means of an example.

Suppose we know the birth rates of women at each age, counting their daughters only. Thus, according to the table below, the annual births of daughters per 1,000 females is 22 at age 17 years, 65 at 22 years, and so on.

Age of Mother	Annual births of daughters per 1,000 females	Number out of 1,000 births surviving to stated age	Births of daughters among survivors
17	22	943	21
22	65	936	62
27	61	928	57
32	41	918	38
37	22	906	20
42	7	889	6
47	1	867	1
Total × 5	1,095		1,020

If the figures in this column are added and multiplied by five to allow for the fact that we have them only for every fifth age, the total comes to 1,095 per 1,000; the ratio is 1.095. This ratio is commonly known as the gross reproduction rate. Since it is derived only from birth rates specific for age of the mother, the gross reproduction rate is not influenced by the size or the age distribution of the prevailing female population.

The gross reproduction rate has another meaning. If we trace 1,000 girl babies from their birth to the end of their reproductive period, assuming that none dies meanwhile and that they give birth to daughters at the rates shown above, they will have altogether

1,095 daughters. The gross reproduction rate thus measures the rate of increase per generation without allowance for deaths.

35. What is meant by "net reproduction rate"?

Let us suppose the generation of 1,000 girl babies of the previous question were traced from birth to the end of their reproductive period, but at the same time allowing for deaths among them. According to the example shown in Question 34, there would survive 943 to age 17 years, 936 to age 22 years, and so on. Now if the survivors to age 17 gave birth to daughters at the rate of 22 per 1,000, then the 943 such survivors would have

$$943 \times \frac{22}{1,000} = 21$$

births of daughters among them; this is the first figure in the last column. In the same way, we may estimate the births of daughters among the survivors to the higher ages. If the figures in this column are added and multiplied by five to allow for the fact that we have them only for every fifth age, the total comes to 1,020 per generation of 1,000 girls traced from birth; the ratio is 1.02. This ratio is known as the net reproduction rate; it will be recognized as the ratio of births of daughters in two successive generations subject to the prescribed birth rates and survivorship rates. If this ratio is greater than one, a continuation of the prescribed rates means that the population will keep increasing. On the other hand, if the ratio should be less than one, the conditions are such as to lead to an eventual decrease in population. In the instance of the example, the excess over one, namely, .02 or 2 percent, is the rate of increase per generation.

36. What do we mean by the "true" rate of natural increase?

To speak in terms of a rate of population increase per generation, as was done at the end of the previous question, is rather vague since length of a generation has not been defined precisely. To avoid this difficulty, a method has been devised to translate the rate of increase per generation to an annual rate of increase. The figure computed by this method is called the "true" or intrinsic rate of natural increase to distinguish it from the annual crude rate of natural increase, which is simply the excess of the crude birth rate over the crude death rate. (See Question 33.)

37. How is the future age composition of the population affected by the trend in the birth rate?

A population maintaining a relatively high birth rate will have a relatively large proportion of its population at the younger ages of life and a small proportion of elderly persons. This was typical of the situation in the United States prior to the era of rapidly declining birth rates. This is also the situation at present in nearly all Latin American countries, where the large proportion of children under age 15 compared to the proportion at the working ages of life seriously impedes industrialization and, therefore, the economic progress of the area. A continual state of low birth rates, such as to yield net reproduction rates below 1, leads to a population with a relatively small proportion of children and young people, and a high proportion of elders.

38. What is the average size of family necessary to maintain a stationary population?

In the current situation of mortality, marriage, fertility, and childlessness, 275 children will be required for every 100 mothers to maintain a stationary population, or an average of 2.75 children per mother. This figure was arrived at from current mortality which shows that out of 1,000 white girl babies traced from birth 920 will survive to age 50, practically the end of their reproductive period. Since 90 percent of the girls eventually marry, if 90 percent of the wives bear children (see Question 9), the number of mothers among the 900 survivors is

$$920 \times .90 \times .90 = 745.2$$

For a stationary population, these 745 mothers will not only have to replace the 1,000 girl babies from which they arose, but they will also have to bear 1,060 boy babies, a total of 2,060 children. The average of 2.75 children per mother is found from a division of 2,060 by 745.

39. What proportion of babies are born prematurely and what are their chances of survival?

It is estimated that about 6 percent of the births in the United States are premature. These are babies born alive with a period of gestation of 28 to 37 weeks, or weighing 5½ pounds or less at birth.

According to one study, about one-fifth died within the first month of life; this is 20 times the rate for full-term infants.

40. What measures are taken to safeguard the lives of premature infants?

Special medical and nursing care is being provided for prematurely born babies by many health departments. Maternity hospitals in many cities are being equipped to care for premature infants until they can be transferred safely to specialized centers in order to supply the careful long-term attention usually required. Transportation for premature infants from homes or hospitals to the centers is often provided by the city.

41. Are fetal deaths and high mortality in early infancy family traits?

Yes. According to New York State data, mothers without a history of fetal death or early death of an infant continued to experience a low fetal death rate and a low rate of early infant loss.

42. How does the mortality of infants in twin births compare with that of single births?

In a New York State study, it was found that the mortality of twins during the first month of life was over three times that of babies from single confinements.

43. What are the principal hazards of maternity?

Infection is the leading cause of maternal mortality, and accounts for over one-quarter of the deaths incidental to childbearing. Some deaths from this cause occur at every stage of maternity—during pregnancy, during childbirth, and after delivery. One-seventh of maternal deaths are due to hemorrhage, trauma, or shock. The toxemias of pregnancy (primarily disturbances of the metabolism) account for one-sixth of the deaths. The remaining deaths are caused by various other puerperal complications.

44. What has been the trend in the chances of death from conditions related to childbearing?

The hazards of maternity are fast declining in the United States. Since 1930, the death rate from diseases of pregnancy and childbirth has been reduced by more than 95 percent from over 60 maternal deaths to the present level of 3.5 deaths per 10,000 live births. Both white and nonwhite mothers have benefited from this improvement, but there is still a wide gap between the two racial groups. The current maternal mortality rate of nonwhite mothers is more than three times that of the white.

45. How does maternal mortality vary geographically within the United States?

Maternal mortality above average is found generally in the South and Southwest, with the highest rates in the East South Central region. Rural areas and the smaller cities show rates on the average about 50 percent above larger cities. This situation probably reflects the limited facilities for satisfactory medical and nursing care for women in these places.

46. What steps are necessary to reduce maternal mortality still further?

It is generally agreed that the hazards of childbearing can be reduced still more at every stage of maternity. This can be accomplished by more widespread and more adequate prenatal care, by the provision of additional hospital facilities for confinement cases among nonwhites, and by raising still higher the standards of obstetrical practice. The recently approved hospital construction program of the federal government should prove of great value in this connection. Special effort should be directed toward safeguarding maternity in areas of the country where the rate is still relatively high, particularly among nonwhite women.

Chapter 3

The Pattern
of Marriage

1. What are the chances for marriage in the United States?

Over 90 percent of the persons entering the marriageable ages in our country may look forward to marrying during the course of their lives.

2. Is marriage more popular now than years ago?

Yes, very much so. At present, somewhat more than two-thirds of the population in the United States at ages 15 and over are married. Only as recently as 1940, the proportion married was three-fifths, a level maintained since 1890. To some extent, the recent increase in the married population results from the decline in mortality and the consequent reduction in the incidence of widowhood. But of much greater importance have been the remarkably high marriage rates during World War II and the immediate postwar period. As a result of this boom in marriages, the proportion of single persons in the population is now at the lowest point since 1890, when data regarding marital status were first compiled for the country as a whole.

3. Do marriages increase in leap years?

There is no evidence that the marriage rate in the United States is higher in leap years than in other years. In fact, since the Civil War period, only twice was the marriage rate in a leap year higher than in the preceding and the following year; the two exceptions were 1896 and 1920.

4. Which month is most popular for marriage?

June is the most popular month for marriage in all but a few areas of the United States. It is also traditionally the most popular month for those entering marriage for the first time.

The seasonal preference of widows and divorcees, however, is not as pronounced. Widows prefer the early fall almost as much as June, and divorcees choose almost equally between June and July. That June is not as appealing to brides who are remarrying may be explained by the fact that many of them are in the labor force or have young children in their care; they probably find the vacation period the most convenient time to be wed. It is also likely that a considerable number of young divorcees remarry shortly after the dissolution of their previous marriage, whatever the month may be.

5. How many marriages are performed annually in the United States?

In 1963, a total of 1,657,000 marriages were performed in the United States, compared with 1,582,000 the year before. The marriage rate was the highest in six years. Canada likewise reported a rise, above the annual number in the preceding three years. The spurt in marriages on both sides of the border reflects the increasing number of people reaching the marriageable ages, a consequence of the baby boom immediately after World War II.

6. What is the marriage rate in the United States?

Currently, there are about 8.8 marriages annually for each 1,000 population. This is much below the high point of 16.4 per 1,000 reached in 1946, the year after the close of World War II, when huge numbers of men were demobilized and assumed marital responsibilities. The marriage rate is now at about the level of that in the Depression years.

7. How does the marriage rate in the United States compare with that of other countries?

The marriage rate in the United States is still among the high insofar as the recorded figures show. These include: the USSR with a rate of 11.0 per 1,000 population in the most recent year; the United Arab Republic 10.9; Romania 9.8; Japan 9.5; West Germany 9.4; and Yugoslavia 9.0. In contrast, many countries with the highest birth rates, such as Peru, Venezuela, Costa Rica, and Mexico have very low marriage rates. The low standing of these countries is explained in part by the wide prevalence of unrecorded arrangements by which couples live together without a formal marriage, and also by the fact that the registration of civil marriages is far from complete.

8. Which states have the highest and lowest marriage rates?

In general, the marriage rate in the United States tends to increase as one moves from North to South and from East to West. There are exceptions to this pattern, due primarily to the fact that many couples are married outside of their own states in order to take advantage of lenient marriage laws.

Thus, the highest marriage rate is recorded in Nevada, which stands in a class by itself. In 1960–62, there were recorded over 200 marriages for each 1,000 persons in that state. This was 12 times the figure for the next highest states; South Carolina 17.3 and Idaho 17.1. The marriage rate is also relatively high in Georgia, Maryland, District of Columbia, and Oklahoma. At the other extreme, the lowest marriage rates in our country during the recent period were recorded in Delaware, Wisconsin, Pennsylvania, and Oregon, with less than six marriages per 1,000 population.

9. Has the marriage rate decreased recently in all regions of our country?

The most pronounced decline was recorded in the Mountain states in spite of the continued popularity of the marriage centers at Reno and Las Vegas, Nevada, which attract thousands of prospective brides and grooms from the adjoining states, especially California.

10. What is the outlook for the number of marriages and the marriage rate in the immediate future?

There should be a sharp increase in the number of marriages by 1965 or 1966, when the young people from the baby boom of 1946–47 reach the late teen ages. If present trends continue the marriages will in all probability again pass the two million mark by 1970, or even before.

11. What are the legal requirements for marriage in the United States?

Under the Constitution of the United States the regulation of marriage is reserved to the individual states. The laws of the states vary greatly in detail and are sometimes in actual conflict; there is, however, some agreement on fundamentals. In all states it is a common policy to require persons who intend to marry to first secure the permission of the state. In order to prevent undesirable marriages, there are a large number of requirements and qualifications which must be met as a prerequisite to the issuance of a license. These have mostly to do with the relationship of the contracting parties, and their mental and physical condition. For example, all states forbid the marriage of parent and child, brother and sister, and grandparent and grandchild. All states also set the minimum age at which a person may marry, and bar subsequent marriages if a prior marriage still exists. There is an additional miscellany of requirements which are precedent conditions to the issuance of a license in some states, such as that the parties be not of different races, inmates of a home for the indigent, or habitual criminals.

12. How many states now have laws requiring premarital examination?

Forty-six states now have laws requiring premarital examination as a requisite to marriage. In addition, Washington requires an affidavit by the prospective groom stating that he is free from venereal disease. Thus, only four states (Maryland, Minnesota, Nevada, and South Carolina) and Washington, D.C., do not require an examination or an affidavit.

Enactment of premarital legislation began over 40 years ago. However, because the earlier laws were inadequate, they were hardly effective in the control of the venereal diseases. Since 1936, when Connecticut passed the first of the newer laws, general recognition by both health officials and citizens of the value of such laws led to their speedy adoption. These laws are not intended to prevent permanently the marriage of persons with venereal infection, but only to delay the marriage of those with communicable or potentially communicable infection until the disease has been rendered noninfectious. The success of these laws is evident from the fact that through them many thousands of cases of syphilis are discovered each year.

13. Do premarital laws depress the marriage rate?

There is evidence that new or amended legislation requiring premarital examination depresses the marriage rate, at least temporarily. For example, Delaware enacted such a law effective July 1, 1947. Immediately, the number of marriages performed in Delaware dropped abruptly from about 600 a month to less than 300. New York also experienced a sharp decline after 1937, when premarital laws became effective in that state. Apparently, such legislation induces some residents to travel to neighboring states to avoid the inconveniences of the new law. More important, it reduces sharply the number of nonresidents who come to the state to avoid the laws of their home states. Eventually, the new law loses its deterring effect on residents. On the other hand, the number of nonresident marriages remains at a lower level.

14. Are there any "Gretna Greens" left in the United States?

Even today there are places in our country which are noted for the large number of marriages performed and for the ease and promptness with which nonresident couples may secure licenses and be married. However, the number of these so-called "Gretna Greens" has diminished considerably in the past two decades as more and more states have enacted legislation requiring a premarital examination and a waiting period before marriage. The most popular marriage centers are those in Reno and Las Vegas, Nevada; Yuma, Arizona; and Elkton, Maryland. For years, Elkton was in the forefront as a "Gretna Green." However, in November 1938, Maryland imposed a two-day waiting period, and marriages in Elkton fell off immediately. Nevertheless, even in 1948 the number of persons married in Cecil County, in which Elkton is located, almost equaled the population of the county. Not all marriage centers owe their existence to relatively lenient license laws. In Chickasaw County, Iowa, for example, a romantic interest which has attached itself to the locality accounts for its popularity as a marriage center.

15. Do all couples who apply for a marriage license get married?

Apparently not, since not all marriage licenses are used. In recent years, for example, the number of marriages performed has varied from 1 to 3 percent below the number of marriage licenses issued.

16. Are most couples married in civil ceremonies?

Marriages by religious ceremony outnumber the civil by about four to one. In two states, Maryland and West Virginia, only religious ceremonies are permitted.

17. Is common-law marriage still recognized in any state of our country?

Common-law marriages are still recognized, though deprecated, in most states scattered throughout our country. Since the pioneer conditions which fostered common-law marriage in the United States have disappeared, an increasing number of states have enacted legislation prohibiting such marriages. Common-law marriage has no foothold among other English-speaking countries, and it is not authorized generally among other peoples. Its continued existence in our country furnishes a means of defeating the effectiveness of reforms, such as laws requiring premarital examination.

18. Is the marriage rate higher in urban areas than in rural areas?

The marriage rate is lower in urban areas. In fact, the rate is generally lowest in the very large cities. In rural areas, on the other hand, the marriage rate is somewhat higher in the small towns and villages than in the farm areas. The differences are, in part at least, explained by the relative proportions of the two sexes in the various communities.

19. Which occupations have the highest and which the lowest marriage rate?

Farmers have the highest marriage rate of all social-economic groups in our country. The high marriage rate among farmers is understandable, since they have to depend so largely on their own family to run both the home and the farm. The desire for companionship is also undoubtedly a factor in this situation.

After farmers, the groups consisting of proprietors and managers, skilled and semiskilled workers, laborers, and clerks follow in order in tendency to marry. The marriage rate for professional persons is lower than for most other classes. This results in large measure from their tendency to postpone marriage while starting a career. Their marriage rate in later life is, however, relatively high, since after age 45 the proportion of professional men who have ever married is practically the same as that for all classes.

20. Are the more educated people less likely to marry?

Among women, the chances for marriage decrease with advance in educational attainment. Thus, in 1947, the proportion of women at ages 35 to 44 who had ever married decreased from almost 95 percent for those with less than seven years of school to about 90 percent for the high-school graduates; the proportion was much lower, 83 percent, for the women with at least a year of college. However, the women with the more extended education who do marry tend to make a better match, insofar as the education of the husband is concerned.

Among men, by way of contrast, the marriage rate is lowest for those who have not completed seven years of school.

21. Do business conditions influence the course of the marriage rate?

Yearly variations in business conditions are an important factor in the fluctuations in the marriage rate. Prosperity encourages marriage and depression discourages it. Young people are not inclined to marry in bad times; as a result, there is an accumulation of eligible men and women who marry in good times. In the short period from 1929 to 1932, while the United States was entering its severest economic depression, the marriage rate fell from 10.1 to 7.9 per 1,000 population. In the years thereafter, the rate moved upward slowly to 11.3 in 1937 as the business situation improved. With the recession of 1938, it dropped again to 10.3, but the prosperity beginning in 1939 brought a rise.

The highest rate of 16.2 per 1,000 was reached in 1946, since which time the rate has declined, in spite of the long period of economic prosperity which the country has enjoyed. There are, therefore, other factors than business conditions which influence the course of the marriage rate.

22. How does war affect the marriage rate?

Generally, the marriage rate rises within the early period of a war, declines during its course, increases sharply in the immediate postwar years, and then reverts more or less to its prewar level. This is illustrated by the experience of the United States during World War II.

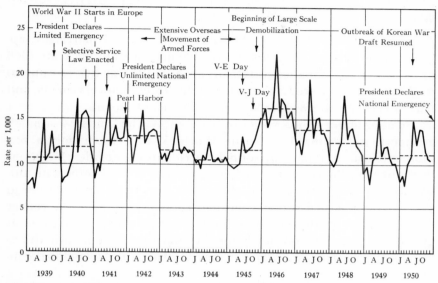

Chart 2.   **Marriages per 1,000 population, United States, 1939–1950.**

The marriage rate started to climb in June, 1940, after the fall of France and the subsequent discussion of conscription. The upswing gained momentum after the attack on Pearl Harbor as thousands hastened into marriage in the hope of escaping induction, or in anticipation of entering the armed forces and of serving abroad. As a result, the rate reached a new peak of 13.1 marriages per 1,000 population in 1942; only three years prior, in 1939, it was 10.7 per 1,000. With the entry of increasing numbers of young men into military service and the shipment of thousands overseas, the marriage rate fell off during 1943, 1944, and the early months of 1945. Then came V-E Day early in May, and V-J Day a few months later, followed shortly thereafter by the start of large-scale demobilization. Each of these events brought an immediate upsweep in the marriage rate, carrying it to its highest level in our history. The peak rate of 16.2 per 1,000 in 1946 resulted mainly from the backlog of delayed marriages among young men who preferred to wait until the war was over, and also from the special appeal of marriage to men who had long been separated from the opposite sex and the comforts of home. In part, too, it was related to the war and postwar boom in divorce, inasmuch as many of the divorces were shortly followed by remarriage. (See Chart 2.)

23. Did many men in our armed forces marry while overseas during World War II and thereafter?

The number was relatively small. Such overseas marriages represented only about 1 percent of our total marriages in the years 1943 to 1947. The principal countries from which the war brides came to the United States were England, Germany, Italy, France, Canada, and Australia. There were also some from China and Japan.

The number of marriages overseas in World War II was much greater than the number during World War I, when only a few thousand army and navy personnel married foreign brides. However, in comparing the experience of the two wars, several important differences must be taken into account. First, American participation in World War II lasted two and one-half times as long as in the earlier conflict. Then again, our forces overseas were almost four times as great. When allowance is made for these factors, there is little difference in the marriage rate for our men abroad in the two global conflicts.

24. How is the course of the marriage rate influenced by that of the birth rate?

The birth rate influences the future marriage rate in two ways. Obviously, a high birth rate at any time means that there will be a relatively large number of young men and women eligible for marriage two decades later. One of the reasons for the record-breaking number of marriages in the United States during the 1940's was the unusually large concentration of men at ages 20 to 25 and of women at ages 18 to 23, people who were born before the very rapid decline in the birth rate. In the same way, the high birth rate in the 40's will increase the marriage rate of the late 60's. The trend of the number of births over the years also has some bearing on the future marriage rate through its influence on the proportions of the two sexes at the ages of marriage.

25. How does immigration affect the marriage rate?

In the past, immigrants as a class generally consisted of young persons, with an excess of men over women. As a result, immigration added to the number of young people, especially men, who were eligible for marriage. Currently, more women than men are coming to our shores but, as in the past, these immigrants are concentrated in the younger adult ages and thus affect the marriage rate appreciably.

26. Is there a greater tendency for marriage in the white population than among nonwhites?

Among both men and women at ages under 25 years, the proportion married is now greater for the white population than for the nonwhite, but the margin is not great. The whites also have a higher proportion married at ages 35 and over. This condition represents a shift from earlier decades, when the nonwhites showed a higher proportion married than the whites. In the last decade the proportion married rose among whites, but declined somewhat among nonwhites. It is this fact which explains the reversal in the position of the two races in recent years. It is noteworthy, however, that whereas years ago common-law marriage without license or ceremony was fairly common among Negroes in the Deep South, and in some urban centers, certain forces in our society have caused them to formalize their marriages. For example, for Negroes who received relief funds during the Depression, the act of marriage acquired a new significance. Selective service exercised an even stronger influence in this direction, as did also the system of allotments and allowances for wives of men in the armed services. Thus, the experience of the two groups has been drawn closer together; marriage at a somewhat earlier age for the Negroes remaining as the most outstanding difference.

27. How common are mixed marriages in our country?

Racial intermarriages are relatively rare in the United States; they probably account for somewhat less than 5 out of every 10,000 marriages. Primarily, this results from the fact that such marriages are legally prohibited in many states in the South where our Negro population is still concentrated. Nevertheless, even in the North, interracial marriages are rather rare.

28. What are the legal requirements in regard to age at marriage?

At common law, a marriage was considered legally binding if the parties had arrived at the age of puberty, which was taken as 14 years in the male and 12 in the female. Today, by statute, the capacity to marry is generally set at 21 years for men and 18 for women. However, if the parents or guardian approve, marriage may be entered into at a lower age. Most states fix this age by statute at 18 years for boys and 16 for girls. In a few states the age is one or two years lower than that prescribed by the majority. Most states, however, have provisions for judicial authorization of marriages where one or both parties are under minimum marriageable age and special circumstances prevail, such as pregnancy.

29. Do people marry earlier nowadays than they did years ago?

The trend in recent decades has been toward earlier marriage. This is evident from the drop in the median age at first marriage, for all men who had ever married, from 26.1 years in 1890 to 22.7 years in 1962. The trend has also been downward for women, but the decrease has been less marked, the median dropping from 22.0 to 20.3 during the past 70 years. Another indication of the downward trend in age at marriage is the change in the proportion of young people who have married. Thus, in 1890 somewhat less than one-half of the women at ages 20 to 24 were or had been married; this rose to a little over half in 1940, but today the figure is more than two-thirds. The increase has been even greater among young men.

30. Do Americans marry at an earlier age than persons in most other countries?

Early marriage is more frequent in the United States than in any other country of the Western world. For example, among our women at ages 20 to 24 years, 69 per cent were already married at the time of the 1960 census. In France, which most closely approaches our experience, the proportion married at these ages at the time of their last census was 43 percent. In Canada and Denmark, the figure was about 40 percent; and in Australia, Italy, and Portugal, it was 31 percent. The prospects for early marriage are relatively low in Ireland and Norway; at the time the last population count was made in these countries, about 20 percent of their young women had married. Although Americans marry relatively young, the age at marriage in our country is not the lowest in the world. In India, for example, close to 9 out of every 10 girls are wed before their twentieth birthday.

31. In what region of our country is early marriage most frequent?

Early marriage is most frequent in the Southern states; in the Northeastern states, on the other hand, people marry about two years later. In 1960, for example, the median age of brides at first marriage in Alabama and Mississippi was 19.1 years; in Connecticut the median age of brides was 21.9; in New York 21.4; in New Jersey 21.8.

32. What is the most popular age for grooms?

The marriage rate for single men is at a maximum at ages 26 and 27, when over one-sixth of them marry.

33. At what age is a single man considered a bachelor?

Although there is no definite age which determines when a single man becomes a confirmed bachelor, for practical purposes it may be set at about 35 years. Beginning with age 18, young men marry in increasing numbers, the marriage rate rising rapidly with each advance in age, and as a result the supply of single men is rapidly diminished. By age 30 about one-sixth of our men are still single; by age 35 the proportion is about one-eighth. While men continue to marry in later life, fewer than half of the single men who have passed age 35 eventually do so. For this reason, single men who have passed their thirty-fifth birthday may be considered as confirmed bachelors. According to this arbitrary definition, there are about three million bachelors in the United States today.

34. What is the most popular age for brides?

The marriage rate for girls is at a maximum at ages 22 to 24 years, when over one-fifth of them marry.

35. At what age is a single woman considered a spinster?

A woman who has passed her thirty-first birthday may be considered a spinster in our country, since the chances are against her eventual marriage after that age. As a matter of fact, most women in the United States who marry do so relatively young. In consequence, less than one-tenth of our women have not been married by their thirty-second birthday. Currently, there are about three million single women over 32 years of age in the United States.

36. How many years, on the average, are grooms older than brides?

On the average, the groom is about three years older than his bride. However, this is not a rigid pattern. For example, the average bride is somewhat less than three years younger than her groom where both are marrying for the first time, but more than four and one-half years younger if one of the partners was previously married. Moreover, this disparity in ages between the spouses increases with advance in age of the groom, from about one year when the groom is under 25 years to more than four years for grooms over age 55.

37. How often do men marry women older than themselves?

About 15 percent of all men marry women older than themselves. However, in most of these marriages only a small difference in age is involved; in only one-fortieth of all marriages the wife is older than her husband by five years or more. In one-tenth of American marriages the spouses are of the same age, and in about two-thirds there is less than five years difference.

38. How frequently do single persons marry persons who have been previously married?

In general, spinsters tend to marry bachelors, and vice versa. However, about 1 out of every 11 single persons who marries takes a spouse who has been previously married. In such cases, the chances are almost four to one that the spouse was previously divorced rather than widowed.

39. Whom do the widowed and divorced marry?

On the whole, persons previously widowed or divorced tend to marry persons who have been married before. Somewhat more than two-fifths of the widows and widowers who remarry choose as their mate someone who has also been previously widowed. In the case of the divorced, one-half take as their new mate another who has been divorced, and about two-fifths enter their remarriage with a single person. Widows have a stronger tendency to marry bachelors than widowers have to marry spinsters; among the divorced, however, marriages with single persons are as frequent for men as for women.

40. Do divorced couples ever remarry each other?

Divorce does not always terminate the personal relationship between the spouses, especially when there are children involved. Thus, the divorced mates may continue to have dealings with each other, and these sometimes culminate in remarriage. However, such remarriages are relatively infrequent.

41. What is the interval between divorce and remarriage?

Most divorced persons who remarry do so within a few years after the dissolution of their last marriage. According to the experience in New York State, about three-tenths remarry the year the divorce is granted, about one-half within the space of two years, and three-fourths before the lapse of five years. However, remarriages do occur even after 20 years, but these account for only 1 or 2 percent of the total divorced who remarry.

42. How common is bigamy in the United States?

From the very nature of the event, one would not expect data on the incidence of bigamy to be available. However, a minimum estimate can be derived from judicial statistics. The most common procedure in the United States for dissolving a bigamous marriage is by annulment. In addition, a number of states include bigamy as a ground for divorce. Judged by these divorce and annulment data, it would appear that close to 2,500 bigamous marriages are contracted annually, or at a rate of about 2 for every 1,000 marriages performed.

43. How does the average age at remarriage compare with the age at first marriage?

In general, there is a substantial difference in age between first marriages and remarriages. Among men, the median age at first marriage was 23.1 in 1960. In contrast, the median age at remarriage for men was 40.7, or 17 years greater than at first marriage. Women remarry, on the average, at an earlier age than men and the difference in their ages between first and remarriage is somewhat smaller than for men, namely, about 15 years.

44. What is the relative importance of remarriages after age 45?

Remarriages, which are relatively infrequent at the younger ages, rapidly increase in importance with each advance in age. At ages over 45, remarriages account for four-fifths of all marriages at that period of life. However, the marriages at these ages have only a negligible influence on the over-all marriage picture, since they represent only about 6 percent of the total.

45. Who has the highest marriage rate—the single, the widowed, or the divorced?

The marriage rate is highest for the divorced and lowest for the single, with the rate for the widowed intermediate. This is the case for both men and women at every age. At the younger ages, the frequency of remarriage for the divorced is very high. Among men and women at ages 20 to 24, at least one-half of the divorced undertake another marital adventure. The marriage rate falls off rapidly after these peaks, but even in the next five years of life the annual proportion who remarry is close to two-fifths.

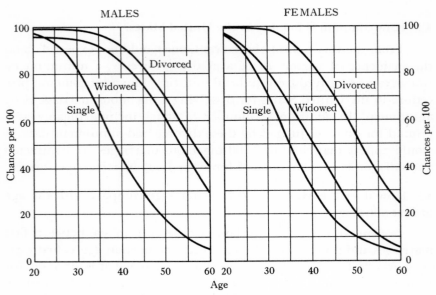

Chart 3.   Chances of eventual marriage for single, widowed, or divorced persons, United States, 1948.

46. Are the prospects for eventual marriage greater for men than for women?

The chances of marriage are greater for men than for women, whether divorced, widowed, or single. However, the differences between the two sexes are least marked among the divorced, and most among the widowed; the single fall in between the two.

Age for age and for both sexes, the chances of marriage are greatest for the divorced, not as high for the widowed, and poorest for the single. For example, a divorcee who is 30 years old has 98 chances in 100 of remarrying, while for a widow of the same age the chances are 81 in 100; a spinster of age 30 has only 70 chances in 100. For both men and women in each of the marital classes, the chances of eventual marriage decrease sharply with advancing age. (See Chart 3.)

47. What effect does the presence of dependent children have on a woman's chances for remarriage?

The presence of dependent children lessens considerably a woman's chances for remarriage.

48. In what proportion of American families has the wife or husband been married before?

In somewhat more than one out of every seven families, either the husband or wife was previously married.

Chapter 4

The Average
American Family

1. What is a family?

The family is the basic unit in all types of society, but its exact definition varies greatly with different cultures. In our society the family serves not only to perpetuate the race and our moral and social ideals, but it is also the basic unit of economic consumption.

For many years in this country no distinction was made in census enumerations between families and households. In 1948, however, the Bureau of the Census redefined the family as a group of two or more persons living together and related to each other by blood, marriage, or adoption. The most common form of family is husband and wife and children. A man living with his grandfather, and a woman with her niece would also constitute families. By this definition there are now close to 47 million families in the United States.

2. What is a household, and how many of them are there in our country?

A household is defined by the Bureau of the Census as a group of persons, related or not, who share common living quarters such as a house, an apartment, or even a single room. There may be more than one family in a household, and there may also be a number of unrelated persons such as lodgers or servants. One person living alone or two unrelated persons sharing quarters constitute households. Quasi households like hotels, large lodging houses, or other institutions are not included in the census count of households. In 1962, there were 54,652,000 households in the country, an increase of 25.5 percent from the figure in 1950. In the same 12-year period the civilian population of the country rose only 20 percent.

3. How many persons live alone?

There were about 13 million persons, comprising over 7 percent of the population, who were not living with relatives in April, 1960. About eight million of them either maintained their own household or shared households with friends. The others lived in hotels, rooming houses, or other quasi households. One-third of the persons not living in families were widows or widowers, one-tenth were divorced, one-tenth separated, and the remainder single. There were a great many older persons among those not in family groups, more than 40 percent of them being at least 65 years of age. The proportion of households containing only one person has increased greatly in recent years.

4. What proportions of the adult population are single, married, separated, widowed, or divorced?

Of the men 25 years old or older in 1960, 10 percent were single, 80 percent married and living with their wives, close to 4 percent married with their wives absent, 4 percent widowed, and 2.5 percent divorced. Of the women at ages 25 and over, 7.5 percent were single, 71 percent married and living with their husbands, 4 percent married with their husbands absent, 15 percent widowed, and 3 percent divorced.

5. What is the average size of a family?

The average size of all families in the United States—both husband-and-wife and other types of family—was 3.65 persons in 1960. The average number of children under age 18 per family was 1.34, and the average number of persons more than 18 years old was 2.31. Urban families had only 3.56 persons, with an average of 1.27 dependent children. Rural nonfarm families contained 3.81 persons; farm families 3.96, including 1.50 children under 18.

6. How do white and colored households compare in size?

Colored households are larger than the white. In 1960, the average size of colored families was one-fifth greater than white families. Most of the difference was made up of dependent children, rather than of other relatives or unrelated persons.

7. What is the average lapse of time from marriage to the birth of the first child?

On an average, about two years pass from the marriage of American couples to the arrival of their first-born. After the first child, births are usually spaced about two or three years apart. In the typical family with three children, all the births occur within the first seven years of marriage.

8. What proportion of husband-and-wife families have dependent children?

Three-fifths of all the husband-and-wife families in the country had children under 18 living with them in April, 1960. The proportion was four-fifths for families where the husband was under 35, three-quarters where he was from 35 to 54 years old, and only about one-seventh where he was 55 or more. In the case of older husbands, most of the children formerly in the family had already grown up and left home. The proportion of husband-and-wife families with dependent children rises from around one-seventh for those married less than a year to about four-fifths for those married 10 to 14 years. It drops off again later to approximately two-fifths for those married 15 years or more.

9 Are there still many large families in the United States?

Almost one-third of all the families in the country in 1960 consisted of only two persons, but there were still a great many good-sized families. Over one-fifth of all families consisted of three persons, one-fifth of four, one-eighth of five, and one-eighth of six or more persons.

10. How does the average size of family vary according to the occupation of the family head?

A survey made some years ago showed that farmers and laborers led in the number of children, with the unemployed not far behind. Craftsmen, foremen, and kindred workers, and service workers were, on the whole, close to the average for all employed persons. Operatives had somewhat larger families, coming between craftsmen and laborers in size of family. Professional and semiprofessional persons, proprietors, managers and officials, and clerical and other white-collar workers tended to have small families, as did those in the non-working population. Size of family varies with the education of the father; in general, the more training required for the job the smaller the families of those who hold it.

11. In what proportion of families have the husband or wife been married more than once?

In about one-eighth of the families in the United States the wife had been married more than once; the proportion was slightly higher for husbands. The proportions were much lower for younger husbands than for older ones, rising to a maximum of one-fifth for the husbands 55 years old and over. A relatively large number of those married more than once also had a spouse married more than once. This was the case even at the younger ages, where there is a choice from many persons who had never been married before.

12. To how many years of married life may a bride and groom look forward?

Under conditions prevailing for the white population in 1948, a bride and groom both aged 20 may expect to live together for 43.5 years, if one considers only the probability of death and not of divorce, annulment, or separation. If the groom is 25 and the bride 20, the average duration of marriage is 40.5 years. If the groom is 30 and the bride 25, they may expect an average of 36 years of married life. These joint expectations of life are necessarily lower than the expectation of life of either the bride or groom considered separately. In the case of the couple aged 20, with a joint expectation of life of 43.5 years, the bride has an expectation of life of nearly 54 years and the groom 49.

13. What is the probability that the wife will outlive her husband?

In most families the wife outlives her husband. Widows today outnumber widowers almost four to one in this country. The chances are almost three in five that the wife will survive her husband when both are the same age. When the husband is five years older, the chances are seven in ten that his wife will outlive him; and when he is ten years older, the chances rise to eight in ten. Only when the husband is around four years younger than his wife are the chances of survival about the same for both.

14. What factors contribute toward the lower mortality of the married?

One study of the married and unmarried in New York State showed that married men had lower mortality rates than bachelors at all ages, but that the differential was greatest among those aged 25 to 44, when family responsibilities were also greatest. Among women, on the other hand, wives had an advantage over spinsters up to age 40; thereafter there was little difference between the mortality rates of the two groups. In part, the lower mortality of the married is the result of selection in favor of those who get married. In addition, of course, there are the direct physical and psychological advantages of family life.

15. What is a broken family?

A broken family is one which has been disrupted by divorce, separation, or the death of either the husband or wife. In April 1960, broken families constituted one-eighth of all families in the United States. Death was by far the chief cause of family disruption. Of the 4,557,000 broken families in the country, 2,549,000 were headed by a widow or a widower, whereas only 1,503,000 were headed by someone who had been separated or divorced and not remarried.

16. Are broken homes common among the colored? How about farm populations?

The proportion of broken homes among the colored is markedly higher than among whites. In 1960, about 25 percent of the colored families, compared with 12 percent of all families, were headed by a person who was separated, widowed, or divorced. Most of this difference was caused by a much larger proportion widowed among the colored, reflecting the higher mortality of nonwhite persons.

Among farm families, only 9 percent were headed by someone who had been separated, widowed, or divorced, relatively fewer than for the country as a whole. There were proportionately fewer widows heading families on farms than in cities or in rural nonfarm areas.

17. In what proportion of broken homes are there children under 18 and what fraction of all children under 18 do they constitute?

Of the 60.3 million children less than 18 years old in 1960, 4.8 million, or about 1 in 12, lived with only one parent. About five-sixths of them were with their mother, and the remaining one-sixth with their father. Over one-third of these fathers with dependent children were widowers, almost one-half were separated from their wives; the rest were divorced and not remarried. Among the women with young children, over one-third were widowed, over one-third were separated, and less than one-third divorced.

18. How many widows are there in the country?

There were close to 8.4 million widows in the United States in 1962; 130,000 were less than 35 years old; 1,326,000 were between 35 and 55, and 6,943,000 were past 55. About one-quarter of the women who become widowed in a year are under 45 years old; another quarter are 45 to 54, about the same proportions are from 55 to 64, and slightly less than one-quarter are over 65. There are fewer men than women widowed. In 1962, there were more than two million widowers in the country, 23,000 of them under age 35, 280,000 between 35 and 54, and 1,825,000 over 55.

19. How do the problems of widowhood vary with age?

Close to 3 out of every 10 widows have children under 18, the proportion declining from more than one-fifth for those widowed less than 2 years to about one-thirtieth for those widowed 10 years or more. Nearly half of the widows whose children are not yet six (too young to be in school) are in the labor force.

The great majority of women recently widowed maintain their

own households, but the proportion decreases with the number of years of widowhood. Of those widowed less than two years, 22 percent are living with relatives, compared with 38 percent of those widowed 10 years or more.

20. How many years of widowhood may a woman at age 45 anticipate? At age 65?

At age 45, if she is white, she can expect to live an additional 32.5 years; at age 65, an additional 15.9 years. If colored, the two figures are 28.0 and 15.2 years, respectively.

With improved longevity, widows at present have many more years ahead of them than widows at corresponding ages 60 years ago.

21. How do the problems of the widower differ from those of the widow?

Fewer widowers have dependent children. Moreover, widowers with dependent children are very likely to remarry. This accounts in part for the fact that only 28 percent of the widowers, compared with 34 percent of the widows, were widowed for 15 years or more.

22. How many children are orphaned a year in the United States?

In 1955, about 350,000 children under 18 became orphans—that is, they lost at least one parent through death. Of these, about 225,000 lost their fathers. One of the unfortunate aspects of orphanhood is that it is most common among those least able to cope with the problems; these are the poorer socio-economic groups who generally experience a mortality above average.

23. What are the chances that a baby just born will be orphaned before 18?

The chances of being orphaned depend upon the ages of the parents. With current mortality, the chances are 4 in 100 that a white infant whose father is 25 years old will lose him before reaching the age of 18; the chances are about 15 in 100 if the father is 40 years old. The likelihood of losing its mother is less; 2 in 100 if the mother is 25, and 8 in 100 if she is 40.

The chances of both paternal and maternal orphanhood have greatly decreased in the last half century, reflecting the extraordinary improvement in mortality of persons at the childbearing ages during this period.

24. How many orphaned children are there in the United States?

It is estimated that there were over three million children under age 18 in 1962 who had lost one or both parents by death. Of this total, about 2,100,000 lost their father only, 850,000 lost their mother only, and 65,000 lost both parents. The proportion orphaned increases rapidly with the age of the children.

25. How many children have been saved from orphanhood by improvement in mortality?

If the mortality conditions prevailing at the turn of the century had continued, there would have been over four times the current number of orphans. The greatest proportional saving was among those who might have lost both parents; next, among those who might have lost their mothers; and third, among those who might have lost their fathers.

26. At what age is the family responsibility of a father at a maximum?

Family responsibility is an all-inclusive concept, but if it is confined to the idea of financial responsibility it may be measured in terms of the normal consumption of adults. An adult consumption unit is the cost of providing food, clothing, shelter, recreation, medical care, and other items required by the average adult male. For the average American man aged 20, consumption measured in this way is about one unit; he is probably still unmarried and need care only for himself. In his twenties, with marriage and the birth of children, responsibilities start rising and come to about three units for the average American man aged 30. The peak of 3.75 units is reached at about the age of 40. Thereafter responsibility declines as grown children leave the home until it amounts to only about two units from age 60 on—just enough for the husband and wife.

27. What proportion of wives work?

In the spring of 1960 slightly less than one-third of the wives living with their husbands were in the labor force; i.e., either working or looking for jobs. Nearly one-half of the women in their first year of marriage had entered or were still in the labor market, but the proportion declined with the duration of marriage.

The proportion of widows working was greater than for wives, and the proportion of divorcees in the labor force was even greater. About 3 out of every 10 widows had jobs or were looking for them.

Of the divorcees, 7 out of every 10 in this country were working women.

28. How much has the typical family income increased since the war years?

In 1962, the average family had an income of $7,140. This is about twice the average for the war years. But this increase must be discounted by the fall in the value of the dollar. The increase in average family income in constant-value dollars is only slightly over 50 percent since the war years.

29. What proportion of families are there at the high, moderate, and low income levels?

Close to one-third of the families in the nation had incomes of less than $4,000 in 1961. The lowest one-fifth of all families averaged about $1,600 in that year. Most of them were farm families. Cash incomes, however, are not a reliable index of farm prosperity, because so many farm families raise a large share of their own food.

30. How does income vary with the age of the head of the family?

Income increases with the age of the family head to a maximum at ages 35 to 44 years, and then starts to fall. The greatest change is between those aged 55 to 64 and those 65 and over. In 1959, the median income of families with the family head under 35 was $5,533; the median income of those with heads 45 to 64 was $6,456, and for those 65 and over, the comparable figure was $3,050. Urban families had a greater income than rural in every age group, but the general age pattern was the same for both urban and rural families.

31. What is the relation of family health to income?

Low income families have more frequent attacks of illness and more days of disability from sickness per person than do families in more comfortable circumstances. A similar relationship exists with respect to mortality. Infant mortality, maternal mortality, and the death rates from a number of causes of death vary inversely with income.

32. What effect does the amount of schooling have on family income?

The average income rises directly with the amount of school years completed. In 1959, the average income of persons 25 years old and over, who had had only one to four years elementary schooling was $1,844; with one to three years of high school, $4,847; while those with four years or more of college amounted to $7,646.

The average income is considerably higher for white than for nonwhite males for each schooling category, but the general pattern of rise with the amount of schooling prevails in both groups.

33. How do most families budget their spending?

Food is the largest single item of expenditure for American families. The table below, based on family income for 1960–61, shows the distribution of expenditures for current consumption by income class of average American urban families. With a rise in income the proportion spent on food and shelter declines, while relatively more is spent on clothing, recreation, and transportation. A study of the distribution of family income in a number of cities

PERCENT DISTRIBUTION OF MAJOR EXPENDITURES FOR CURRENT CONSUMPTION BY INCOME CLASS— ALL URBAN FAMILIES—UNITED STATES 1960–61*

Item	All Families	$1,000 to 1,999	$2,000 to 2,999	$3,000 to 3,999	$6,000 to 7,499	$7,500 to 9,999	$15,000 and over
All Items	100.0	100.0	100.0	100.0	100.0	100.0	100.0
Food & Beverages	26.0	30.9	29.6	27.4	25.9	25.8	21.0
Home & Operations[1]	24.3	35.4	30.2	26.6	23.6	22.2	24.3
Furnishings & Equipment	5.1	3.6	3.9	4.7	5.5	5.4	5.3
Clothing	10.4	6.1	8.2	9.0	10.3	11.1	12.3
Transportation	14.7	5.4	8.6	13.1	15.3	16.0	14.2
Medical	6.6	8.0	8.1	7.3	6.5	6.3	6.2
Other Goods & Services[2]	10.7	8.1	9.5	10.0	10.7	11.1	11.7
Other Costs	2.2	2.4	1.9	1.7	2.1	2.0	5.0

* *Source*—Bureau of Labor Statistics Report 237-38—April 1964.
[1] Includes shelter, fuel, light, refrigeration, water, and household operations.
[2] Includes tobacco, personal care, recreation, reading, and education.

shows little relative change in the proportion of total spending for each of the main consumption items. The table makes no provision for savings, gifts and contributions, personal insurance, and taxes as these are not consumption items.

34. How do family expenditures vary with increased income?

With a rise in income the proportion spent on food and shelter declines, while relatively more is spent on clothing, recreation, and on automobiles. Home furnishings take an increasing share, and savings, insurance, and charitable donations also rise proportionately, but medical care apparently consumes about the same fraction of total expenditures for families within most income groups.

35. How do family savings vary as the head of the family ages?

Family savings, on the average, increase with the age of the head of the family. The greatest proportion of families with relatively small annual savings in relation to their incomes are found among those whose heads are less than 25 years old. Even among those in the 25- to 34-year-old group, a large number of families save very little. Not only are the costs of getting a family going, buying a home, and all the other expenses of the first 10 years of married life high, but men under 35 are still far from their peak earnings. After about the age of 45, there is a spurt in the proportion of families saving in relation to their incomes. Because of decreased family costs and increased income, this spurt in savings may continue until the head of the family retires from active employment.

36. What factors enter into a consideration of the money value of a man to his family?

Broadly speaking, the money value of a man to his family is the present worth of his future earnings less the cost of his maintenance. Calculation of this amount involves a consideration of the chances of employment, probable future earnings for each period of his career, the expected chances of survival, the probable savings at each age, future interest rates, and the size of the family.

A study made in 1946 of the money value of the net future earnings for men of specific age and annual earnings showed a value of $32,300 for a man 30 years of age and earning $2,500; a value of $53,200 for a man at this age earning $3,500; and close to $100,000 for a young man in the $5,000 income class. At higher income levels, the net values of future earnings are much greater.

37. What proportion of homes are owned by their occupants?

Of the 53,000,000 dwelling units occupied by residents in the United States in 1960, about 62 percent were owned by the families who lived in them. In urban areas only about 61 percent were owner-occupied, compared with about 74 percent in rural areas. Since 1940 there has been a marked rise in owner occupancy. Before World War II only 44 percent of all homes in the nation were owned by the persons living in them.

38. How many persons are there per room in most households?

The average number of persons per room in 1960 was 3.0, slightly higher in owner-occupied housing units (3.1) and lower in rented housing units. On the basis of persons per room, housing units on the average were less crowded in 1960 than they were in 1950 or 1940. About 12 percent of the occupied units in 1960 had more than one person per room, compared with 16 percent in 1950 and 20 percent in 1940.

39. What rents do most people pay in the United States?

About 25 percent of the tenant-occupied dwelling units in urban and in rural nonfarm locations rented for less than $40 a month in 1960; 10.5 percent paid a monthly rental of $100 or more. The amount of rent paid increased with the number of rooms in the unit rented.

40. What parts do governmental programs and private insurance play in family protection?

Securing the family against the economic and health hazards of modern life is one of the major aims of the society in which we live. Life insurance and annuities help families and the survivors of death-broken homes to stay together. In addition, private health and hospitalization insurance now aid the large majority of the population in meeting the financial problems of illness and accidents. Private pension and retirement plans are being rapidly extended. Private insurance and personal savings are the primary source of protection for most families. The federal, state, and local governments, however, provide a variety of financial aids. The federal government operates old-age and survivor's insurance, paying benefits to persons reaching 62 and to their wives, or under the survivor's plan to the dependents of insured persons who have died. In addition, the federal government contributes to the state unemployment insurance and public assistance programs which aid needy families and children and also the blind, as well as those out of work. Under state laws, various workmen's compensation benefits are available to workers or their widows in case of occupational accidents or illness. Several states also have laws providing for the insurance of workers against total loss of income because of illness. And finally, the states and localities operate general assistance programs for those not eligible for the other forms of aid.

Private and public contributions to the protection of the family are tremendous. In 1962, for example, 2,264,000 life insurance death claims were paid by private companies in the United States, the total benefits reaching nearly $4 billion. In that year 85 percent of all husband-wife families were covered by some kind of life insurance, and the average amount of life insurance owned per family was $11,400. The various governmental programs in 1962 were paying benefits to approximately 1 out of every 10 persons, though this figure includes some duplications for those receiving payments under more than one government assistance plan.

Chapter 5

Marital Dissolution
by Divorce,[1]
Separation, and Death

1. What are the chances that a marriage will end in divorce?

Currently, about 1 out of every 10 marriages is dissolved by divorce or annulment within the first five years of marriage and about one out of every six within the first 10 years. If recent trends in divorce and mortality continue unchanged, about one out of every three marriages started in the past decade will eventually end in divorce and two-thirds will last until the death of either the husband or wife.

[1] In this chapter, the term "divorce" includes absolute divorce and annulment; limited divorces such as bed and board, legal separation, and separate maintenance decrees are grouped together under the general term "separation," and are treated only in questions 45 to 48.

2. How many divorces are granted annually in the United States?

Almost 400,000 divorces and annulments are now granted each year. This is a sharp drop from the peak year 1946, when about 629,000 were granted. By contrast, however, in no year prior to World War II did the figure reach as high as 300,000. The greater number of divorces granted currently is due in part to the increase of our married population, but more especially to the rise of the divorce rate.

3. What has been the trend of our divorce rate?

The divorce rate in the United States has risen with few interruptions throughout our history. In a period of roughly 90 years, it has increased sixfold. Immediately after the Civil War, the rate was less than 2 divorces annually per 1,000 married couples; by the beginning of World War I, it was about 5 per 1,000; and at the time of Pearl Harbor, it was almost 10 per 1,000. At present, about 10 divorces are granted each year for every 1,000 married couples. Although this is a pronounced drop from the postwar peak of 18.2 in 1946, it exceeds the rate for every year prior to 1941.

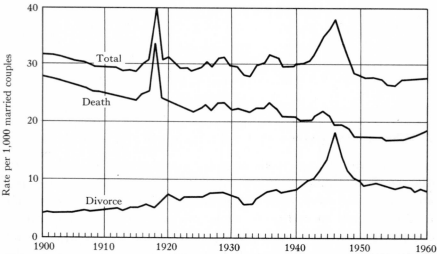

Chart 4. Marital dissolutions by death and divorce, United States, 1900–1960.

4. Are there more divorced (and not remarried) women than men in the United States?

In 1960, close to three-fifths of our divorced (and not remarried) population were women. In fact, every federal census since 1890—the first to make available statistics by marital status—has reported more divorced women than men. The excess of divorcees results primarily from the fact that the remarriage rate is higher for divorced men than women, and also from the higher mortality rate for men.

5. Is there a most popular month for divorce?

Although there is some seasonal variation in divorce, it results primarily from the laws and court procedure rather than from the choice of those getting divorced. Since most courts take a summer recess, fewer divorces are granted during those months. In 1950, for example, the daily average number of divorces in August was the lowest for the year.

6. How does the divorce rate in the United States compare with that in other countries?

With the possible exception of Egypt, the divorce rate in the United States is probably the highest in the world. In 1960, the most recent period for which reasonably comparable data are available, the rate in Egypt (UAR) was 2.5 per 1,000 population. Our rate—2.2—was about double that of Austria, West Germany, and the USSR, and four times that of England and Wales—0.51.

Throughout the world the long-term trend of divorce since World War II has been upward almost universally. In consequence, the disparity among most nations is much smaller today than before the World War, or at the turn of the century.

7. What is the trend in the rate of divorce in various regions of our country?

Substantial increases in the rate of divorce have been recorded in all regions. The most pronounced rise, however, has occurred in the South and on the West Coast. The lowest rate is in the Northeast region, followed by the North Central, the South, and the West. The rate is almost four times as high in the West as in the Northeast.

In general, the frequency of divorce tends to increase as one moves from east to west, and from north to south.

8. How do urban and rural divorce rates compare?

The divorce rate has long been higher among the urban than the rural population. As a consequence, the rapid growth of urban communities in our country has contributed to the rise in the national divorce rate. However, the indications are that since 1940 the divorce rate has increased more rapidly among the farm population than among city dwellers.

9. Do all states grant divorce?

Today, all states grant divorce. South Carolina, which from 1878 to 1948 had no divorce law and granted only annulments, was the last to enact such legislation.

10. Which state has the strictest divorce law?

New York State stands in a class by itself, since absolute divorce may be granted only for adultery or for presumed death after an absence for five consecutive years (Enoch Arden decree). Moreover, the New York law prohibits for three years the remarriage of the guilty party in an adultery case. The result is that New York State, which contains almost one-tenth of the country's population, grants less than one-fortieth of the absolute divorce decrees.

11. In what states and cities is it easiest to obtain a divorce in our country?

Reno and Las Vegas, Nevada, and Miami, Florida, undoubtedly attract the largest number of persons in the United States who migrate for the purpose of securing a divorce. This is understandable since both Nevada and Florida have liberal divorce laws; in each, the decree is final upon entry of the court's judgment and either party may remarry at once. In Florida, only 90 days' residence is necessary before bringing suit, and in Nevada only six weeks. Moreover, in all three of the cities mentioned, the hotel and entertainment facilities are conducive to residence long enough to meet the legal requirements.

12. Do any states besides Nevada and Florida have liberal residence requirements?

Arkansas and Wyoming require a residence of 60 days, and Idaho only six weeks. In contrast, in Connecticut and Massachusetts at least three years' residence is necessary before divorce proceedings may be instituted. Most other states require a residence of one year.

13. How many go outside the country for a divorce?

Fewer than 3,000 of our marriages are dissolved annually by divorces obtained outside the country. Mexico probably accounts for at least nine-tenths of the total. Our possession in the Virgin Islands is also said to be catering to divorce-seekers from the States. Although the number of these decrees in the Virgin Islands has been increasing slowly, it has not yet reached much above 150 a year. Divorces secured in recent years in other foreign places are even fewer in number.

14. Are all applications for divorce granted?

In the country as a whole, only about three-fourths are granted. The proportion varies considerably from state to state, and even from county to county within a state, according to the customs and practices of the courts.

15. How does war affect the divorce rate?

Immediately after the end of a war, the divorce rate generally rises sharply. This was certainly the case in our country after the two World Wars, and there is evidence that a postwar rise also occurred after the Civil War. Apparently, hasty courtship, long separation, and the general difficulty of readjustment to postwar life lead to instability in many war marriages. After the recent war, the rise in divorce was sharpest among those married less than five years—essentially those married during the war.

16. How do business conditions affect the divorce rate?

In general, there are more divorces in periods of prosperity and fewer in depressions. With the improvement of economic conditions in the years preceding Pearl Harbor, the divorce rate in the United States rose. The last war and postwar boom in divorce may also be explained in part by the war-induced economic prosperity. This is especially true for the early war years when the divorce rate went up most abruptly among couples married 10 years or longer. Very likely, some of these divorces were postponed from the Depression period. Inability to pay alimony and the costs of court litigation are undoubtedly factors in the decline of marital dissolutions during periods of deflation. But that is not all: hard times may also curtail hasty marriages.

17. Which occupations have the highest divorce rate?

In general, divorce rates are high in occupations involving irregular hours or frequent absence from home overnight, and those requiring association with the opposite sex with little or no community chaperonage. Actors, traveling salesmen, musicians, military personnel, seamen, and physicians appear to have more than their share of divorces, while clergymen, farmers, and miners have fewer than average.

18. Is the divorce rate higher for native white Americans than for the foreign-born?

Yes, and among the native whites the third generation Americans have a higher divorce rate than the second generation. The relatively low divorce rate among the foreign-born results from a number of factors. Since the rate in the country from which they have emigrated is comparatively low, the foreign-born are culturally less inclined to seek divorce in case of marital difficulty. General distrust of courts and language difficulties also contribute to the low frequency of divorce among them.

19. Is the divorce rate lower for Negroes than for the white population?

The best available evidence indicates that nationally the divorce rate is lower among Negroes. Desertion and informal separation, however, have long been common occurrences among them. This is especially the case in the rural South, but these practices have also been carried along generally with the Negro in his migration to northern and urban centers. In addition, the cost of divorce is a greater deterrent to Negroes because of their lower income. Thus, Negroes in our large cities contribute a disproportionate share of desertions, but not of divorces. In recent years, however, the situation has been changing. The divorce rate has increased more rapidly among Negroes than whites. In some areas, the Negro rate has already surpassed the rate for whites.

20. Are divorce rates affected by the marriage rate?

A rise in the marriage rate means proportionately more newly married couples. Because the divorce rate is highest in the early years of marriage, the number of divorces rises faster than the total number of married persons; this situation leads to an increased divorce rate. The relationship works both ways; a decline in the marriage rate is subsequently followed by a decrease in the divorce rate.

21. What has been the trend in the divorce rate among newly married couples?

The divorce rate has risen sharply at all stages of married life. Since 1922–24, the rate among couples married less than five years has almost doubled. Smaller increases were recorded for families of 5 to 20 years standing; for longer-term marriages, the rate has increased by about one-quarter during this period.

22. What proportion of divorces are granted in the first 10 years of marriage?

Currently, about two-fifths of all divorces and annulments are granted to couples married less than five years, and one-fourth to those married for five to nine years. The remaining divorces are spread out over many years of marriage, with the proportion decreasing as the duration of marriage is extended. Even so, couples married 20 years or more are granted about one-ninth of all divorces.

23. How frequent are divorces among couples married more than 20 years?

Currently 6 divorces are granted annually for every 1,000 couples married 20 years or longer. The divorce rate, of course, is not uniform for all years of marriage after the twentieth. From under 6 per 1,000 at the twentieth anniversary, it falls steeply to almost 1 per 1,000 by the fortieth year of marriage. A few couples get divorced even after their golden wedding anniversary. In many of the divorces effected decades after marriage, the husband and wife have already been living apart for years.

24. What is the average duration of marriages which terminate in divorce?

In 1960, more than 30 percent of the divorces occurred in less than four years after marriage, and over one-half occurred in less than eight years. Previous marital experience of husband and wife affects the duration of marriage prior to divorce.

25. Do the chances of divorce vary with the age at marriage?

The chances of divorce do not change much within the normal range of age at marriage—from around 17 to 40—but beyond these very rough limits, the likelihood of divorce appears to be greater. Similarly, there seems to be little variation in the frequency of divorce in marriages where the wife is older by not more than 5 years or where the husband is older by not more than 10 years. Where there are great age gaps between marriage partners, there is a tendency toward extremes in adjustment—either very good or very poor. The younger party to such a marriage, or either one if both are relatively young, is likely to seek divorce once marital difficulties arise, because the chances of remarriage are still good.

26. At what age is divorce most frequent?

The divorce rate is at a maximum among men and women not yet 25; thereafter, it declines throughout life. For husbands past 55 and wives past 50, the rate is less than one-half the average for married persons of all ages.

27. What is the chance of remarriage for the divorced?

The remarriage rate for the divorced rose sharply after the two world wars, reaching the maximum of 357 per 1,000 for divorced men in 1946, and 285 per 1,000 for divorced women in that year. The remarriage rates of the divorced have steadily declined since, but are still much higher than for the single or widowed.

The remarriage rate declined perceptibly during the years of the Depression period.

28. Are the divorced and widowed good marriage risks?

In general, they are not. Although many second marriages are successful, as a group the divorced and widowed who have remarried experience a relatively high divorce rate. In Iowa, for example, where remarrying brides and grooms constitute only one-sixth of the total marriages, persons married more than once account for one-fourth of all divorces. Moreover, it appears that the frequency of divorce rises substantially with each successive marriage.

Children in Divorce

29. Are most divorced couples childless?

In the 16 states for which data were available for the year 1959, there were no children under 18 years of age in 35.6 percent of the cases; one child was involved in 22.2 percent; two children in 16.0 percent; and three or more in 13.2 percent; and no information about children reported in 13.1 percent. The figures vary, however, from state to state.

The proportion of divorced couples with children also varies with the duration of marriage—from very low figures in the marriages of short duration to a maximum of about two in every three divorces with duration of 18 years. Children are actually involved in more than half of the divorces granted to couples married 7 to 23 years. At the longer durations of marriage, the proportion of divorces which involve dependent children is again small because most of the off-spring have already grown up and left home.

30. Do children lessen the chances of divorce?

Thirty years ago, divorce was more than three times as frequent among the childless as among those with children. More recently, however, the difference between couples without and with children has greatly diminished. In 1955, divorce was less than two times as frequent among the childless as among those with children. After the twentieth year of marriage, the differential between the childless and those with children diminishes rapidly and disappears completely by the thirtieth. The rate of divorce also drops with rise in the number of children. For couples with four or more children, it is considerably less than half what it is for those with only one child. (See Charts 5 and 6.)

Although it would seem reasonable to ascribe some of these dif-ferences to parental affection and responsibility, it is probably also

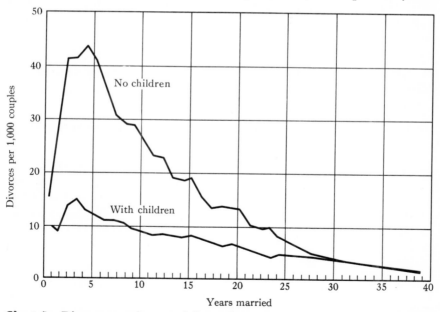

Chart 5. Divorce rate for married couples with and without children under age 18, according to duration of marriage, United States, 1948.

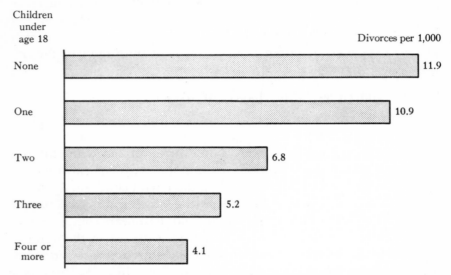

Chart 6. **Divorces per 1,000 married couples by size of family, United States, 1955.**

true that the absence of children is in itself not necessarily a cause of divorce. Both divorce and childlessness result from more fundamental factors in the marital relationship.

31. How many children are affected by divorce?

Over one-third of a million children have been affected by divorces or annulments granted in each of the recent years, or roughly, one for every marriage dissolved.

32. Is the number of children affected by divorce increasing more rapidly than the number of divorces?

Both have increased, but the uptrend has been sharper for the number of children affected. The proportion of divorces involving children has grown from about 38 percent during the period 1922–32 to 64.4 percent in 1959. As a result, the average number of children per divorce has risen appreciably.

33. To whose custody are children of divorced couples generally entrusted?

The mother receives custody of the children in two-thirds to five-sixths of the cases; the husband is awarded custody in about one-tenth. In the small remaining proportion of divorces, the children are awarded to someone else, or no provision is written into the decree. Generally, children are awarded to the petitioner for divorce, which is usually the wife. In most instances in which the husband is the plaintiff, he is awarded the children. There is also some tendency for the mother to be given custody of girls and the father of boys. Regardless of the custody award, however, most divorce decrees make provision for the other parent to visit or to be visited by the children.

Court Procedure

34. What proportion of divorces are granted to the wife?

Divorces are normally granted to the plaintiff, i.e., the one who starts the court action. This is the wife in two out of every three cases. The reason the plaintiff usually gets the divorce is that all but a handful of divorce actions are uncontested.

35. What are the legal grounds most frequently alleged in divorce actions?

In 1959, cruelty was the principal legal ground for divorce, accounting for 51.6 percent of the total divorces reported by 16 states. This was followed by desertion, 23.2 percent. The remaining grounds for divorce such as adultery, drunkenness, and a long list of others, account for only a small percentage of the divorces. The figures for each vary from state to state, reflecting the laws in the respective states. After the twenty-fifth year of marriage, desertion is the most frequent recorded cause.

36. In what proportion of divorce cases is alimony granted?

Alimony is granted in a little more than one-fourth of the divorces ordered. The chances of receiving alimony, maintenance, or support vary from state to state, and are about five times as great in Wisconsin as in Florida. There are some indications that the trend is toward curtailment of alimony, and many decrees now stipulate that payments shall cease upon remarriage of the ex-wife, or that there be a mandatory revision of payments upon her remarriage.

37. Are husbands ever granted alimony?

In recent years there have been court decisions to the effect that husbands are also entitled to alimony under certain circumstances. However, requests for alimony by husbands are extremely rare and can only be granted in those states in which specific statutory authority allows it. In general, requests for alimony are granted most frequently when the welfare of children is involved. As most children are awarded to the custody of the wife rather than the husband, husbands rarely get alimony.

Annulment

38. What is the difference between annulment of a marriage and divorce?

An annulment of a marriage is a legal decree that no valid marriage was contracted because of some condition which existed at the time of marriage. A divorce, on the other hand, is a legal decree which dissolves or partially suspends a legally recognized union for some action or occurrence after the establishment of the marriage. In modern law, the term "divorce" is usually specifically applied to *Divorce A Vinculo Matrimonii* or absolute divorce, in contrast to *Divorce A Mensa Et Thoro* or separation from bed and board. The first type of divorce puts an end to the marriage; the second authorizes separate maintenance, but leaves the marriage bond in full force.

39. What are the grounds for most annulments?

Fraudulent representation, being under the legal age for marriage, and bigamy, in the order named, are the most frequent grounds for annulment in the United States and account for fully four-fifths of the total. "Fraudulent representation," which is by far the more popular cause alleged in California and New York, is a general phrase covering a number of specific causes, such as misrepresentation of financial standing or willingness to have children, deception as to character, and physical incapacity. In most other states, bigamy accounts for the largest number of annulments.

40. How many annulments are granted annually in the United States?

An average of about 13,000 annulments have been granted annually in recent years. The number rose to an all-time high of about 22,000 in 1946, but has since declined.

41. Do annulments constitute a large proportion of all legal marital dissolutions?

In the country as a whole, annulments constitute only a little more than 3 percent of the total legal marital dissolutions. In California and New York, however, they account for much greater proportions; in California about one-ninth, and in New York almost two-fifths. Both states have relatively restrictive laws governing absolute divorce; in California, there is a one-year interlocutory period before a decree becomes final; and in New York, aside from Enoch Arden decrees, adultery is the only ground for absolute divorce and the guilty party may not remarry for at least three years.

42. Have annulments risen more rapidly than divorces in recent years?

After World War I, annulments represented about 2 percent of all legal marital dissolutions in the United States; today, they account for more than 3 percent.

43. In what period of marriage are annulments granted?

In New York State, about four-fifths are granted in the first five years of marriage. In general, however, there is no time limit within which an annulment must be requested. In fact, a small number occur even after 20 years of marriage.

44. Are annulments ever granted to couples who have children?

If there are legal grounds for annulment, the presence of children does not prevent its being obtained. At common law, the children of couples whose marriages had been annulled were considered illegitimate, but many states now have statutes which specify the legitimacy of such offspring. Some states have even modified their divorce law to include the grounds for annulment, in order to protect the interests of the offspring and parties to a marriage which is annulled.

Separations

45. How many legal separations (bed and board decrees) are granted in the United States each year?

Probably fewer than 15,000 legal separations a year are granted in the United States. This is roughly equivalent to one legal separation for every 25 absolute divorces or annulments granted. Some of these separations are followed by absolute divorces in subsequent years. Legal separations are, of course, not the only kind which occur. Some separations are informal, as separation by private agreement, abandonment, or desertion.

46. How many abandonments or desertions occur each year?

It has been estimated that more than 50,000 abandonments or desertions take place each year, with the husband usually the deserter. Desertions, or "poor men's divorces," are not always permanent; the deserter in many instances returns voluntarily to his family, perhaps only to repeat the performance in a subsequent year. In some cases, however, the act of desertion becomes the basis for a later divorce.

47. How many couples separated either legally or informally are there in the United States?

At any one time, the husbands and wives in close to one million marriages—almost 3 percent of the total of all couples—are living apart in the United States. This figure includes those who have already applied for an absolute divorce, those separated legally, and those separated by private agreement or no agreement at all. Since some of them continue to live apart for the balance of their lives without ever getting divorced, there is a gradual increase in the frequency of separated couples with advance in age.

48. Are there more separated couples in states with low divorce rates?

In general, no. Nevada, for example, with one of the most liberal divorce laws and the highest recorded divorce rate, also ranks first in frequency of separated couples. At the other extreme, South Carolina, which used to grant no absolute divorce, has one of the lowest recorded rates for separated families. Some of the Northeastern states, however, are exceptions to the rule. New York State, with the strictest divorce law and one of the lowest recorded divorce rates, ranks near the top in the frequency of separated couples. Similarly, Connecticut, Massachusetts, New Jersey, and Rhode Island have low divorce rates, but in all four states a relatively large number of husbands and wives live apart.

Role of Mortality in Marital Dissolutions

49. How many families are broken annually through the death of either husband or wife?

About 800,000 families are broken up each year by death, two-thirds of them by the death of the husband. The husband usually dies first because the rate of mortality among men is higher than among women and because the husband is generally several years older than his wife.

50. What are the chances that a wife will outlive her husband?[2]

51. To how many years of life together may a bride and groom look forward?[3]

52. Are more children affected by divorce than become orphaned?

Despite the decline of mortality and the rise of divorce, the annual toll of orphans is still greater than the number of children affected by divorce. Currently close to 400,000 children under 18 become orphaned each year, whereas not quite 350,000 children under 18 are annually affected by divorce.

53. What is the relative contribution of death and divorce to the total of marital dissolutions?

Death breaks more families than divorce, but the relative importance of divorce has been increasing almost steadily throughout our history. In 1890, divorce accounted for less than one-tenth of all marital dissolutions; today, the figure is close to four-tenths. The relative contribution of death and divorce in breaking up families varies with the duration of marriage. In the early years of marriage, divorce constitutes a far greater hazard to the continuity of family life than death. In the third year of marriage, for example, the divorce rate is about three and a half times the disruption rate from the death of either husband or wife. It is not until about the fifteenth year that divorce becomes less frequent than death. Thereafter, the frequency of divorce continues to fall and death takes an increasing toll.

54. Has the breakup of families become more frequent?

Not in the past 60 years at least. The upswing of divorce has been more than offset by the decline in family disruptions due to mortality. From 1890 to 1915, the combined rate of marital dissolutions dropped from 33 families broken annually per 1,000 to 29 because of decreasing mortality. The rise in marriage dissolutions in 1918 to a high of 40 per 1,000 was also primarily a reflection

[2] This is answered in Question 13 of Chapter 4, page 52.
[3] This is answered in Question 12 of Chapter 4, page 51.

of the death rate, in this case of the influenza pandemic which struck in the autumn of that year. (See Chart 4 on page 62.)

After the influenza outbreak and until the beginning of World War II, the rate of marital dissolutions fluctuated with no definite upward or downward trend, although early in the Depression the rate dropped to the lowest point of the entire series—very likely the lowest in our history. Throughout World War II, marital dissolutions rose rapidly as a result of the mounting divorce rate and reached a high of 38 per 1,000 in 1946. With the readjustment to peacetime life, the divorce rate receded so sharply that the level of total dissolutions is now back to where it had been before the war.

Chapter 6

The Sick
and Their Care

1. What is health?

Although there are many concepts of health, perhaps the best is that stated in the charter of the World Health Organization. According to this definition, "Health is the state of complete physical, mental, and social well-being and not merely the absence of disease or infirmity."

2. Through what agencies is this ideal achieved?

First and foremost are the medical and the allied professions. They care for the sick and conduct the research which extends our knowledge of the causes of diseases and the best ways to treat them. They direct the huge facilities which have been built to protect the health of the people and are a powerful force in educating the people in personal hygiene.

Next are the public health authorities, primarily concerned with preventive measures. They protect our food and water supplies, maintain sanitary standards, provide for immunizations, maternal and child health clinics, and for a multitude of services which help to maintain the health of the people. Our voluntary health agencies are an important element in our health system. They have pioneered in demonstrating new fields of health control, they support medical research, and they carry on intensive campaigns of health education directly to the public.

Finally, there is the informed public who because of their knowledge cooperate with the medical profession, the public health authorities, and the voluntary health agencies. The public also supports our voluntary agencies. These joint forces—medicine, public health, voluntary agencies, and enlightened public—are our best guarantee for the achievement of the ideal of good health.

3. What is illness?

To define illness is difficult, for it is not an entirely objective phenomenon. It depends somewhat upon individual circumstances and personal idiosyncracies. There are many millions of gainfully occupied persons with handicaps and chronic ailments which they do not recognize. Even if they do, they may not consider the ailments as serious or regard themselves as being so ill that they cannot continue their normal activities. Others with the same impairments may consider themselves so seriously ill as to interfere with gainful work or other ordinary activity. Economic conditions also play a part. Some may regard themselves as disabled when employment is hard to find, but return to work when jobs are plentiful.

In surveys to ascertain the prevalence of illness, the definition of illness has sometimes been broad. In such cases it may include all those whom the household informant has considered as ill, whether they have been under medical attention or not and whether the illness did or did not interfere with employment or other normal activities. On other occasions, the definition has been restricted to those confined in the home, hospital, or institution, and unable to work or follow their usual activities for a definite period of time. The difference between *disabling* illness and *all* illness, including that which is nondisabling, is thus usually marked. Consequently, in any discussion of sickness, the first point of consideration is the definition of illness and, second, the use to which the record will be put.

4. How many people are unable to work or carry on their usual activities because of illness on any given day in the United States?

The number has varied from 1.5 to over 5 percent of the population in the various surveys of illness made during the past 45 or more years. The results reflect the definition of illness, the method of gathering the data, the season of the year in which the count is made, and the emphasis placed on securing a complete record of the blind, crippled, and mental defectives, as well as the number of patients in institutions. The general economic conditions at the time of the survey likewise affect such figures materially. During the year 1962, close to 2 percent of the working population were away from work on an average day because of illness.

5. How does season affect the amount of illness reported?

The amount of illness varies with the season of the year in northern climates. From a high recorded in January and February, the prevalence of illness drops to a low in the late summer and then rises toward the end of the year. Seasonal variation in the amount of reported illness is mainly due to fluctuations in the amount of short-term illness; in this, the respiratory diseases are a major factor. Improved sanitation and closer supervision of milk, food, and water supplies have reduced the prevalence of the diarrheal diseases which formerly caused a secondary peak in the summer months.

6. What proportion of the population suffer no illness in the year; one illness; two illnesses; etc.?

Considering as illness all frank and recognized attacks of disease accompanied by discomfort, pain, loss of function, or disability, whether there is medical attention or not, it was found in one survey that almost one-half of the persons reported no illness during the year. One illness was reported for about one-third of the group, two illnesses for one-eighth, and three illnesses for only one-twentieth. Less than 1 in 100 were ill five or more times during the year. It is difficult to believe, however, that so large a fraction of any group of people could go through a year without so much as a severe headache or a minor sprain. This only shows how uncertain are the results of health surveys which depend so much on the accuracy of the memory of the respondent, on his disposition or attitude of mind toward the inquiry, and on other fortuitous factors. In other surveys with more complete records of minor (especially respiratory) illness, there were smaller proportions with no illness and larger proportions with one or more cases.

7. At what rate do cases of illness occur annually?

In a survey conducted by the United States Public Health Service, 1961–62, the average frequency of acute conditions requiring medical attention or reduced activity was 2.22 cases per person per year. Twenty years earlier, in a survey made in the Eastern Health District of Baltimore, the incidence of illness was at a rate of 1.3 cases per person per year. In this instance, illness was reported only if it was disabling. Clearly, the exact figure depends upon the definition of illness which is used in collecting the data.

8. How does the incidence of acute disabling illness vary with sex and age?

Illnesses arise more frequently among females than males. While there is little difference in the incidence for the two sexes during the first 15 years of life, at the higher ages the rate for females exceeds that for males. During the period 1961–62, the excess was greatest in the age range 25 to 44 years, but declined thereafter with advance in age.

Beginning with a very high rate among infants and young children (3.7 cases per child under 5 per year), the incidence of acute conditions declined steadily with each age to a minimum of 1.3 cases per person per year at ages 65 and over.

9. What proportion of all acute illnesses are disabling?

This same health survey (1961–62) reported that 37.0 percent of all cases caused restriction of activity but did not require medical attention; 24.8 percent required medical attention but did not result in activity restriction; and 38.2 percent required medical attention and resulted in activity restriction. These proportions varied considerably by type of condition, and by age period. The data excluded cases involving no restricted activity and not requiring medical attention.

10. How much time is lost currently by employed persons because of illness?

The answer depends greatly on what is meant by disability. Data from the United States National Health Survey for the period July

1961 to June 1962, indicates that the average loss of work time was about 5.8 days a year per employed person—about three-quarters resulting from illness, and the rest from injuries of one kind or another. The days lost rise with advancing age and are higher for females than for males, up to age 44, after which age the days lost by males are appreciably higher. During 1962, close to 2 percent of the working civilian population was absent from work because of illness in an average day. The highest losses were sustained by farm workers.

11. How much time is lost by grade-school children because of sickness?

Data from a National Health Survey showed that during the 12 months ending June 1962, boys and girls 6 to 16 years of age missed about the same number of days from school because of illness and injury (5.7 days, including both acute and chronic illness). Here, too, different surveys have given different results, much depending on the prevalence of the communicable diseases during the period of the study. The extent to which the communicable diseases prevail affects school attendance materially, since regulations require those with common childhood diseases to stay at home until the period of communicability is past. On the average, urban children missed a greater number of days from school than either rural nonfarm or rural farm children.

12. Do the unemployed experience more days of disability owing to illness than do the employed?

The National Health Survey for 1961–62 showed that illness or injury among those unemployed was responsible for 22 days of restricted activity per year compared with 12 days per currently employed persons per year. While lack of employment may contribute to a high illness rate, long disablement may also lead to the loss of employment. Both factors tend to increase the rate of disability among the unemployed.

13. What proportion of the disabling illnesses confine the patient to the house, to the hospital, to an institution?

According to one survey, nine-tenths of those disabled were confined indoors; of these, about one-eighth were in a hospital, and less than 1 in 100 in some other institution.

14. What proportion of work-loss days are due to acute and to chronic conditions?

Much depends on the age of the workers. At the younger ages (under 25) the acute conditions account for over 80 percent of the work-loss days; at 45 and over, the chronic conditions account for almost two-thirds of the work-loss days.

15. How is the extent of chronic illness related to social-economic status?

In a recent study it was found that the prevalence of chronic diseases was much higher for the "poor" than for the "well-to-do"; the prevalence for the intermediate classes was close to that of the "well-to-do."

16. What are the most common *acute* illnesses?

The respiratory diseases are by far the most common cause of acute illness. The upper respiratory diseases (chiefly common colds) and influenzalike illnesses caused more than one-half of all acute conditions during 1962–1963 according to the National Health Survey. Each of these illnesses required either medical attention or restriction of usual daily activities. Injuries and infective and parasitic diseases ranked second and third, each causing about one-eighth of all acute conditions.

17. What are the most common *chronic* conditions causing limitation of activity?

During 1959–61, about 17 percent of all chronically limited persons reported that heart conditions caused their activity limitation, 16 percent reported arthritis and rheumatism as the cause; 7.0 percent, mental and nervous conditions; 6.8 percent, high blood pressure; and 6.8 percent, impairments of the lower extremities and hips.

18. What is the average duration in days of restricted activity for various acute conditions?

During 1962–63, the average upper respiratory illness caused 2.4 days of reduced activity. Common childhood diseases caused an average of 6.3 days of restricted activity; illnesses reported as influenza, 4.2 days; pneumonia, 16.1 days; digestive system diseases, 3.6 days;

fractures and dislocations, 17.1 days; sprains and strains, 6.8 days; and other injuries, 3.9 days.

19. What percentage of all illness is under the care of a doctor?

In one study where illness included all frank and recognized attacks of disease, four out of five cases received some kind of medical care, exclusive of that provided by nurses, druggists, neighbors, or other lay persons. For all cases of illness attended by a doctor, the number of calls averaged close to five per case. In the more recent National Health Survey of 1961–62, covering all *acute* illnesses, 63 percent of all cases required some type of medical attention.

20. What proportion of persons receive hospital care in the course of a year?

About 12 percent, or an average of one out of eight Americans now receive care in general hospitals in the course of a year. The proportion has increased rapidly in recent years because of the increasing urbanization of our population, the rise in public demand for hospital care, the great growth in hospital insurance plans, and the increased tendency of physicians to organize their practice around hospitals where their patients can receive the help of laboratory tests, special treatments, and the constant supervision needed in their treatment.

21. What proportion of the illnesses in the care of a physician require laboratory service, x-ray service, and physiotherapy?

The use of x-ray and laboratory tests as an aid to diagnosis is now a commonplace. In a group of 6,420 hospital cases reported in 1942, 85.5 percent required laboratory service and 23.4 percent x-ray service. Other items in the list of special services were physiotherapy, 1.7 percent; electrocardiography, 1.4 percent; basal metabolism, 1.8 percent; oxygen therapy, 1.4 percent and radium therapy, 0.2 percent.

22. In what proportion of illnesses are medicines or drugs procured?

In a group of 9,000 families surveyed some years ago, medicine of some kind was procured in 58 percent of the reported cases. This was exclusive of those which were treated by home remedies or from the home stock of medicines.

The medicine was obtained on a doctor's prescription in 43 percent of the cases; on a druggist's recommendation in 3 percent; and by purchase over the counter without either a doctor's prescription or a druggist's recommendation in 12 percent of the cases.

23. How much is expended annually for health purposes in the United States?

The nation as a whole spent about $31.8 billion for medical and health services of all kinds, including medical research and facilities construction, in 1962. This is equivalent to about $170 per capita. *Private* expenditures in that year for these purposes amounted to $23.8 billion. The remaining $7.95 billion were *public* expenditures. Of the $31.8 billion expended, $1.4 billion were for construction of hospitals and related medical facilities, and $1.0 billion were for research. The remaining $29.3 billion were for currently consumed private and public health services.

24. What is the annual cost of the medical care provided for veterans?

The Veterans Administration spent about $993 million in the fiscal year 1962 for its medical care program. This figure includes the expenses of maintaining the 170 Veterans Hospitals with their outpatient departments which provide medical and dental care, and the expenses of operating the general, psychiatric, and tuberculosis hospitals, as well as the "hometown" medical program.

25. What does the average family spend for medical care?

While the average American family spends about 5.5 percent of its budget on medical care, the actual amounts spent vary widely in individual cases. Many families spend little or nothing during the year, buying only patent medicine and supplies; other families, at the same time, suffer serious illnesses, often involving very heavy expense.

In 1962, private consumer expenditures for medical care, including the net cost of health insurance, amounted to $119.44 per capita. Expenditures for hospital care were 27.8 percent, for physicians' services 26.5 percent, for dental services 10.0 percent, and for drugs 18.9 percent of the total. Expenditures for other professional services, eyeglasses and appliances, nursing home care, and the net cost of health insurance comprised the rest.

26. What factors influence the amounts spent on medical care?

The amounts expended on medical care depend on the type of illness involved, on the size of the family, the ages of its members, and on the income class of the family. According to one report, the annual expenditures for medical care varied from an average of $165 for families with an income of less than $2,000 per year to $411 for families with incomes of $7,500 and over.

In an earlier study, the amount spent annually for medical care by well-to-do families was 10 times that in the poorest families. The size of the community also affects the cost of illness. The average annual expenditures are in general higher in large cities than in medium-size cities; they are lowest in rural areas. In many cases, the low expenditures by the poorest families are supplemented by services received without charge.

27. What amount is spent annually for hospital services?

In 1962, the expenditures for patient care for all hospitals totaled about $10.5 billion. Of this amount, $6.1 billion were spent by consumers, about $260 million were philanthropic contributions, and $4.2 billion represented expenditures by federal, state, and local governments. Total expenditures in federal facilities were $1.5 billion and in non-federal $9.0 billion. These figures exclude expenditures for construction and fixed equipment.

28. What change has there been in the expenditure for hospital care over the years?

The cost of hospital service today is much greater than it was even 10 years ago. The average operating cost for a patient each day in voluntary nonprofit hospitals rose from $18.35 in 1952 to $36.83 in 1962. This rise was occasioned by the increase in the number and variety of services provided. In addition, wages of hospital personnel, notoriously low in the past, have risen. The cost of operating hospitals has also been affected by the higher price level of all commodities. Offsetting all this, as far as the patient is concerned, has been the steady decline until recently in the average length of the hospital stay. Nationally the decline in length of stay appears to be ended now, and, in fact, length of stay may be rising.

29. What is the average charge for a hospitalized illness?

In 1962, the average income of general hospitals per patient day was $36.83. This is exclusive of income from gifts, endowments, or funds from special campaigns. With an average stay of 7.6 days, the average hospital charge for each patient is thus about $279.91.

There are no up-to-date reliable figures on total charges for illnesses in which the patient at one time or another received general hospital care. Such charges would include physicians' charges for services during and before and after hospitalization, special nursing, if any, drugs before and after hospitalization. One might guess that such charges would equal, on the average, at least 50 percent of the cost of hospital care by itself.

30. How many people are insured against hospital expense under Blue Cross and other types of insurance?

The exact figure for the number of persons insured against hospital expenses is difficult to determine because of overlapping of the various plans. One estimate is about 141,000,000 persons, or three-fourths of the civilian population.[1]

More than 60,000,000 persons are now covered by the hospital-sponsored Blue Cross. The insurance companies reported over 85,-000,000, while other millions are enrolled for various types of hospital insurance provided by industrial medical plans, private group clinics, consumer-sponsored plans, and university health service. Quite a number of persons are insured under more than one plan.

31. What proportion of insured persons are admitted to hospital care each year?

About 13 percent of all insured persons are admitted to hospitals annually. The percentage varies with sex, age, marital status, and type of contract.

32. What is the average length of hospital stay of insured and uninsured patients?

In 1962, the average length of stay of patients in short-term general hospitals was 7.6 days. The trend in recent years has been slightly upward. Children have the shortest stay, 5.4 days; the longest stay was incurred by patients 55 years and over. Those with hospital insurance had somewhat shorter average stay than those without coverage.

[1] See answer to Question 44 of this chapter, page 90.

33. What proportions of hospitals are proprietary, private non-profit, and governmental?

The largest number of hospitals in the United States in 1962 was in the nonprofit group. Out of a total of 7,028 hospitals registered, 3,623 were church and other nonprofit hospitals; the state, county, and city hospitals numbered 1,968, and federal hospitals, 447. There were 990 proprietary hospitals.

The several categories of hospitals differ in their number of beds, bassinets, admissions, and average census. On these bases, the classes of hospitals were distributed as follows in 1962 (total = 100%):

Type of Hospital	*Hospitals*	*Beds*	*Bassinets*	*Admissions*	*Average Census*
Total	100.0	100.0	100.0	100.0	100.0
Federal	6.4	10.5	4.0	6.0	11.0
Governmental, nonfederal	28.0	56.5	20.8	21.0	58.7
Private nonprofit	51.6	30.0	69.2	66.5	27.9
Proprietary	14.0	3.0	6.0	6.5	2.4

34. Under what auspices do general hospitals operate?

Private voluntary agencies maintain about four-fifths of the general hospitals. These furnish most of the facilities for acute illnesses. The government customarily assumes responsibility for the care of patients suffering from tuberculosis, and nervous and mental disorders requiring long hospitalization. In addition, the federal government looks after veterans in certain circumstances, all military personnel, and some of the dependents of the latter.

35. What variation is there in hospital facilities among states?

The 7,028 registered hospitals in the United States in 1962 had a capacity of 1,689,414 beds. This amounts to an average of approximately 9.1 beds per 1,000 population, including the armed forces.

There is wide variation in the distribution of these hospital facilities among states. The District of Columbia had a high of 20.5 beds per 1,000 population, while New Mexico had a low of 6.4 per 1,000. The location of large federal facilities in certain of the states accounts for part of the variation, but some of it reflects the relative wealth of the states. The Southern states have the fewest hospital beds per capita.

36. How many general hospital beds are there per 1,000 population?

In 1962, there were 769,870 beds, or about 4 per 1,000 population, in general hospitals in the United States. Of these, 106,207, or nearly one-seventh, were in federal hospitals. Many patients in the hospitals of the U.S. Public Health Service, the Veterans Administration, Indian Affairs, and even some of those in the hospitals of the Army, Navy, and Air Force are from the civilian population.

37. What legislative provisions have been made to assist in the construction of needed hospitals and other health facilities in this country?

In 1946, Congress enacted the Hospital Survey and Construction Act—popularly known as the Hill-Burton Program—to provide grants or loans to states to assist in constructing and equipping needed public and voluntary nonprofit hospitals and public health centers. In 1954, the program was broadened to also provide grants for nursing homes, diagnostic and treatment centers, and rehabilitation facilities.

Since 1947, Congress has made annual appropriations from $65 million to $220 million for the construction of these health facilities. The federal share varies from state to state, ranging from one-third to two-thirds of the cost of construction and equipment of each project.

By December 31, 1963, more than 7,000 projects had been approved since the beginning of the program. These projects, providing 298,392 beds in hospitals and nursing homes and also providing 1,974 other types of health facilities, involved a total cost of $6.4 billion. The federal contribution amounted to $2.0 billion with the remaining $4.4 billion paid by states, local communities, and voluntary nonprofit groups.

38. How many physicians are there in the United States?

In 1963, the number of licensed physicians in the United States was 278,275. More than one-third of them were classified as specialists. Those who were engaged in "rendering medical services directly to the civilian population" were 175,523. The rest were engaged in teaching, administration, preventative medicine, etc. A sizable number were not in medical practice at all.

In the United States, doctors average 1 to each 683 persons in the population. Considering only those in active private practice, there is 1 physician to 1,082 persons. As might be expected, the larger cities with their better medical facilities and higher economic incentives attract more doctors, while the rural areas have a much lower ratio of physicians to persons.

39. How many medical schools are there, what is the number of students, and how many are graduated each year?

There were 87 approved medical schools in the United States in the academic year 1962–63. Of these, 83 were approved 4-year schools. The total enrollment in these schools in that year was 31,491. There were 7,265 graduates.

40. How many registered nurses are there in the United States and in what types of service are they?

The American Nurses Association estimates that as of January 1962 there were 550,000 active professional nurses in the United States. Of this number, approximately 80 percent were employed in hospitals and related institutions or in private duty. The distribution of active registered nurses by the fields of nursing was as follows in 1962:

ESTIMATES OF PROFESSIONAL NURSES EMPLOYED FULL- AND PART-TIME IN THE UNITED STATES, BY FIELD OF NURSING, AS OF JANUARY 1962*

Field of Nursing	1962
Totals	550,000
Hospitals and related institutions	367,250
Private duty	69,500
Office	40,000
Public health	34,700
Occupational health	17,000
Nursing education	
Professional nursing programs	16,750
Practical nursing programs	2,800
Other	2,000

* Data supplied by American Nurses Association, Inc.

41. How many schools of nursing are there, what is the number of students and how many graduates are there each year?

According to the National League for Nursing, there were in October 1962, 1,136 state-approved initial programs in professional nursing in the United States and Puerto Rico. Enrollment in these programs totaled 123,861 on that date. Also, during the academic year 1961–62 there were 49,805 admissions and 31,186 graduations of students in the initial, or basic, professional programs.

42. How many practical nurses are there in the United States?

The exact number of practical nurses is not known. In 1962, there were approximately 225,000 practical nurses and of that number a significant proportion were graduates of one-year training programs and most practical nurses were licensed. There has been a large increase in their number in recent years. Practical nurses and attendants care for patients in their homes or in hospitals or institutions. They perform a combination of housekeeping and nursing duties, applying knowledge acquired primarily through practical experience.

43. How many dentists are there in the United States?

As of mid-1962, there were 107,995 dentists listed in the United States, of whom it is estimated that 95,000 were active in the profession. Approximately 92,000 practiced dentistry, i.e., worked at the chair, and some 3,000 were engaged in teaching, research, administration, etc. About 87,000 were in private practice.

There were 48 dental schools in the United States, including Puerto Rico, and the number of students enrolled in 1962 was 13,576.

44. How many people are insured against cost of sickness under various plans?

As already indicated, about 141 million persons in the United States were insured for hospital expenses under voluntary plans by 1962. Of this number, 131 million were covered for surgical expenses; over 38 million for major medical expenses; and close to 45 million were insured against loss of income. These numbers have grown rapidly in recent years in each one of these several categories.

45. In how many states are there voluntary prepayment medical care programs?

All states have voluntary health insurance programs. Insurance companies function in all of them. There are Blue Cross plans (or Blue Shield plans covering hospitalization) in all states, except Nevada, South Dakota, and Alaska, and all three are served to some extent by plans in other states. There are Blue Shield plans (or Blue Cross plans writing surgical-medical benefits) in all states, except Nevada and Alaska, and both are served by plans in other states.

46. How many states provide insurance against disability?

Rhode Island, California, New Jersey, and New York have insurance plans against nonoccupational disability. 'Rhode Island, where operations began in 1943, has a cash sickness compensation plan, wholly compulsory with the state as the insurer. The California plan, which began payments December 1, 1946, provides for a state unemployment insurance disability fund; but voluntary plans, either through self-insurance, benefit associations, or commercial insurance companies, are also allowed. In New Jersey, where benefits became payable January 1, 1949, there is a state disability fund with provisions for contracting insurance privately outside of it. The New York plan, with payments beginning July 1, 1950, permits self-insurance or insurance with authorized commercial companies; it also has a state insurance fund.[2]

47. What types of disability insurance are provided under social insurance and related programs?

Disability payments are made under the federal old-age, survivors, and disability insurance program to a person who is unable to engage in any substantial gainful activity because of a disability that is expected to be of a long-continued and indefinite duration or to result in death. Benefits are also paid to dependents of a disabled worker.

Railroad workers have social insurance protection against permanent or total disabilities under the Railroad Retirement Act and most federal, state, and local public employees have similar protection under their retirement programs. The Veterans' compensation and pension programs provide cash benefits for veterans with service-connected disabilities and in some cases for veterans with non-service-connected disabilities. In four states and the railroad industry, there are social insurance programs providing workers with partial compensation for loss of wages caused by temporary nonoccupational disability. Workman's compensation programs in every state provide cash benefits and medical care when a worker is injured in connection with his job.

[2] See answer to Question 45 of Chapter 18, page 291.

Chapter 7

Mortality—
In General

1. How many people die in the world annually?

The number of deaths in the world may fluctuate widely from one year to the next, depending upon the presence of epidemic or famine in the poorly developed areas. A rough estimate of the annual number of deaths is 60,000,000 or about 2 every second. About two-thirds of these deaths are in Asia, somewhat less than one-sixth in Europe, about one-tenth in Africa, and one-twelfth in the Western Hemisphere.

2. What purposes are served by the mortality records of a community?

Mortality records are essential for the planning and effective operation of a community's medical and health services. Properly analyzed, these records point to the need for specific health services and facilities of various types, for example, hospital beds, health centers, clinics of various kinds, and specialist services. Statistics on fatal accidents guide the direction of safety campaigns. They indicate the degree of hazard in specific occupations, the causes of automobile fatalities, and even the dangers in the home. The success of specific programs for the control of disease or fatal accident can be evaluated by mortality records. Such records are also of great service in medical research.

3. How is the mortality of the community measured?

The mortality of a community is measured by its death rate. This is obtained by dividing the number of deaths in a period of time, say a year, by the average population living during the year. For example, in 1962 there were recorded 1,757,000 deaths in the United States. The estimated population July 1 was 186,591,000; this may be regarded as the average for the year. Dividing 1,757,000 by 186,591,000 yields .00941; multiplying this result by 1,000 gives a death rate of 9.41 per 1,000 population. This is called the "crude" death rate because it applies to the total population without consideration to the composition of the population by age, sex, or other characteristics.

4. How does mortality vary from age to age?

A death rate for a specific age may be computed by dividing the annual number of deaths in the community at that age by the number of persons at the same age and multiplying the result by 1,000. In this way it is possible to secure death rates or mortality rates at the various ages of life. Mortality is high among infants, especially during the first month of life.[1] The rate then drops sharply as the infant goes into childhood, and remains at a rather low level throughout adolescence. The mortality then increases with advance in age, first gradually and after about age 40 more rapidly. It is not until near age 65 that the mortality rate is again as high as in the first year of life. At age 85, the mortality rate is more than four times that at age 65.

5. At what year of age is the number of deaths greatest?

The number of deaths is greatest in the first year after birth. In 1961, there were 107,956 infant deaths reported in the United

[1] See Chapter 14, pages 209, 210.

States. This was more than the number for each age from 1 through 55 years. A secondary peak in the number of deaths occurs near age 77.

6. What is the safest age from the standpoint of mortality?

Age 10 is the safest year of life. Children of that age have passed the hazards of the acute infections of infancy and early childhood. They have yet to face the chronic diseases of the later years. Among children 10 years of age, accidents constitute the most frequent cause of death.

7. What is the relation between mortality and longevity?

In a sense it might be said that longevity is the inverse of mortality. Generally speaking, where differences in death rate are large, one may be rather sure that there will also be large differences in longevity. However, the relation between mortality, as measured by the crude death rate, and longevity, as measured by expectation of life at birth, is quite complex. It is usually not safe to infer that of two communities which show a small difference in their crude death rates, the one with the lower rate will have the greater longevity. It is necessary to know the mortality rate at various ages of life to be able to measure longevity or the expectation of life of a community or of a group of people. This calls for the construction of what is known as a "life table."[2]

8. How does the mortality of men differ from that of women?

Men have a higher mortality than women at every year of age. In the first year of life the mortality of white males was about one-third higher than that for white females in 1961. The ratio of male to female mortality rises to 2 at age 14 and to almost 3 in the early twenties.

This ratio of double mortality of males continues for about 10 years. Another peak in the ratio of male to female mortality, about 2.1, is reached near age 55 and from that point on the ratio diminishes steadily with advance in age. The higher mortality of males, as compared with females, has been found in most species of animals as well as man. (See Chart 7.)

[2] See answer to Question 12 of Chapter 24, page 397.

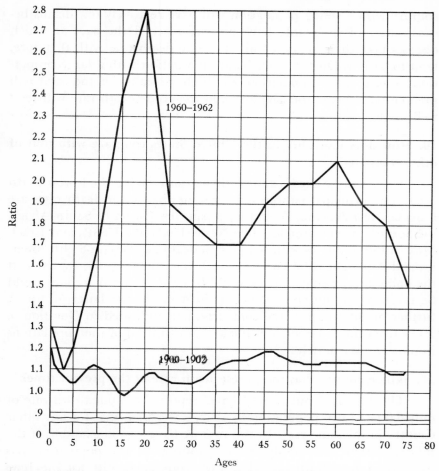

Chart 7. **Ratio of mortality rates at each age, white males to white females, United States, 1900–1902 (Original Registration States) and 1960–62.**

9. What difficulties are there in international comparisons of mortality?

Two main problems arise in comparing crude death rates for different countries. First, many deaths in underdeveloped countries may not enter into the reports because of an inefficient system of registration, while the reporting of deaths is fairly complete in the more developed countries. The second difficulty arises from the fact that the crude death rate is strongly influenced by the age and sex distribution of the population; countries can differ greatly in this regard. A country with a young population will have relatively few deaths because most of its people have not yet reached the ages at which diseases take their greatest toll. Its crude death rate will, therefore, tend to be low. On the other hand, in a nation with a large proportion of aged in its population, the high mortality of the aged will predominate in the total picture and the crude death rate will tend to be high.

10. How does mortality in the United States compare with that of other countries?

The United States is among the nations having the lowest death rates. The principal nations having somewhat lower death rates are Canada, New Zealand, Australia, Japan, the Union of South Africa, the Scandinavian countries, The Netherlands, the USSR, and Israel. Most of the countries with the highest death rates are in South America and Asia. The differences in death rates between the leaders and the underdeveloped countries would be even greater if account could be taken of the unreported deaths in many of the latter group. A further qualification in the comparison, as indicated in Question 9, arises from the differences in the age constitution of the populations in the various countries.

11. Which country has the lowest death rate at the present time?

The Jewish population of Israel reported a crude death rate of only 6.0 per 1,000 population in 1962, lower than that for any other country in the same year. In this case we have a good example of the influence that a favorable age distribution of the population has upon the crude death rate. The low crude death rate for the Jews in Israel reflects the low average age of that country's population, a result of the recent influx of young immigrants. The crude death rate is not a good measure of their mortality. For a truer measure of the mortality of Israel in relation to other nations, it would be necessary to compare death rates among them at different ages of life.

12. How are the difficulties of international comparison of mortality minimized?

It is entirely possible for two nations to have practically identical death rates at the various ages of life and yet have markedly different crude death rates. Such a situation would arise if one of the nations had a larger proportion of aged than the other. In order to obtain a better index of mortality for purposes of comparison, the death rates are "age-adjusted." The procedure is, first, to take some common age distribution of the population as a standard. In this standard population we then find the expected number of deaths by multiplying the number of people at each age by the corresponding death rate for that age in the nation in question. The sum of expected deaths for each age computed in this way, when divided by the total population of the standard, yields the age-adjusted death rate. It will be recognized that two nations having practically identical death rates at each stage of life will also have practically identical age-adjusted death rates.

13. How do urban and rural areas compare in mortality?

In years past, mortality was lower in rural areas than in urban centers. In 1940, for example, the age-adjusted death rate for cities was one-sixth higher than for rural areas. In recent years, however, this differential in favor of rural areas has disappeared. In fact, the advantage in mortality has been reversed. In some degree this may be the result of a change in the definition of urban and rural by the Census Bureau. More important, however, is the great concentration of medical and public health facilities in the cities and the better standards of living that prevail there.

14. How do the states rank as to mortality?

The states with the most favorable mortality are the Midwest, the Mountain and Pacific Coast states. The two new states, Alaska and Hawaii, report exceedingly low death rates. One should keep in mind in this connection, the marked increase of population in the Pacific Coast area of young people. This has had the effect of reducing the crude death rate materially.

There is, in fact, little evidence to show a marked difference in true mortality in the various states of the nation. This results largely from the great progress in the growth of health services throughout the country, with only few exceptions.

15. What difference is there in the mortality of the white and non-white populations of the United States?

The mortality of the nonwhite population is higher than that of the white. In 1961, the death rate of white persons was 9.3 per 1,000, while that for nonwhites was 9.6. This reflects the extraordinary improvement in the mortality of the nonwhites in recent years. In 1940, the rates were 10.4 and 13.8 per 1,000, white and nonwhite respectively.

16. How does the mortality of the married differ from that of the single, widowed, or divorced?

Among both men and women, the married have lower death rates than the single, widowed, or divorced. However, the differences are greater for men than for women. In 1940, the age-adjusted death rate for single men was one and one-half times that for the married men. The widowers had a death rate twice that for the married men, while the divorced had a ratio of over twice the married. Among women, the single had a death rate only 10 percent higher than that for the married. However, the death rate of widowed and divorced women was over one and one-half times that for married women. The advantage for married women is now found even at the principal childbearing ages, 20 to 29. Formerly this was not the case, owing to the high maternal mortality which once prevailed.[3]

17. How does the mortality of the native-born compare with that of the foreign-born?

In 1900, the mortality of the foreign-born was about one-fifth greater than for the native-born, but the differential has since been eliminated. The excess of mortality among the foreign-born was generally attributed to the substandard living conditions of immigrants. Many of them lived in crowded slum sections of cities under poor sanitary and working conditions. More recently the foreign-born—fewer in numbers—no longer face the great handicaps of those who came here years ago. The early immigrants are now largely in the older age groups and have used their opportunity to become acclimated and well established in this country. They have benefited greatly with the remainder of the population from improved surroundings and higher standards of living.

18. Has occupation any relation to mortality?[4]

Occupation may affect mortality both directly and indirectly. Men in certain types of work—steeplejacks, structural iron workers, and electric power linemen, for example—have high accident rates.

[3] See answer to Question 14 of Chapter 4, page 52.
[4] See Chapter 18, page 283.

Some other workers are exposed to dust, abnormal temperatures, or chemicals which may result in a high mortality from certain diseases or conditions. In addition to these direct effects, occupation may also have an indirect influence on mortality through the standard of living which results therefrom. The relatively low income of un-skilled laborers may mean inadequate food, crowded and unhealthful living quarters, and the need to work during periods of sickness.

19. How does mortality in the world today compare with that of ancient times?

Fossil remains indicate that prehistoric man seldom achieved old age. Death by violence was very frequent. Mortality in infancy must have been extremely high in ancient times, even in the best period of Greece and Rome. Deaths might easily have been at the rate of 50 per 1,000 persons each year. The corresponding rate for the more advanced countries today is one-fifth as high.

20. What has been the trend of mortality in the last century?

The death rate in the United States during the last century has declined very rapidly. Although the public health movement had its start about 100 years ago, preventive medicine did not make real headway until the turn of the century. Mortality from tuberculosis has been cut by more than 90 percent, infant mortality by almost as much, and mortality from pneumonia by more than two-thirds. Since 1900 alone, the death rate for all causes of death in the United States has been cut by almost 50 percent. Typhoid fever, diphtheria, measles, scarlet fever, whooping cough, and smallpox have been virtually eradicated as causes of death.

21. What are some of the principal factors in the recent improvement in mortality?

Fundamentally, the great reduction in mortality during our time is a result of the great advances in medical science, in public health practice, and more generally, in our standard of living. By eliminating foci of infection, by broad scale immunizations, and by more effective medical care, it has been possible to alter greatly the picture which prevailed at the beginning of the century. At that time the first three leading causes of death were the infectious conditions, namely pneumonia and influenza, tuberculosis, and diarrhea and enteritis. Diphtheria ranked ninth and meningitis, tenth. Today, pneumonia and influenza rank sixth in order, followed by arterio-sclerosis and diabetes. Tuberculosis and diarrhea and enteritis are now of relatively minor importance as causes of death, while diphtheria and meningitis are practically out of the mortality tables. For most of the great reductions in mortality it is possible to point to some specific advance in medicine and sanitation. We should not overlook, however, the contribution from our rising standard of living which has given us better food, improved surroundings in our home and place of work, a shorter work day, and more opportunity for healthful recreation. These improvements have undoubtedly strengthened our resistance against many diseases.[5]

22. At which ages has the reduction in mortality been greatest?

Mortality has been reduced most rapidly in infancy and early childhood. There have also been sharp decreases in death rates up through middle life; even the higher ages through 65 years have shown substantial reductions. For example, mortality in infancy is now less than one-fifth of what it was at the beginning of the century. Also, at age 30, current mortality is only one-fifth of that in 1900. Even at age 50 the death rate today is one-half, and at age 70 the reduction comes to over one-third. Contrary to general impression, substantial improvement in mortality is observed even at the older ages.

23. How does the reduction in mortality of men compare with that of women?

Quite generally, the reduction in the mortality for women has been greater than for men. At age 30, for example, the mortality for white males in 1960 was one-sixth of that in 1900, whereas for white females the ratio was about one-eighth. At age 70, the recent mortality rate for white males was three-quarters of that at the beginning of the century, but for white females the ratio was a little over one-half. In infancy, both sexes experienced about the same rate of improvement.

24. How does the reduction in mortality of the white compare with the nonwhite population?

During the last three decades the death rates for the nonwhite population have been declining much more rapidly than for the white population. For example, from the period 1930 to 1960, the

[5] See answer to Question 9 of Chapter 24, page 395.

decline in the death rates for the nonwhites amounted to 38 percent, compared with only about 12 percent for the white population. The more favorable showing for the nonwhites reflects the more rapid improvement in their living conditions. The marked difference in mortality in the two groups which prevailed in earlier decades is being rapidly eliminated. Today, the mortality of nonwhites is approximately that of the whites only 15 years ago.

25. How many lives are saved annually because of the reduction in mortality since 1900?

If the mortality rates of 1900 had prevailed in the population in 1960, there would have been over 3,000,000 deaths. Instead, there were approximately 1,700,000. In other words, 1,300,000 lives were saved from premature death in that one year as a result of the improvement in mortality conditions during the past 60 years.

26. What are the common causes of death today?

Diseases of the heart rank first as causes of death, accounting currently for a little under one-third of all deaths. Cancer, with almost one-seventh of all deaths, ranks second. Next in order is cerebral hemorrhage, to which is ascribed about one-ninth of all the deaths. Accidents are the cause of about one-eighteenth of the total. The causes of death following in order are: premature births, pneumonia and influenza, arteriosclerosis, diabetes, and finally, congenital malformations and cirrhosis of the liver. These first 10 leading causes of death constitute 84 percent of the total.

27. What changes in rank have the leading causes of death shown since the turn of the century?

These changes are evident in the table on page 103.

28. How have the chances of eventually dying of an acute or chronic disease changed since the beginning of the century?

With the great reduction in mortality from the infectious conditions, the chances of dying from an acute disease have declined sharply. In 1901, these chances were somewhat greater than one in three for the newly born baby. By 1945, the chances of eventually dying from an acute condition had declined to only 1 in 10. Since then, the probability has declined further. With death a certainty, there has been, contrariwise, a sharp rise in the chances of eventually dying from a chronic disease. These chances were one in two for the baby born in 1901, but they have risen to over four in five for the present-day baby. There has been relatively little change in the chances of eventually dying from external causes during this period. (See Chart 8 below.)

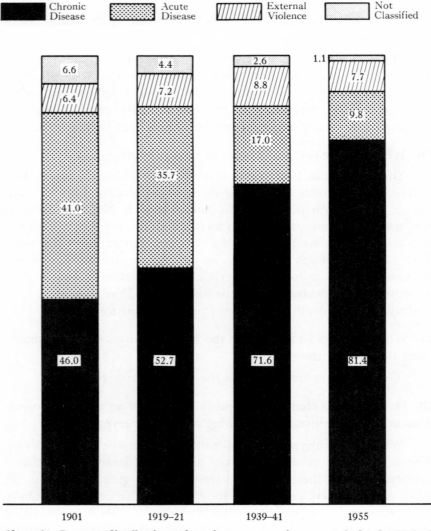

Chart 8. **Percent distribution of major groups of causes of death, United States, 1901, 1919–21, 1939–41, 1955.**

THE TEN LEADING CAUSES OF DEATH IN THE UNITED STATES, 1900 AND 1960

Rank	Cause of Death	Death Rate per 100,000 Population	Percent of Deaths from All Causes
	1960		
	All causes	955	100.0
1	Diseases of heart	369	38.7
2	Cancer	149	15.6
3	Cerebral hemorrhage	108	11.3
4	Accidents	52	5.5
5	Premature birth	37	3.9
6	Pneumonia and influenza	37	3.9
7	Arteriosclerosis	20	2.1
8	Diabetes	17	1.8
9	Congenital malformations	12	1.3
10	Cirrhosis of the liver	11	1.2
	First ten causes	813	85.3
	1900		
	All causes	1,719	100.0
1	Pneumonia and influenza	202	11.8
2	Tuberculosis	194	11.3
3	Diarrhea and enteritis	143	8.3
4	Diseases of heart	137	8.0
5	Cerebral hemorrhage	107	6.2
6	Nephritis	89	5.2
7	Accidents	72	4.2
8	Cancer	64	3.7
9	Diphtheria	40	2.3
10	Meningitis	34	2.0
	First ten causes	1,082	63.0

29. What factors account for the sharp drop in mortality from the infectious diseases?

The control of these diseases has resulted from efforts on three fronts. First came the discovery of the manner by which the diseases were spread and their causative organisms. Next in importance were the intensive campaigns carried on by public and voluntary health agencies to prevent infection by blocking the transmission of the diseases. Finally, there were the techniques used for building up immunity. The advances along these lines were made possible by the efforts of the medical profession, public health authorities, scientific workers in many fields, and the cooperation of the general public.

The control of typhoid fever, for example, followed the development of sewage disposal systems, the purification of water, the protection of milk supplies, the elimination of insect carriers, the supervision of human carriers, and, finally, the more general use of inoculation. In the case of yellow fever, the turning point came when Walter Reed demonstrated that the disease was transmitted by the mosquito. Extensive measures to eradicate it came soon after. Diarrhea and enteritis were brought under control by the general improvement in sanitary conditions and by the protection of food supplies, particularly through the pasteurization of milk.

The conquest of poliomyelitis, which today appears to have been accomplished, was brought about by a series of interesting steps. First, there was the discovery and identification of its viral causative organisms. Next came the development of methods of growing these viruses in quantity and pure culture. Then followed the preparation and wide use of the Salk vaccine, supplemented more recently by the introduction of Sabin's oral vaccine. Currently, a death from this disease is a rarity, all of which reflects an extraordinary accomplishment of modern medicine.

30. What recent developments in medical science have sharply reduced mortality?

The treatment of many acute conditions has been revolutionized by the development of specific serums, by chemotherapy, and by antibiotics. A good example of the beneficial effects of these new treatments is provided by the trend of mortality from pneumonia. The introduction of serum treatment about 1935 brought down the death rate from this disease shortly thereafter. After the sulfa drugs were introduced about 1937, mortality again dropped, but this time somewhat more rapidly. A major decline in the death rate was brought about since World War II through the introduction of penicillin and other antibiotics. Among other conditions brought under control through these new developments is sepsis, as a result of which the chances of recovery in surgical operations have greatly improved.

31. What are the leading causes of death at the various ages of life?

The leading causes of death change dramatically with advance in age. In infancy, morbid conditions associated with birth take the largest toll. For children under one year of age, the leading causes of death in order of importance are premature birth, congenital malformations, pneumonia and influenza, injury at birth, and diarrhea and enteritis. In early childhood, ages one to four, accidents are the greatest danger, followed by the infectious conditions. Malignant neoplasms and congenital malformations exact equally serious tolls. At ages 5 to 14, the chief killer is again accidents, followed by malignant neoplasms. Accidents continue as the leading cause of death at ages 15 to 24 years, followed in turn by malignant neoplasms. Diseases of the heart already play an important role in mortality. Beginning with age 25, the lead among the causes of death is held by diseases of the heart for the rest of life. Accidents hold second place at ages 25 through 44, followed closely by cancer. After age 45, cancer holds second rank among the causes of death, cerebral hemorrhage third, and accidents fourth.

32. What are the prospects for still further improvement in mortality?

With the continued advance of medical science and of public health work, there will undoubtedly be further sharp reductions in maternal mortality, infant mortality, and from such infections as pneumonia and tuberculosis and, finally, in accident fatalities. The increasing concentration of research and medical facilities on the diseases of the cardiovascular-renal system and on cancer will undoubtedly bring considerable improvement in these directions.

33. What was the effect of World War I on mortality in the United States?

War deaths were but a small fraction of the total deaths for the United States in the years of World War I. The direct battle losses among members of the Army, Navy, and Marine Corps came to 52,692 deaths. Nonbattle deaths in the armed forces, chiefly from the influenza epidemic, totaled 55,868. During this period, the annual number of deaths for the country was about 1,000,000.

34. What was the effect of World War II on mortality in the United States?

The loss from battle deaths among members of the armed forces during World War II was about 300,000. Nonbattle deaths came to approximately 110,000. There was amazingly low mortality from disease among the armed forces, but on the other hand the record for nonbattle fatalities was high. Almost half of the nonbattle fatalities were the result of aviation accidents. The civilian population of the

United States experienced a very favorable death rate during the war years; the intensified efforts by government and by voluntary health agencies to preserve the public health were undoubtedly factors in this development. The acceleration of medical research during the war also had some beneficial effect. In 1946, the first postwar year, the death rate was down to 10 per 1,000, the lowest recorded for the country up to that time. It has declined only slightly from this level in the years since.

35. How does mortality vary with the seasons?

Mortality is highest in January and February, and lowest in July, August, and September. In 1960, for example, when the crude death rate for the entire year was 9.5 deaths per 1,000 population, the winter high of 11.2 occurred in February and the summer low of 8.5 came in August. Most of the seasonal fluctuation in mortality is the result of the seasonal changes in the respiratory diseases, particularly influenza and pneumonia. The maximum mortality from these two diseases occurred likewise in February, and the minimum in August. Heart disease shows some seasonal variation, partly because heart patients not infrequently succumb to pneumonia. In many diseases, such as tuberculosis and cancer and those associated with childbirth, there is relatively little seasonal influence on mortality.

36. What has been the effect of decreasing mortality on population growth?

The decline in mortality since the industrial revolution has resulted in a rapid increase in the population of the world. From 1800 to 1936, just before World War II, the population doubled. Mortality reduction was concentrated, for the most part, in the countries of the Western world. Because of this reduction, and more recently in the underdeveloped countries, the doubling of the population may now be expected before the close of the present century. More attention is now being given to the control of disease in the less developed areas of the world, and population increase will continue on a large scale if present birth rates are maintained.

37. What has been the effect of decreasing mortality on the age distribution of the population?

The rapid decrease in mortality has been one of the factors contributing to the aging of our population. The other two factors are the reduction in the birth rate prior to World War II and the curtailment of immigration. The decline in mortality, which has been concentrated largely before midlife, has increased the chances of survival to the older ages. According to health conditions prevailing in 1900, the chances of surviving from birth to age 65 were 41 in 100. In 1960, these chances were close to 75 in 100.

38. Does heredity or environment have the greater effect on mortality?

The changes in environment brought about by our rising standard of living and the advances in public health administration, in addition to the progress of medicine, have profoundly affected our mortality experience. Compared with the reduction in death rates produced by these forces, the differences in mortality observed between groups with long-lived parents and groups with short-lived parents are relatively minor.

39. Which diseases are holding back progress of underdeveloped areas?[6]

Malaria still saps the energies and abilities of many millions of people in these areas. It is estimated that hundreds of millions suffer from the disease and that perhaps two million a year die from it. Malaria is particularly prevalent in hot countries, and infests many of the most densely populated areas of the world.

Tuberculosis and the venereal diseases also cost many lives annually and are a constant drain on the energies of many nations, particularly the underdeveloped ones. Great progress has been made in developing controls over these two sources of premature death and disability through the activities of the World Health Organization.

Among the nutritional diseases that are debilitating are beriberi, pellagra, and scurvy. All of these are still common in various areas of Asia.

40. What are the principal epidemic diseases still in the world?

No epidemic disease has yet been brought under complete control on a world-wide basis. The principal ones—cholera, malaria, plague, typhoid, typhus, yellow fever, and smallpox, for example—continue to smolder in endemic form in various regions of the world, periodically flare up to epidemic proportions and continue to pose

[6] See also Chapter 21, page 336 ff.

serious threats to populations elsewhere where, through the application of modern public health measures, these diseases have virtually reached the point of eradication. These threats of rapid spread have been magnified by the ease and speed of modern airplane travel. As our knowledge of the reservoirs of infection, the modes of transmission (personal contact, airborne spread, insect vectors) and the mechanisms of natural or induced immunity improve, many of these diseases could be eradicated on a global basis. The attainment of such goals in large measure awaits only the application of known and available public health skills.

41. What effect will rapid declines in mortality have on the future of underdeveloped countries?

Recent demonstrations have shown that expert medical and public health workers with a moderate expenditure of funds can practically eliminate certain of the infectious diseases. In Ceylon, for example, an island-wide antimosquito campaign, conducted by only 1,000 workers using DDT, was so effective that within a few years the total mortality was cut one-third. Dramatic results have also been recorded in other areas, notably in Greece and Sardinia. In practically all of the underdeveloped countries that have benefited from rapid declines in mortality, birth rates have remained at a high level. This means that the crude rate of natural increase, the difference between the birth rate and the death rate, will move upward rapidly. These countries, most of which are subject to great population pressure, may thus have this pressure increased. A solution is being sought by helping them to expand their agriculture and industry, and by spreading knowledge of birth control.

42. How are international relations affected by the existing reservoirs of high mortality?

High mortality is not only a frequent result of a low standard of living, but is also often the cause of it. In many underdeveloped areas, living conditions are appalling because malaria and other diseases impose a heavy burden on the people. They are poor and lack the resources in trained personnel and equipment to cope with the most common infectious conditions. Present efforts to promote public health work in the East will unquestionably strengthen many of these nations and make them more influential in international relations. The dissatisfaction with health conditions by many people is only a part of a more general situation which has recently received the attention of the United Nations and of our own country in its various aid programs.

43. What international agencies exist to combat high mortality?

Although large-scale active efforts toward world-wide eradication of disease are relatively new, there have been organizations interested in international public health for many years. The International Red Cross, which is now a century old, and many national Red Cross organizations dating back many decades have been engaged in health work transcending national boundaries. The Pan American Sanitary Organization was started in 1902. The Health Organization of the League of Nations came after the first World War. Many private charities have also had international activities for years. The International Health Division of the Rockefeller Foundation, for example, antedates World War I.

Since World War II, the Pan American Sanitary Organization, the Health Organization of the League of Nations, and the International Office of Public Health have been absorbed by the World Health Organization of the United Nations. W.H.O. membership, which is open to any nation in the world, now includes 107 countries. At present its primary aim is the reduction of mortality from malaria, tuberculosis, schistosomiasis, and venereal disease in all parts of the world, but particularly in the underdeveloped nations. Teams of W.H.O. experts are now working in Africa, Asia, and Europe to control disease-carrying mosquitoes and other vectors, to test populations for tuberculosis, to administer antituberculosis BCG serum, and to use drug treatments for venereal disease.

W.H.O. also has an epidemiologic section with a chain of stations for reporting outbreaks of epidemic disease. When cholera erupted in Egypt in 1947, the W.H.O. Interim Commission mobilized the world's resources for producing vaccine and ended the epidemic in record time. In 1949, when there was an outbreak of typhus in Afghanistan, it was the W.H.O. again which arranged for shipments of antityphus vaccine and of DDT to kill the lice which spread the infection.

Chapter 8

The Conquest
of Tuberculosis

1. What is the annual death toll from tuberculosis in the United States?

Tuberculosis currently accounts for about 9,500 deaths a year in this country, or for less than .6 of 1 percent of the total mortality. The death rate from the disease is currently 5.1 per 100,000 population, which places tuberculosis among the lesser causes of death in the nation. The death toll alone, however, is an inadequate measure of the social and economic loss which the disease still inflicts upon the individual, his family, and the community. As a chronic disease, tuberculosis often entails considerable medical and hospital costs either to the patient or to the community, as well as loss of income in many families.

2. How does tuberculosis rank among the causes of death?

In the United States tuberculosis is now in sixteenth place among the causes of death according to the International List of causes of death. Only 60 years ago tuberculosis was the second-ranking cause of death and the most common cause of misery and destitution among American families.[1] Social and economic progress, public health work, and the extension and improvement of medical care have helped to bring about this extraordinary improvement in the tuberculosis situation.

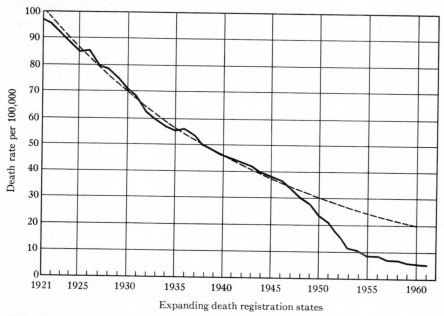

Chart 9. Decline in tuberculosis mortality, United States, 1921-61.

3. What has been the trend of mortality from tuberculosis?

The decline in the death rate from tuberculosis is one of the outstanding achievements of public health work in the United States. Since 1900, when the death rate from tuberculosis was 194 per 100,000 population, the decline has been almost continuous. By 1940, the death rate from the disease was down to 46 per 100,000. In the decade following, the death rate fell 51 percent to 22.5 per 100,000, and since then with acceleration to the amazingly low figure of 5.1 per 100,000. (See Chart 9.)

[1] See Table in Chapter 7, page 103.

4. What does the decline in the tuberculosis rate since 1900 mean in number of lives saved?

If the 1900 death rate from tuberculosis at various ages had continued to the present time, the annual number of deaths from the disease in our population of 190 million would be about 368,600. Instead of that, only about 9,500 deaths occurred in 1962. That represents a savings of close to 360,000 lives in that year alone.

5. What is tuberculosis?

Tuberculosis is an infectious disease caused by the tubercle bacillus. It is communicable and is spread when persons with active disease cough or otherwise excrete bacilli into the air that others breathe. Externally noticeable symptoms do not usually appear until the disease is well advanced; detection is accomplished by tuberculin skin testing followed by chest x-ray for those who react, or by chest x-ray initially for adults in high-prevalence populations. Although characteristically a chronic disease, tuberculosis in the past often occurred in acute form, when it could cause death within a few months. Among infants, the disease was particularly likely to develop rapidly in the form of generalized tuberculosis.

6. Can a person be infected with tuberculosis but not come down with the disease?

Millions of Americans have been infected with tuberculosis but have not become diseased. Being infected merely means that tubercle bacilli have entered the body and established themselves but not necessarily that they are reproducing to cause destruction of tissue. One is ill with tuberculosis when the infection has progressed to the point when there is evidence of destruction of tissue in the lungs or other parts of the body. The disease may be revealed by x-ray, or, as it advances, by such symptoms as loss of weight, fatigue, elevated temperature, and persistent cough. Only a small proportion of those infected ever develop the disease, but some people infected at an early age develop disease late in life.

7. Can the presence of infection with tuberculosis be tested?

A characteristic reaction of the body to tuberculin, a chemical product of the tubercle bacillus, reveals whether or not there is an infection with the bacillus. The test is made by injecting tuberculin into the skin. There are various preparations of tuberculin in use today, the most generally accepted is called P.P.D. (Purified Protein Derivative).

8. What parts of the body may be attacked by tuberculosis?

Although tuberculosis may attack any part of the body, it has a very decided preference for the lungs. Deaths from tuberculosis of the lungs and other respiratory organs account for more than 90 percent of all the deaths from the disease. The remaining deaths are the result of a generalized spread of the disease throughout the body or due to tuberculosis of the central nervous system. Relatively rare are deaths from tuberculosis of the intestines and peritoneum, the vertebral column, the genitourinary system, or of the bones and joints.

9. How many cases of tuberculosis are there in the country?

At the present time, there are about 330,000 cases of tuberculosis on the registers of health departments; 110,000 of them are active cases, about 46,000 hospitalized. Tuberculosis is a reportable illness, yet some cases go undetected and, therefore, unrecorded unless death occurs from the disease. About 4 percent of newly reported cases are first reported at death. In 1962, the number of reported new cases was 53,315, but the actual number of new cases is undoubtedly greater. With better methods of casefinding, the number of new cases reported to the health authorities may increase.

10. What has been the trend in the age distribution of tuberculosis deaths?

The decline in tuberculosis mortality has not been uniform for all ages; the greatest progress has been made among the age groups which used to suffer the highest death rate from the disease. Fifty years ago, the peak in the tuberculosis death rate for white males was in the age group 35 to 44, and for white females, 25 to 34. With the largest improvements registered in childhood and in the early adult years, the peaks of mortality are now in ages over 65 for both white males and white females. In other words, tuberculosis has taken on the same age pattern as most other chronic diseases, with the heaviest death toll among the old, instead of concentrating among the young, as formerly.

11. Has infection with the tubercle bacillus been decreasing in this country?

Infection has been decreasing in striking fashion as health measures have provided for better detection of active cases and for increasing segregation of those capable of spreading the disease. Tuberculosis, which once was so common that in some areas hardly anyone avoided contact with it, is becoming so rare in many sections that there is little chance to become infected. Recent tuberculin tests by health authorities in school populations in Midwestern states reveal very few cases of infection, indicating virtual eradication of tuberculosis among those 15 years old or less. In the relatively more crowded city of Minneapolis, the annual infection rate among high-school students in recent years has been 1 in 300, about one-tenth of the rate of two decades earlier.

12. What are the chances in the United States of dying from tuberculosis?

Even on the basis of current mortality rates, the chances are less than 1 in 100 that a newly born white baby will eventually succumb to tuberculosis. But the situation with reference to this disease is constantly improving. Much of the tuberculosis that now occurs in persons beyond middle life is due to the breakdown of infection acquired early in life when tubercle bacilli were widely present in the environment. Because this is no longer true and the opportunities to become infected are less common, only a few reaching adulthood or old age will have been infected in the past, so that cases due to endogenous breakdown will be fewer. Treatment will undoutedly also improve in the immediate future. The risk of dying from tuberculosis should, therefore, be much lower than the figure of 1 percent; only 40 years ago the chances were about 10 percent. The indications are that risk of dying from tuberculosis will in the near future reach a low minimum. That is what is meant when we say that tuberculosis can be eradicated.

13. How did the United States compare with other countries in tuberculosis mortality before World War II?

Only four countries in the world with reliable mortality statistics had lower tuberculosis death rates than the United States in 1939, the last prewar year. They were Denmark, The Netherlands, Australia, and New Zealand. For that year, the death rate in our country was about 47 per 100,000, compared with 34 in Denmark, 39 in Australia, 40 in New Zealand, and 41 in The Netherlands. The other countries in Western Europe lagged behind with the rate in England and Wales at 62, Italy 76, and Switzerland 80. The highest rates were recorded in the Orient and in extremely cold climates. The figure for China was estimated at about 400 to 500 annual deaths per 100,000 persons, and in Greenland around 550. Even the then American territory of Alaska had a death rate of 437 per 100,000 from tuberculosis in 1939.

14. How did World War II affect the tuberculosis death rate?

The effect of World War II on tuberculosis mortality varied in different areas. Where there was active fighting and destruction, with a tremendous deterioration in living conditions, tuberculosis mortality rose appreciably. In the United States and Canada, however, tuberculosis continued to decline as a result of increased efforts to detect new cases and of improved methods of therapy. In this country in particular, the x-ray examination of millions of young persons who came up for military service and again on discharge greatly advanced the case detection work. After the end of hostilities, mass x-ray examination of the general population increased; many health departments conducted these examinations free for local residents.

In most of continental Europe, the death rate from tuberculosis skyrocketed during the war. Although Denmark and Norway were able to keep some of their health services operating, most of the nations overrun by the Nazis suffered almost complete destruction of their public health organizations and equipment. In The Netherlands, for example, the tuberculosis death rate more than doubled from 1939 to 1945. In cities like Vienna and Berlin, the wartime peaks were at least twice the prewar levels; in Warsaw they were more than three times as high. Even in London, tuberculosis mortality rose 75 percent during the early years of fighting. Postwar overcrowding in half-destroyed communities, the continuation of low levels of diet, the poor state of morale in many countries, and the grossly inadequate medical facilities in large areas of continental Europe combined to make the immediate postwar, as well as the war years, serious for tuberculosis.

The two decades since the close of the war have seen remarkable advances in the control of tuberculosis throughout the world but, more particularly, in the countries of Europe, the Americas, and the antipodes. Some death rates are less than those prevailing in the United States: The Netherlands, 2.7 per 100,000; Denmark, 4.2; Australia, 4.2, and New Zealand, 4.8. The rate in England and Wales is down to 7.2 per 100,000; in West Germany to 14.2; in Italy, 17.5; France, 20.4 per 100,000. All of these reflect the remarkable improvement of recent years. It is only in such East European areas as

Hungary with a rate of 28.6 per 100,000; Poland, 39.1; Yugoslavia, 42.1 per 100,000, that we are confronted with what are still sizable death rates from tuberculosis.

15. What is the United Nations doing to combat tuberculosis?

In cooperation with the United Nations International Children's Emergency Fund and the Scandinavian relief societies, the World Health Organization of the United Nations has been conducting mass case-finding campaigns on millions of children and vaccinating those free from tuberculosis infection. The vaccine, BCG (Bacillus Calmette-Guérin), is prepared from an attenuated strain of tubercle bacilli. By this time, many millions of children and young adults have been tested, about half of them vaccinated under the United Nations program. Tuberculosis centers have been established in many countries. Their effectiveness is attested by the decreasing incidence of, and mortality from, this disease. The World Health Organization is conducting research in the chemotherapy of tuberculosis, especially in the use of the new antibiotics like streptomycin, paraamino salicylic acid (PAS), and isoniazid. Their extensive use has revolutionized the treatment of tuberculosis.

16. How do the death rates from tuberculosis for males and females compare in the United States?

Many more males than females in this country die of tuberculosis. The mortality from the disease among white males is from two to three times that among white females. Among the colored, the mortality of males is likewise much greater than that of females. The excess of male deaths is found particularly at the later ages.

17. How do tuberculosis death rates for white and colored persons compare?

In recent years, the death rate from tuberculosis among the colored was more than three times that among the whites. At certain ages, particularly in the early adult years, the rates for the colored population are more than seven times the rate for the white population. Among the colored races themselves, there are also considerable differences. The American Indians and the Chinese have an overall mortality from tuberculosis higher than for Negroes; however, mortality from tuberculosis for the Japanese is somewhat lower than for the Negroes.

18. At what ages is tuberculosis mortality at the minimum?

The lowest tuberculosis mortality is found today among children at ages 5 to 14 years. This is the case in the United States for both sexes and for whites and nonwhites.

19. Can tuberculosis be inherited?

The disease itself cannot be inherited, any more than one can inherit a cold or whooping cough. There is often, to be sure, a high familial incidence of tuberculosis. This is largely explained by the close contact in which family members live, a situation which involves danger of infection when any single member has a communicable disease. An added factor is thought to be the inheritance of a susceptibility to the disease. Also, certain types of body build have been associated with a proneness to the development of tuberculosis in persons who are infected. Thus three factors—the tubercle bacillus, environment, and body constitution—bear on the susceptibility of any individual to tuberculosis. Inheritance alone cannot account for the disease.

20. Is there a high mortality from tuberculosis among the husbands and wives of known tuberculosis patients?

The familial pattern of tuberculosis manifests itself not only in a high mortality from the disease among the children, parents, or siblings of the known tuberculous, but also among their husbands and wives. Here again is further evidence that the disease is infectious and that it is likely to be transmitted from active cases to those who are in close contact with them. In some recent studies, the mortality from tuberculosis of the surviving husbands or wives of consorts who had succumbed to the disease was found to be three times that expected on the basis of general population death rates.

21. How does the tuberculosis death rate vary geographically within this country?

The lowest death rates from tuberculosis are found in the Plains, North Central, and Rocky Mountain states, while the South, Southwest, and Middle Atlantic states have the highest rates. More than half of the states had death rates less than 5 per 100,000 in 1962. Idaho, Nebraska, North Dakota, Utah, and Wyoming had the lowest mortality from tuberculosis—less than 2 per 100,000 in 1962, and

Kentucky and Arizona were at the other extreme of the table with rates of 9.8 and 9.7 per 100,000 respectively. Less than 15 years earlier, the rate in Arizona was 82, which is a striking illustration of the extent of the improvement in recent years. The relatively high rates still prevailing in the South reflect the lower living standards in that area.

22. Do many localities lack adequate facilities to care for the tuberculous?

This lack exists not only in some of the poorer and more backward areas but also in some of the more progressive places. In many areas, including some large metropolitan centers, for example, adequate facilities are not available for care of patients who are not hospitalized. These, under the newer methods of care, include not only public health nurses to follow up cases in the home but, equally important, clinics where they can receive medical care, laboratory and x-ray examinations, as well as drugs, which they must take for long periods of time.

23. Is tuberculosis an urban disease?

Because the concentration of population helps to spread the disease, tuberculosis is more of a health problem in the cities than in the country. Thus the death rate in the largest cities in 1962 was 9.3 per 100,000 when it was 5.1 for the nation as a whole, and only 4.1 for the other areas of the country, exclusive of large cities.

Tuberculosis cases also tend to be concentrated in urban areas. In 1962, the cities with more than 500,000 people had a new active case rate of 56.0, while the rate for the nation was 28.7.

It should be pointed out that the highest case and death rates from this disease invariably are found in the slum districts of our large cities and that the nonwhite males in these areas have the highest rates in the nation.

24. Is tuberculosis an occupational hazard?[2]

25. Do social and economic factors influence the prevalence of tuberculosis?

From the beginning of the campaign against tuberculosis it was evident that the disease is most common among the poor. The death

[2] See answer to Question 27 of Chapter 18, page 284.

rates are high where the standard of living is low and the general state of the people depressed. The decrease in tuberculosis in this country has come about during a period which witnessed not only extension and improvement in medical service, but also a rising standard of living. The real income of the average family in this country has gone up sharply and with that rise has come the opportunity for a better diet, better housing, more recreation, and a higher level of education. Studies have shown that lowering the caloric, animal protein, and vitamin-C content of a diet leads to greater susceptibility to tuberculosis. Poor and overcrowded housing obviously make for greater hazard of infection should there be any tuberculosis around. In general, the better off economically a population group is, the less likely it is to suffer from tuberculosis.

26. What has been the program of the antituberculosis campaign?

Since the beginning of the century an extensive and organized campaign against tuberculosis has been waged by public health agencies, the medical profession, and voluntary health groups. Case-finding has been stressed, especially in the early stages of the disease. In most instances the tuberculosis section of the local public health department has been the center for this work. Cases, once discovered, are registered and either treated in hospitals or sanitoria, when appropriate and practical, or are followed up in such other ways as will aid the patient and prevent his spreading the disease. The members of the families of new cases are examined carefully since they are a likely source for other active cases. Patients sufficiently recovered to resume work are helped to establish themselves in fields of employment suited to their capacity. Physicians and technical personnel are given specialized training in the detection and treatment of tuberculosis. Voluntary agencies and, more particularly, the thousands of local affiliates of the National Tuberculosis Association have done most of the work of educating the public with regard to the problem and the importance of being examined for the disease. They are also instrumental in obtaining adequate facilities for handling the disease and in providing funds for research.

27. At what stage of tuberculosis are the chances of cure best?

For patients who receive appropriate chemotherapy, the chances of cure are very good no matter what the stage of their disease. Those with minimal disease can be rendered noninfectious within a few weeks and will recover from their disease in essentially all cases. Under proper management, over 90 percent of advanced cases will also recover. Minimal cases, of course, have less residual scarring of the lung.

Another advantage of tuberculosis being discovered at the minimal stage is that the patient has had less opportunity to spread the disease to others.

28. What measures have been taken to prevent tuberculosis infection from animals?

Tuberculosis is a disease of many animals as well as man, and particularly of dairy cattle. Fifty years ago many children in this country contracted tuberculosis by drinking the milk of diseased cows. Bovine tuberculosis was then widespread all over the world. A campaign in which both federal and state authorities cooperated to discover tuberculous cattle and destroy them, compensating farmers for the loss, was phenomenally successful. Bovine tuberculosis has been virtually wiped out in the United States. In addition, the policy of pasteurizing most milk for human consumption has resulted in almost complete elimination of cattle as a source of human tuberculosis infection in this country.

29. How has the sanatorium movement advanced tuberculosis control?

The sanatorium movement has made two major contributions to the campaign against tuberculosis. First, by isolating active tuberculosis patients from their families and the general public, sanatoria have prevented the spread of the disease. Secondly, by treating patients, by developing new medical and surgical methods, and more recently utilizing the newer drug therapy, and by proving the importance of rest and relaxation, the sanatoria have contributed greatly to the welfare of the tuberculosis patient. They have cured or arrested the disease in many patients and have enabled them to return to their families and to normal lives.

30. How many beds are available in hospitals and sanatoria for tuberculous patients?

At present there are about 60,000 beds for tuberculous patients in tuberculosis hospitals and sanatoria, including both private institutions and those of the local, state, and federal governments. Because of the decline in the incidence of the disease and the greater effectiveness of the newer chemotherapy, the number of admissions and the average length of stay of patients have been greatly reduced. As a result, many tuberculosis hospitals have closed their doors. Some tuberculosis patients are now cared for in general hospitals, and this will undoubtedly increase in the future. There is no longer the waiting period before admission which in the past handicapped many patients in their ability to receive treatment.

31. Are additional tuberculosis facilities needed?

Recent surveys indicate that not more hospital beds for the care of the tuberculous, but better use of the facilities already available is the prime requisite, especially in those areas where case rates are still appreciable. In such areas there is need for better case detection and the concentration of trained personnel, particularly in the states with high death rates and large colored populations, to find and treat all active cases of the disease.

32. What lines of research are now being followed in the campaign against tuberculosis?

Although eradication of tuberculosis in this country is possible with present means, it would be greatly speeded if more short-term cures could be effected. With that in mind, the Public Health Service and many private agencies are concentrating on research in chemotherapy. In addition, studies are also being made in the field of prevention. The Public Health Service is engaged in a long-term study of the usefulness of isoniazid in preventing tuberculosis, and is also testing various tuberculin, histoplasmin, and other antigens. Work is being done on improved methods of diagnosing tuberculosis and in the production of a simple and accurate tuberculin test that can be applied and read by nonmedical personnel. Improvements are constantly being made in the design and use of x-ray and radiofluoroscopic equipment.

33. What has been the effect of the use of chemotherapy in the recent treatment of tuberculosis?

The use of the newer drugs, including streptomycin, paraaminosalicylic acid (PAS), and isoniazid, has proved most effective in the treatment of tuberculosis. A course of drug treatment usually results in the arrest of the disease, with the closing of the lesions which prevents the escape of the infective organisms to the environment. An added advantage is that these drugs reduce the period of hospitalization, the patient can continue his treatment at home or at the district tuberculosis clinic. These drugs have effected a veritable revolution in the treatment of the disease.

34. What part does occupational rehabilitation of the ex-tuberculous play in controlling the disease?

Now that tuberculosis can be treated successfully with drugs, most tuberculosis patients, when their disease has become inactive, are able to return to whatever jobs they had before becoming ill. Occupational rehabilitation is needed, therefore, only for those whose educational level is so low as to make them unemployable, or for persons who have had such extensive disease as to make them pulmonary cripples.

35. Who have been the leading figures in the fight against tuberculosis?

The outstanding men in the fight against tuberculosis have lived in relatively modern times. René T. H. Laennec (1781–1826), a French clinician, developed the stethoscope and also introduced auscultation as a means of diagnosis. Robert Koch (1843–1910), the famous German bacteriologist, discovered the tubercle bacillus in 1882 and proved that it was the cause of tuberculosis. He also contributed to the discovery of tuberculin tests and, as director of the Institute of Infectious Diseases in Berlin, helped to train many medical researchers. Wilhelm Roentgen (1845–1923), German physicist, discovered the use of x-ray to examine inner parts of the body. Sir Robert Philip (1857–1939) was largely responsible for working out what are now routine procedures in dealing with tuberculosis as a community health problem. This Scottish physician set up the first tuberculosis clinic on record and established many corollary services, including home supervision of some patients and treatment of others in sanatoria. Edward L. Trudeau (1848–1915) was the American doctor who pioneered the sanatorium movement in this country. At his small camp at Saranac, New York, in 1885, he began demonstrating the efficacy of rest, fresh air, and adequate diet in tuberculosis, the only effective treatment known at the time. His first two-bed little red cottage was the precursor of the chain of the hundreds of specialized sanatoria and tuberculosis hospitals in the country today.

Hermann M. Biggs (1859–1923), for many years Medical Officer of Health of New York City, organized the first city health department laboratory and invited physicians to use it to test their patients' sputum. He introduced compulsory registration of tuberculosis cases and led in the establishment of one of the first state tuberculosis campaigns. Léon Charles Albert Calmette (1863–1933) and Camille Guérin (1872–1961) were the French scientists who developed the now standard vaccine against tuberculosis known as Bacillus Calmette-Guérin, or BCG. Manoel de Abreu (1892–1961), Brazilian physician, developed small-film x-ray technique. Selman A. Waksman (1888–   ), American biologist, isolated streptomycin, first drug used successfully against tuberculosis. Jorgen Lehman (1898–   ), Swedish scientist, introduced paraaminosalicylic acid (PAS), a drug now widely used in combination with other drugs. The American and European pharmaceutic industry introduced isoniazid, now the most useful of all antituberculosis drugs.

36. How did the campaign against tuberculosis develop in this country?

The organized campaign against tuberculosis dates back to the end of the nineteenth century. In 1892, the Pennsylvania Society for the Prevention of Tuberculosis was founded, with Dr. L. F. Flick as one of its leaders. A number of other small tuberculosis organizations, many of them lasting only a short while, came into being in the next dozen years. In 1904, at a convention of the American Medical Association, the National Association for the Study and Prevention of Tuberculosis was formed, with Dr. Flick again instrumental in its founding. Since then, the national association has grown until now it has affiliated agencies in all states. It has led in the education of the public on the subject of tuberculosis, in helping to train technical personnel, in persuading government officials of the importance of the disease and of the need for tuberculosis facilities, in raising funds for sanatoria, hospitals, research, case-finding, and other branches of the antituberculosis campaign. The Christmas seal drive alone has brought in close to $30,000,000 annually in recent years. Since 1942, there has been a special branch or division concerned with tuberculosis in the United States Public Health Service, but most public health activities in this country are carried on by local and state health departments. Tuberculosis was early recognized as one of the major health problems of the nation, but the efforts of

50 years by official and voluntary agencies have resulted in a great public health victory.

37. What effect has the decline in tuberculosis had on the American population and economy?

Sixty years ago, tuberculosis had its peak mortality among white males at about 25 to 40—the ages when family responsibility was greatest—and at about 30 for white females, when many of them had young children to care for. The sharp decline in tuberculosis mortality since then has, therefore, had an incalculable effect on home life. The preservation of millions of families that otherwise would have been broken has meant not only that there were proportionately far fewer orphans, but also that great advances were made in production, and the general well-being of the population.

Many hundreds of thousands of working men have been saved from the disease by the improvements in medical and social science in the last half century. The men thus saved were able to do constructive work which has contributed greatly to the economy of the nation. Were it not for the advances in health and welfare—and the decrease in tuberculosis was one of the most important—the United States could not have attained its present pre-eminent position among the nations of the world.

38. What is the outlook for eventual control of tuberculosis?

The outlook is very favorable for virtually complete control of this disease. The death rate has been decreased nearly 60 percent in the past decade, and the case rate has been decreased 46 percent. The numbers of new cases reported, however, remain rather high, and local, state, and federal agencies are working for the establishment of more effective tuberculosis facilities. The federal government aids the states with grants for improvement of community services to tuberculosis patients, their families, and others needing diagnosis or treatment for tuberculosis. Hospitals and sanatoria now must provide more intensive care, although for shorter periods. Educational programs must be set up for physicians, nurses, and other tuberculosis workers, and for the general public. The combination of these efforts promises ultimate success in bringing tuberculosis to a minor place among the causes of illness and death in this country. There is no good reason why tuberculosis cannot be eradicated.

Chapter 9

The Mystery
of Cancer

1. Where does cancer rank among the causes of death in the United States?

Cancer is now outranked only by heart disease as a cause of death in this country. Among women 15 to 54 years old, it is the leading cause of death from disease. A half century ago, cancer was outranked by tuberculosis, pneumonia, diseases of the heart, and nephritis. Although cancer is commonly a disease of adults, it is nevertheless one of the leading child killers. Among children aged five to nine, cancer, including the leukemias and Hodgkin's disease, has been for some time the leading cause of death from disease.

2. What is cancer?

"Cancer" is the generic name for a group of diseases, all characterized by uncontrolled cell reproduction. Cancerous growths usually have no clear boundaries setting them off from normal tissues; cancer cells may intrude between the healthy cells and spread throughout the body. Cancers of practically every part of the body have been reported, although the heart, circulatory system, and muscles seem generally unaffected. A variety of cancerous growths, such as sarcoma and carcinoma, have been identified.

Cancer is not a germ disease, but there is evidence that some cancers may be caused by a virus. Cancer is not infectious, at least not in man, and to date has not been combated by the usual methods of artificial immunization. Plants as well as animals are susceptible to it, and it is among the diseases reported in early medical literature. The only cures now known involve destruction of the cancerous growth, either by surgery or radiation, or both. Drugs have been found which may alleviate suffering from the disease and in some instances cause temporary recession and improvement, but so far no drug cure has been discovered.

3. How does cancer kill?

Cancer kills by extending into the healthy tissue around it, robbing the neighboring parts of their nutrition, and in other ways interfering with their normal function. In addition, after a cancer has developed at one site, some of its cells may be carried by the lymph or blood to other parts of the body where they begin a new cancerous growth.

4. What are the usual signs of cancer?

There are seven symptoms which are sometimes called the danger signals of cancer. However, the appearance of any one or more of them does not necessarily mean that the individual has cancer; it does call for a careful checkup by a physician without delay. Even persons presumably in good health should have a physical examination annually, and women over 35, semiannually. The seven danger signals are:

1. Any sore that does not heal
2. A lump or thickening in the breast or elsewhere
3. Unusual bleeding or discharge
4. Any change in a wart or mole
5. Persistent indigestion or difficulty in swallowing
6. Persistent hoarseness or cough
7. Any change in normal bowel habits

Significantly, pain is absent from the list of signs of cancer. Pain is usually not evident in cancer cases until the disease is far advanced.

5. How many persons a year die of cancer in this country?

In 1962, cancer of all types caused approximately one out of every six deaths in the United States, killing more than 278,000 persons. The death rate from cancer was 149.9 per 100,000 population.

6. By how much is the expectation of life reduced by cancer?

If cancer were eliminated as a cause of death, the expectation of life of American men entering middle age would be increased by about a year and a half, and of women by two years.

7. What is the probable number of cancer cases in our country?

The number of new cancer cases discovered annually has been about a half million. An additional third of a million previously diagnosed cases are still under treatment. Unfortunately, in many areas there is still little concerted effort to detect cancer cases, so that the true extent to which the population of this country suffers from the disease is not known. If present trends continue, it is conservatively estimated that one-fourth of those now living will suffer from this disease.

8. How does the United States compare with other countries in cancer mortality?

The United Kingdom, France, Switzerland, Austria, and many other countries of Western Europe have reported higher death rates from cancer than this country in recent years. It is significant that the countries with high recorded cancer mortality are also those with a generally high level of public health and medical practice. Thus, a good part of the international variation may be the result of efficiency in diagnosing cancer, in reporting it as a cause of death, and of the proportion of older people in the population. England and Wales, which had a cancer death rate of 216 per 100,000 population in 1961 —one of the highest in the world—also has a high expectation of life. Countries like Mexico and Egypt, with reported cancer death rates of 35 or under per 100,000, have very poor records of longevity.

9. What has been the trend in cancer mortality in this country since 1900?

The recorded death rate from cancer has more than doubled since the turn of the century. Sixty years ago, 64 persons per 100,000 were reported dying from cancer, compared with 149.9 in 1962. In the same period, there has been a very great drop in mortality from many diseases, particularly tuberculosis, pneumonia, and the communicable diseases of childhood. The only important natural causes of death other than cancer which have shown a rise in mortality are the cardiovascular ailments.

10. Has there been a real increase in the chance of dying from cancer?

The marked rise in the crude death rate probably does not reflect the true cancer situation. In all likelihood the disease is only moderately more prevalent, age for age, today than in 1900. Mortality from the disease has always been much higher among the old than among children or young adults, and the proportion of the popula-

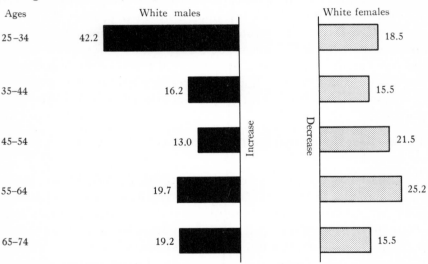

Ages	White males	White females
25–34	42.2	18.5
35–44	16.2	15.5
45–54	13.0	21.5
55–64	19.7	25.2
65–74	19.2	15.5

Chart 10. Percent increase or decrease in cancer death rates by sex and age group, Metropolitan Life Insurance Company, Industrial Experience, 1911–1960.

tion surviving to old age has been growing steadily. Persons saved from premature death from tuberculosis, pneumonia, or one of the acute diseases may now live to the ages at which cancer and heart disease take their great toll. If allowance is made for the changes in the age composition of the population, the present cancer death rate would be only one and one-half instead of more than two times that of 1900.

The great improvement in the diagnosis and reporting of cancer in the last 60 years has also added to an exaggerated impression of the trend of cancer mortality. With increasing urbanization has come an increase in hospitalization for serious illness and more frequent use of x-rays and laboratory techniques. A great many deaths formerly ascribed to other causes are now properly attributed to cancer.

In the last decade or so the death rates for certain types of cancer have fallen off after allowance is made for changes in the age and sex composition of the population, despite the continuing improvements in diagnosis. This suggests that the real peak in cancer mortality for these sites may be past. (See Chart 10.)

11. What is meant by "accessible" and "inaccessible" cancers?

"Accessible" cancers are those relatively easily reached for diagnosis or treatment. The most obvious example is cancer of the skin, which can be detected by sight and feel soon after developing, and is open to the simplest form of surgery or x-ray treatment. "Inaccessible" cancers are those of the internal organs, especially the ones not reached through any of the body openings. Cancer of the stomach, liver, lung, and brain are relatively "inaccessible." They would usually not be noticed early in their development unless uncovered by tests or complicated examinations, and their treatment is likely to require the more radical surgery.

12. Do men and women have different cancer death rates?

The differences between the death rate from cancer in the two sexes stem primarily from the different sites of cancer and become manifest in the several age periods of life. Mortality from cancer is now lower among females than among males; in earlier years the reverse was true. Females still have a higher mortality than males at ages 25 to 54, but beyond these ages, males uniformly have higher death rates. In this connection, it should be observed that females have more accessible cancers than males. These are more likely to be noticed early, resulting in more effective treatment as well as in better reporting of cases.

13. Is cancer principally a disease of later life?

Despite the fact that it ranks among the leading causes of death at almost every period of life, cancer is for the most part a disease of the middle-aged and the old. Some forms may take as long as 20 years to develop to the point where they cause death. In 1962, more than nine-tenths of all cancer deaths were among persons 45 years old and over. Less than 3 percent of the cancer deaths that year occurred among individuals under age 25.

14. Are there racial differences in cancer mortality?

There are material differences in the recorded mortality of colored and white persons, but it is not possible to say whether they are the result of different susceptibilities, of differences in the quality and quantity of medical service available, or of other social factors. In 1962, the death rates for colored males exceeded those for white males at ages 35 to 74; the rates for colored females were in excess of the white rates in the age range 25 to 74. At other ages, the rates for the whites were somewhat higher.

Cancer of the skin is much less common among the colored than among white persons. Some interesting differences in the frequency of cancer of the various organs or sites of the body have been observed among various Asiatic peoples, but there is no good evidence that the total frequency among them is far different from that in the United States. It has been commonly observed that cancer of the cervix is less frequent among Jewish women than among the neighbors in their communities.

15. Are there geographic variations in cancer incidence and mortality?

Although cancer is more frequently reported in the South, the North has the highest mortality. The reason for the apparent contradiction is that cancer of the skin, which has a very low fatality rate, is much more frequent among white Southerners. As for cancers other than those of the skin, there is little regional difference in incidence among white males and only small variations among white females. One cause for the difference between the South and North in respiratory cancer may be the greater degree of urbanization and industrialization in the North, with consequently a higher concentration of soot, petroleum-combustion products, and other impurities in the atmosphere.

16. Is cancer more prevalent in urban or rural areas?

The combined death rate from all forms of cancer is higher in urban areas than in rural. The reported mortality from cancer varies from a minimum for predominantly rural states to a maximum for those which have been most industrialized and urbanized. Also, the reported cancer mortality rises from a minimum in those states having proportionately the fewest doctors, to a maximum in those having proportionately the most doctors. Evidently, a great deal of urban-rural variation in cancer mortality reflects differences in the efficiency of diagnosing and reporting the disease.

17. Does cancer mortality and incidence vary with social-economic status?

Certain types of cancer seem to be more common among those at the lower end of the economic scale. Studies in England, for example, indicated a higher rate of cancer of the upper alimentary tract among the poor than among the rich. Certain skin cancers showed the same feature. These variations have been attributed to habits, diet, cleanliness, occupations, housing, and general exposure to soot, coal dust, etc. It is also clear that diagnosis is important in cure and that treatment is often expensive. Those in the lower social-economic groups may not be well enough educated in the advantages of routine examinations, early signs, nor have as ready access to medical facilities.

18. How does environment affect the chances of having cancer?

Under certain conditions, cancer can be caused by a number of environmental factors. Malignant growths are known to be caused by actinic rays, x-rays, radium radiation, and constant chemical or mechanical irritation. About 300 substances, ranging from the dust of some metallic elements to complex organic compounds, have been shown to have resulted in a high incidence of cancer among those exposed to them. Many of these chemicals are becoming quite common in modern industry. The relatively high incidence of cancer of the skin, especially of the exposed portions of the body, among white sailors and farmers is an example of environmental cancer. Apparently pigmentation of the skin influences the susceptibility to cancers caused by sunlight, since such growths are about seven times as common among white persons as among colored.

19. Is cancer an occupational disease?

There are a few occupations with a cancer incidence higher than average; of these, radiologists provide a good example.[1]

[1] See answer to Question 30 of Chapter 18, page 285.

20. How does diet affect cancer?

Apparently susceptibility to certain types of cancer is related to diet. For example, cancer of the thyroid, like goiter, is found to a greater degree than elsewhere among residents of areas where the drinking water is iodine deficient.

In experimental animals it has been found that diets just barely sufficient in variety and in caloric content to support life result in a lower susceptibility to cancer than overly generous diets. Life insurance data also show that persons overweight at the time of applying for insurance have a cancer incidence later in life that is greater than average. Being overweight is a contributory factor in other diseases as well, including ailments of the heart and the circulatory system.

21. Can cancer be inherited?

Cancer in man is not believed to be inherited, but there is evidence that a susceptibility to the disease runs in families. Studies indicate that identical twins are much more likely than fraternal twins to have the same type of cancer, in some cases even developing the disease simultaneously. There are families in medical history in which there has been a strikingly high incidence of the disease. A person will not necessarily have cancer if other members of his family had the disease, but such persons should be examined at frequent intervals.

22. What has been the recent trend in cancer mortality among women?

After allowance is made for the increasing proportion of aged in the population, it is found that cancer mortality among females in the United States has been declining since about 1927.

23. What has been the recent trend in cancer mortality among men?

Mortality from cancer among men is rising consistently, even after allowing for the aging of the population. However, the current rate of increase is not as great as it was two decades ago.

24. What are the most common sites for cancer among women?

In order of frequency the most common sites among women are the breast, uterus, skin, and intestines. Together they account for three-fifths of the cancers in women. Among the less common sites for females are the genital organs other than uterus, digestive organs other than intestines, urinary tract, and leukemias. Three-fifths of all cancers among females—those of the breast, uterus, skin, rectum and anus, mouth, and thyroid—are relatively accessible to diagnosis and treatment.

25. What are the most common sites for cancer among men?

The most common site for cancer in men is the skin, followed by the lungs, prostate, intestines, stomach, rectum , and anus, and bladder. The digestive organs, excluding the rectum and anus, account for one-fourth of all male cancers and are among the relatively inaccessible sites of malignant growths. Only a little more than one-third of the cancers among males—those of the skin, mouth, rectum and anus, prostate, and thyroid—are relatively accessible to diagnosis and treatment.

26. What has been the trend in mortality from the accessible cancers?

Within the last 25 years there has been a definite reduction in the death rates from accessible cancers among both males and females, according to the experience among Industrial policyholders of the Metropolitan Life Insurance Company. The greatest improvements among men were in mortality from cancers of the mouth and of the skin, and among women in mortality from cancers of the vulva and vagina, the mouth, the uterus, and the skin. Although the recent gains have been proportionately about the same for both sexes, the mortality of females from accessible cancers is still around three times that of males. This is largely because of the high incidence of cancer of the breast and uterus among women.

27. What has been the trend in mortality from the inaccessible cancers?

According to Metropolitan Life Insurance Company data, cancer at inaccessible sites has continued to show a high mortality, though there are some where gains have been made. Among women, mortality from inaccessible cancers has been reduced since about 1935, but the improvement was only about half as great as that for accessible cancers. The best record was made in cancers of the stomach, liver, esophagus, and bladder. The death rate from inaccessible cancers among men has shown an overall rise in recent years; however, decreases have been recorded in mortality from cancer of the stomach, liver, esophagus, and bladder. Mortality from cancer of the respiratory system, especially the lungs and bronchus, has increased very rapidly in the last few decades.

28. What has been the trend in mortality from cancer of the skin?

Cancer of the skin, while the most common form of the disease, is also one of the most readily cured. Since skin cancers are likely to be noticed early in their development, there is a good chance that they will receive treatment before they have had time to spread to other organs. Although skin cancers account for more than one-sixth of all cancers among males in this country, they cause only about one-fortieth of the male cancer deaths. The death rate from skin cancer has been falling for a number of years. The mortality of women from skin cancer is even lower than that of men.

29. Is there any relation between smoking and cancer of the lung?

It has been observed, in a number of surveys, that among lung cancer patients the proportion of heavy cigarette smokers is much larger than among patients with other cancers. Even more convincing are the results of more recent studies in which large numbers of individuals, smokers and nonsmokers, were carefully followed up for a number of years. In each case it was found that the the incidence of cancer of the respiratory system was many times greater among the heavy smokers of cigarettes than among the nonsmokers. This probability of developing respiratory cancer appeared to depend on the amount of cigarette smoking. As a result of these studies, the Surgeon General of the U.S. Public Health Service has finally declared that the smoking of cigarettes is a serious health hazard; he is urging the public to discontinue this indulgence, and is taking other steps to safeguard the public.

30. What indications are there of improvement in the cancer situation?

The most important sign of an improvement has been a reduction in the death rate from cancer among women. Cancer research has been intensified on all fronts. The facilities for dealing with cancer have been and still are being expanded, the awareness of the population has been heightened, and the skill of doctors in dealing with cancer also increased. As a result, the rate of survival for cancer patients receiving treatment has risen markedly in many areas.

31. Why is the early reporting of cancer symptoms so important?

With present methods of treatment, the chances of cure are immeasurably better when the cancer is caught in the early stages. It is possible under those circumstances to remove or kill the cancer cells completely, using surgery or radiation, or both. Once the growth has spread to other parts of the body, treatment is more difficult and the chance of cure seriously reduced.

32. Are many cases now diagnosed within a month of the appearance of symptoms?

Within the last two decades the proportion of patients seeking medical aid within a month of the first symptoms of the disease has risen 50 percent. Nearly 30 percent of the cases of cancer of the breast are now brought to the attention of a doctor within a month of the patient's first realization that something was wrong. A study in Vermont in 1947 showed that 60 percent of all cancer cases reported were still in the early stages, as compared with only 20 percent 10 years earlier. The time lag between diagnosis and treatment has also been cut almost in half within the last two decades according to data from Massachusetts.

33. Is there evidence that medical and surgical treatment of cancer is improving?

Increasing numbers of cancer patients are being discovered in early stages of the disease and are receiving more adequate care. This is generally true throughout the country. As a result, there has been a steady rise in the survival rate of cancer patients.

34. What are the chances of developing cancer?

The chances at birth of eventually developing cancer are about two in seven for females and slightly less for males (two in eight).

35. What are the chances of eventually dying of cancer?

At present the chances at birth are about 2 in 13 that a white male in the United States will eventually die of cancer, and about 2 in 11 that a white female will. It has been estimated that with present medical and surgical techniques, mortality from cancer could be reduced one-third from its present level by early detection of more cases and by increasing the availability of adequate treatment.

36. How much is being spent annually on cancer research in this country?

For fiscal 1964, the National Cancer Institute has appropriated $145 million, most of which was for research. The American Cancer Society appropriated $12 million last year for its National Research Grants Program, while the Atomic Energy Commission spent $6 million for cancer research. The Damon Runyon Memorial Fund raised over $1 million for this purpose. Other private foundations, medical schools, and hospitals also had expenditures of varying amounts for cancer research.

37. What are the main fields for cancer research today?

The attack on cancer is being advanced from many different directions—in the fields of both pure and applied science. In addition to the medical profession, physicists, biologists, immunologists, virologists, and geneticists, as well as statisticians are engaged in cancer research on a broad front. Fundamentally, the study of cancer now involves the study of life and growth. Since the development of cancers from healthy cells results from a misdirected form of reproduction and normal life processes, much of the basic biological and biochemical research now carried out has value in the study of cancer. There is, therefore, a special concentration on investigating the simpler forms of life and, more especially, the viruses, to throw light on the processes of cell division and the action of the chromosomes and of the chemical constituents of the hereditary substance (DNA). The development of embryos is also being studied, and new agents are being sought which act as cancer producers and cancer inhibitors in experimental animals.

The chemistry of the body is being explored with emphasis on the enzymes, hormones, and the glandular systems of mammals, with particular reference to inhibiting cancers of the primary and secondary sex organs. Animals with and without cancers are being fed a variety of diets to see what effect deficiencies and excesses of certain substances have on cancer growth.

There has been a concentration of much research on the viruses, not only in mammary cancer of mice but also in other animals and in other malignant tumors. Tests to detect cancer-causing viruses are being sought on a wide scale and with some success.

A variety of chemotherapeutic agents are being sought which can arrest cancer development or possibly even cause complete regression of tumors. A number of such are already in wide use. Unfortunately, some of these agents do not have all the qualities needed and have serious toxic effects, but they point out directions for important further work.

At the same time, improvements are constantly being made in surgery and radiation, and in both chemical and x-ray methods to diagnose the disease. The radioactive isotopes produced by the Atomic Energy Commission have an affinity for specific organs and make possible the introduction of cancer-killing rays into previously inaccessible parts of the body. Such isotopes are also being used as tracers in metabolism studies to follow the course of ingested substances through the body. Smear tests and blood tests have been developed to aid in the early discovery of cancers of certain internal organs.

Of great importance in the search is the fact that all the major agencies supporting cancer work are encouraging, through grants, the training under competent auspices of a large body of young scientists who are dedicating their lives to the investigation of the cancer problem. This is one of the most promising activities in the wide field of cancer research.

As the result of the concentration of money and well-directed effort, advances are now being made in almost all sectors of cancer research. In view of the great accomplishments of recent years, it would not be surprising if the cancer riddle were resolved within a few more decades.

38. Why is the accumulation of statistical data so important in cancer research?

Since the mechanism of cancer is not yet fully understood, it is often by following out statistical leads that new knowledge is gained. Studies may reveal, for example, that among two groups of mice living under almost identical and controlled conditions and as similar genetically as possible, there is a much greater incidence of cancer in those subjected to long periods of ultraviolet radiation. Such radiation might then be added to the list of statistically proven carcinogenic agents. In like manner, the recent statistical studies of the relation of cancer morbidity and mortality to the smoking habit have demonstrated an unmistakable hazard due to heavy cigarette smoking. Because there are such wide gaps in knowledge about cancer, the statistical, mathematical approach is even more important in cancer research than in most other fields of medical work.

39. How does a cancer registry help in cancer research?

A cancer registry, which is a record of all tumor and cancer cases within a given institution or geographic area such as a state, helps in cancer research because it is a source of statistical data about the incidence and the death rate of the disease. A cancer registry should include fairly complete information on the diagnosis and treatment of each case, as well as the personal history of the patient; it should follow up each individual at least once a year after the cessation of treatment for information on possible recurrence of the disease. In 1962, 27 states had state-wide cancer registries or planned them, 17 states had regional cancer registries, and 7 states had none. The three oldest registries, all of which have already contributed a great deal to our knowledge of cancer, are in Connecticut, Massachusetts, and New York.

40. What facilities are there for the detection of cancer in this country?

The great majority of cancer cases are discovered by general practitioners and by general hospital staffs. There are, however, a few hundred cancer detection centers in the country accommodating thousands of patients a week. These are scattered through the nation, in almost every state. Some states operate traveling detection and diagnostic units, and one state has a group of specialists who can on occasion act as a traveling tumor board.

41. What facilities are there for diagnosis and treatment?

Complete diagnosis of cancer—determination of the type of growth, the primary and all secondary sites, etc.—often require special laboratory equipment and tests. In 1933, in its first list of approved cancer programs, the American College of Surgeons named 140 institutions. By 1950, this list had grown to 575 institutions, and in 1963, there were 972 approved institutions, including 11 cancer hospitals in the United States and Canada. Only two states had no specialized cancer diagnostic or treatment clinics in 1963.

42. What government and voluntary agencies are working to combat cancer?

The organizations in the field of cancer range from voluntary fund-raising groups and endowed foundations to a federally supported center for research. In the area of money-raising and the provision of local service, the largest organization is the American Cancer Society, which devotes its resources to education about cancer, the support of detection centers, aid to cancer patients, the establishment of new clinics, and to research. The Damon Runyon Fund raises money solely for research purposes, and the National Cancer Foundation is primarily concerned with aiding cancer patients. On the government side, there are the local and state health agencies and the National Cancer Institute of the Public Health Service. The latter not only does its own research but also provides major funds for other research groups and helps pay for the construction of new cancer facilities.

43. To what extent is the public informed about cancer?

A number of surveys during the last two decades by the American Cancer Society and other organizations have disclosed the extent of the knowledge the public has about cancer, and also the public's attitude in dealing with the various aspects of the cancer problem. A number of findings are of interest: apparently, the general public has an increasing background of knowledge about the disease; that it is possible to have cancer, even though one feels well; that it is not a contagious condition; that it is a serious disease in childhood and, in fact, in most other age periods of life; that a large fraction of the population is aware of one or more of the danger signals calling for medical attention. With this growing knowledge of the facts of cancer has also come a better attitude toward the condition. Fewer persons would now maintain secrecy with regard to symptoms, or would avoid medical intervention or medical examination. In fact, a large fraction believe that cancer is curable. Younger persons, as might be expected, are far better informed on the subject than older ones, among whom cancer is more prevalent. There has thus been great improvement in recent years in these evidences of increasing knowledge of the disease and in constructive attitudes toward its control. Nevertheless, there is still plenty of room for further education of the public. Such increase in knowledge will undoubtedly help to bring down the mortality from cancer.

Chapter 10

The Control
of Diabetes

1. What is diabetes?

Diabetes mellitus is a disease in which the ability of the body to get energy from sugars and starches (carbohydrates) is impaired. Unlike the normal person, the diabetic cannot get full benefit from his food. Sugar accumulates in his blood and is then eliminated in the urine. In this way, one of the main energy constituents of food is lost to the diabetic, who also loses both weight and strength as a result. A vicious cycle is established in which the diabetic is driven to eat to satisfy his hunger but cannot properly use the extra food he consumes.

2. What causes diabetes?

The real cause of the disease has not yet been discovered. It is known that diabetics lack a substance called insulin, altogether or in an effective form. Insulin is secreted by clusters of cells known as the islands of Langerhans which are located in the pancreas, a gland behind the stomach. Without adequate quantities of effective insulin, sugars and starches cannot properly be utilized. The diabetic either produces too little insulin or the insulin he does produce is counteracted by antibodies or the secretions of other glands.

3. What are the symptoms of diabetes?

At the onset of diabetes there are generally no obvious symptoms. In later stages, the disease is marked by excessive thirst and hunger, frequent urination, the loss of weight and strength, and easy tiring. In some instances, diabetes may first be noticed because of blurring of vision, the slow healing of wounds, itching, or even the occurrence of gangrene of the toes or feet. But these are already evidences of far-advanced disease.

4. How is diabetes usually diagnosed?

Even before symptoms develop, diabetes can often but not always be detected by simple laboratory tests. In the presence of the symptoms described previously, the finding of sizable amounts of glucose in the urine is usually sufficient to make the diagnosis, but generally a test is also made to determine the amount of sugar in the blood. In some instances where the results are still not clear, a special procedure known as the glucose tolerance test is used. This involves testing the blood for sugar just before administering a measured amount of sugar or glucose and testing again at half-hour or hourly intervals for two to three hours afterward.

5. How is diabetes usually discovered?

It is unfortunately still true that the disease is usually not diagnosed until the symptoms appear, until there are serious complications, or until it is discovered accidentally on medical examination during illness or in preparation for an operation. An increasing number of cases, however, are being discovered in the course of routine private, industrial, and life insurance medical examinations.

6. How many diabetic individuals are there in the United States?

On the basis of the data collected in the U.S. National Health Survey, 1957–59, it is estimated that there are approximately 1,600,-000 known cases of diabetes in the United States. In addition, there are almost as many others who have the disease but do not know it. Because cases of diabetes are not reported to public health authorities, there are no exact figures available. The number of cases in the United States has grown in the past two decades, largely because of the increase in population, particularly at the older ages, and the increased longevity of diabetics. Likewise, the improved facilities for the detection of new cases, and the interest of physicians and the general public in this area, add to the number of known cases.

7. How many new cases occur each year?

The number of new cases is at least 75,000 annually. This is an estimate based upon statistics of deaths from the disease and facts on the average length of life of patients. The figure given is a minimal estimate; the true number is probably appreciably higher.

8. How many die from diabetes each year in the United States?

About 31,000 deaths in the United States in 1962 were classified as due to diabetes; the death rate was 16.8 per 100,000 population. Not all the deaths of people with diabetes, however, are ascribed to diabetes. In fact, these are exceeded by deaths of diabetic patients ascribed to other causes. Available studies show that the number of deaths of individuals with diabetes is now more than 60,000 a year.

9. How does diabetes rank among the diseases?

Diabetes is a serious health problem, although the leading chronic diseases—heart disease and cancer—involve many more cases. In 1962, diabetes ranked eighth among all the diseases causing death in this country, and accounted for 1.8 percent of all deaths.

10. How does the prevalence of diabetes in the United States compare with that in other countries?

Diabetes is a universal disease. It is found in all countries and among all races, but with wide variations in frequency. Accurate information on the number of cases of the disease is not available, but mortality statistics indicate that diabetes is at least as prevalent in the United States as in any other country in the world. The death rates from diabetes are relatively high in Western Europe and in the white population of the countries in the British Commonwealth; they are generally low in Eastern and Southern Europe and in Latin

America. Little is known about diabetes in the tropics or the Far East, but if the recorded mortality in Japan is a guide, the disease is comparatively rare in the Orient. Altogether, the range of the reported mortality rates is from less than 5 per 100,000 in some countries to 25 in Belgium. A few countries report even higher death rates but these are small and no great reliability can be attached to their mortality data. Where doctors and medical facilities are lacking, many cases obviously escape diagnosis and the recorded death rate from diabetes is accordingly low. The sex and age distribution of the population and the prevailing standard of living also play a part in determining the level of diabetes death rates.

11. What geographic variations in diabetes are found within the United States?

In 1960–61, when the annual death rate for the nation as a whole was 16.5 per 100,000, the rates for the states varied from a minimum of 8.5 in New Mexico to a maximum of 33.0 in Rhode Island. In general, the higher death rates are found in the Northeast and the lower ones in the South and Southwest. In part, the state variations reflect the differences in the age and sex composition of the population, but again the low rates in some areas are probably the result of failure to diagnose the disease because of inadequate medical facilities.

12. Is death from diabetes more frequent in cities than in the country?

Death rates from diabetes are about 60 percent higher in cities of the United States than in the country, even when adjustments are made for differences in the average age in the two groups. Diabetes mortality is highest in the largest cities (100,000 or more population). The rates for moderate-size communities (10,000 to 100,000 population) and for small places (2,500 to 10,000) are somewhat lower, but still above those for rural areas.

13. How does the onset of diabetes vary according to age?

Diabetes may occur at any age, but it is comparatively rare among children and young people. The rate of onset increases with advancing age, especially after 30 or 35. Less than 1 new case out of 20 is found among persons under 25 years old; about one-seventh of the new cases occur among those from 25 to 44; more than half at ages 45 to 64; and one-quarter at 65 and over. (See Chart 11 below.)

14. How do the prevalence and mortality of diabetes vary with age?

The same general pattern of increasing rates with advance in age is found both in the prevalence of diabetes and in diabetes mortality. The peak in the prevalence rate, shortly after age 70, comes several years after the peak of onset, about age 65; the maximum death rate is even later in life. Of the existing cases, slightly less than one-fifth are under 45, a little less than one-half between ages 45 and 64, and about one-third are 65 and over.

15. How do the sexes compare in the prevalence and mortality from diabetes?

About five out of every eight known diabetic individuals are females. The death rates, especially in later life, are considerably higher for females than for males. These differences between the two sexes must be considered in the light of the fact that there probably is more unrecognized diabetes among men than among women.

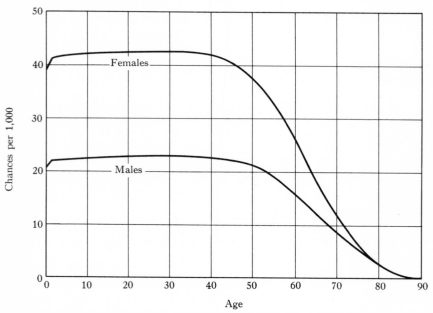

Chart 11. **Chances per 1,000 of eventually becoming diabetic, according to sex and age.**

16. Does the death rate from diabetes vary according to marital status?

The mortality from diabetes is higher among married women than among the single, but there is no significant difference by marital status among men. The excess of deaths among married women is found at all ages above 25, but is markedly so beyond age 45. Among younger women the rate for the unmarried is higher, suggesting that girls with diabetes are less likely to marry than those without diabetes. In part, the excess of diabetes among married females may be caused by strain on the endocrine system during pregnancy and menopause. In any case, the occurrence of sugar in the urine during pregnancy is not uncommon, and the gain in weight during pregnancy is not infrequently retained.

17. Is diabetes more common in thin or fat people?

Except in childhood and early adult life, overweight usually precedes the onset of diabetes. Insurance studies show that diabetes develops much more often in fat persons than in those of average weight or less. The greater the excess of weight, the higher the prevalence of diabetes. One study of males showed that individuals 25 percent or more overweight had a death rate from diabetes 13 times as high as those who were underweight. A study of women 15 to 34 percent overweight showed a death rate from diabetes 62 percent above the average. These findings are confirmed by clinical studies. For example, slightly more than one-half of the diabetic men and three out of five of the diabetic women in one survey were at least 20 percent above average weight. Frank obesity (40 percent or more overweight) was found in one out of every six men and one out of every four women with diabetes. Fatness was particularly common among those whose diabetes began after middle life, especially among women. Studies of females with diabetes show that married women weigh more than the single. Apparently single women are much more figure-conscious than married women.

18. Are there any marked differences in the diabetes death rates of national and racial groups within this country?

There are wide differences in the reported mortality rates from diabetes for various groups, but they may to a degree reflect variations in medical care or economic status. Jews have long been observed to have a high death rate from the disease. A study in New

York City showed that mortality from diabetes after the age of 45 was more than one and three-quarters times as high among Jews as among non-Jews.

About 50 years ago, persons of German and Irish origin in this country also had diabetes death rates above the average, while those of Italian descent had low rates. Now, these nationality differences appear to be much smaller. The prevalence of diabetes among Italians in this country was reported recently to have risen much closer to the figure for the population as a whole. Negroes were also thought at one time to be relatively free from diabetes, but today their death rates are higher than among whites. This is true for both sexes and most age groups.

19. Is there any connection between occupation and diabetes?

There are large differences in the death rates from the disease in various occupational groups. Persons engaged in the sale or serving of food and drink have high rates. In this group are hotel keepers, grocers, and butchers. Bakers, on the other hand, have a mortality only a little above average. At the low end of the mortality scale are those doing strenuous physical labor: building workers, coal miners, and stevedores. These occupational groups, of course, vary with respect to income so that to some extent the differences in death rates from diabetes may reflect differences in nutrition and in medical care. There is also the factor of selection. People with diabetes are not likely to be engaged in occupations requiring strenuous physical labor.

20. Is there a seasonal variation in the onset of diabetes?

It is not known whether the onset of diabetes has any seasonal pattern because the onset is usually slow and cannot be pinned down to a particular week or month. Mortality from the disease does show marked differences according to season, with the rates rising in winter and falling in summer. This seasonal change is characteristic of most chronic diseases and reflects largely the frequency of fatal respiratory complications among those suffering from chronic disease.

21. Is there any relation between populations or areas with high sugar consumption and diabetes frequency?

There is apparently little, if any, direct connection between sugar consumption and the frequency of diabetes. Those areas in which the consumption of sugar is high do not show an excessively high frequency of diabetes. The trends in sugar consumption and diabetes frequency have often been in opposite directions. No significant conclusion should be drawn from this finding, however.

22. Can diabetes be caused by injury?

Instances of diabetes developing directly from an injury are exceedingly rare because this could happen only if there were a major injury to the pancreas, which has a well-protected position in the body. In any case, it is doubtful whether such a development would occur unless a predisposition to the disease already existed. An injury thus might accelerate the onset of the disease. A temporary increase in the severity of existing diabetes often follows an injury.

In most instances where diabetes is supposed to have been caused by an accident, the disease was simply discovered in the examination following the accident. This is not an unusual way in which new cases are found, particularly among older people. The development of gangrene, after even so slight an injury as stubbing a toe, is too often the circumstance that leads to the discovery of the disease.

23. Can diabetes be caused by nervous strain?

There is no good evidence of this. It is true that sugar is sometimes found in the urine during and after a period of nervous tension, but such glycosuria is transitory. If continued nervous strain were a factor in causing diabetes, one might expect to find a high prevalence of the disease among aviators and among soldiers in combat for long periods, but this is not the case.

24. Is diabetes inherited?

Diabetes itself is not inherited, but there is ample evidence that predisposition to the disease is. Studies show that diabetes runs in families, and occurs about as often as would be expected if a predisposition to the disease were an inheritable recessive characteristic. This means that the parents of anyone with diabetes must at least be carriers of the disease in the genetic sense, even though they may not themselves have diabetes. On this theory, if both parents have diabetes, all their children would be susceptible to the disease. If one parent has diabetes and the other is a carrier, the chances are that half their children would be susceptible. And if neither has diabetes but both are carriers, one-fourth of their children are susceptible.

Evidence of a hereditary factor in diabetes is also found in the occurrence of diabetes in twins. In one study, diabetes occurred in both of the twins in nearly 50 percent of the pairs of *identical* twins, against only 3 percent in the pairs of *fraternal* twins. Other surveys show that diabetes is found much more often in the parents and grandparents of children with diabetes than would be expected on the basis of the prevalence of the disease in the general population.

25. Is the prevalence of diabetes increasing or decreasing?

There is no doubt that the number of individuals with known diabetes has increased faster than the population. This is partly explained by the large increase in the number of older persons, particularly women, among whom the incidence of diabetes is highest. In addition, more cases, particularly of the mild type, are detected now than years ago because the opportunities for discovering diabetes have so greatly expanded. Urinalysis has become a routine part of almost all medical examinations in the physician's office, at admission to the hospital, at admission to school or college, or on examinations for life insurance, for military service, or for employment. There has also been a sizable growth in the diabetic population because those with diabetes now live longer than they formerly did. It is not known, however, whether there has been a definite increase in the rate at which new cases occur in any age group. Some authorities believe that there has been an increase, at least in those countries where food has been plentiful and the pace of mechanization in industry, agriculture, and in the home has been rapid.

26. What is the trend in the mortality of diabetes by sex and age?

Since the discovery and extended use of insulin, there has been a sharp downward trend in the death rate from diabetes among children and young people in this country. Among men, the reductions in the death rate extend up to age 55, and among women to age 45. At the older ages the mortality continued to increase until 1940. Since that year, however, there has been a sharp decrease in the death rates even in middle and later life. The death rates from the disease are now lower than in the preinsulin years at all ages up to 65 among men and up to age 55 among women. At ages under 35 the reductions exceed 50 percent in each sex.

27. What has been the trend of mortality from diabetes in different parts of the world?

Recent and reliable statistics on mortality are available for only relatively few countries. Prewar data showed that death rates from diabetes were rising almost continuously in most parts of the world. In the 15-year interval between 1919–20 and 1934–35, increases as large as 50 percent were common. In general, these increases were confined to the middle and older ages. Death rates among young people have been sharply on the decline in all Western countries since insulin came into general use. More recently, declines in mortality have occurred widely among middle-aged persons and, to a lesser degree, even at the older ages. Only at the most advanced years have death rates increased appreciably.

28. What is insulin, and by whom was it discovered?

The insulin used in the regulation of diabetes is manufactured chiefly from the pancreas of cattle and hogs. Although it had been known for some time that a deficiency in the secretion of the pancreas in some way was involved in the genesis of diabetes, technical difficulties prevented the isolation of insulin from the other secretions of the gland and, therefore, its use as a corrective of the condition. Its isolation was successfully accomplished in the late summer of 1921 by Frederick Banting, a young Canadian surgeon, aided by Charles H. Best, who was then a student in the medical school of the University of Toronto. The discovery was also assisted by Professors MacLeod and Collip of the university. For this work, Banting and MacLeod were awarded the Nobel Prize in Medicine for 1923, which they shared with Best and Collip. Primary credit for the discovery, however, rests with Banting who conceived the methods of separating out insulin and who developed his idea with persistence despite many rebuffs and discouragements.

The original insulin was a rather crude preparation, but many new types have since been prepared and tried. Today, a number of insulins are on the market. The major differences in the preparations are in their rapidity and duration of action.

29. How has improvement in the treatment of diabetes by insulin affected the longevity of individuals with diabetes?

The expectation of life of those with known diabetes has increased at every age since the discovery of insulin. The drug has revolutionized the management of the disease. It brought new life and vigor to persons with diabetes so that most of them could live virtually normal lives. It cut down the hazard of injuries and infections and eliminated or postponed many complications of the disease. In addition, its discovery was a spur to more effective diabetes research. (See Chart 12 below.)

30. At which ages has the improvement in longevity been greatest?

In general, the younger the age, the greater has been the gain in longevity in those with diabetes. Before insulin, the child with di-

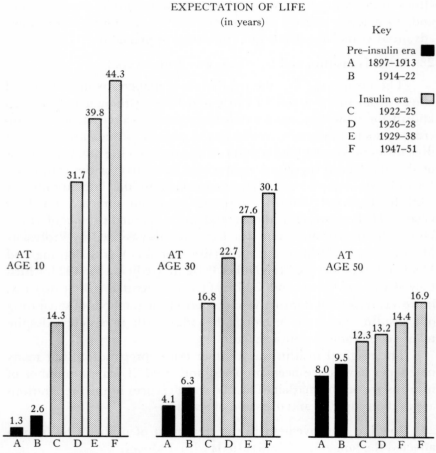

EXPECTATION OF LIFE
(in years)

Key

Pre–insulin era ■
A   1897–1913
B   1914–22

Insulin era ▨
C   1922–25
D   1926–28
E   1929–38
F   1947–51

AT AGE 10: A 1.3, B 2.6, C 31.7, D 39.8, [E/F] 14.3, 44.3

AT AGE 30: A 4.1, B 6.3, C 16.8, D 22.7, E 27.6, F 30.1

AT AGE 50: A 8.0, B 9.5, C 12.3, D 13.2, F 14.4, F 16.9

Chart 12. **The increasing longevity of diabetics; experience of the George F. Baker Clinic, Boston, Mass., 1897–1951. (Excludes deaths within one week of first observation or hospital discharge.)**

abetes was doomed to an early death. Few survived more than a year, and even this short period was one of bare existence. Insulin changed the picture overnight; children with diabetes can now do the same things as those without diabetes. They can go to school and take part in all kinds of sports. They can plan careers, and they can later marry and have children.[1]

31. Do all diabetics need insulin?

Virtually all children who have diabetes and most young adults with the disease need insulin. The proportion requiring the drug is less at the older ages, when the disease is more easily controlled by diet and exercise. Many older patients with mild diabetes who are not on insulin are doing well with the oral hypoglycemic compounds. All who have diabetes, however, should know how to use insulin so that they can take it in an emergency.

32. What is meant by a diabetic diet?

Because the person with diabetes is unable to utilize sugars and starches his diet contains a restricted amount of carbohydrates. Under present methods of treatment the restriction is moderate. Diabetic diets today generally contain about half as much carbohydrate as a normal diet, or between 150 and 250 gm a day, depending on the age and activity of the patient. Additional fatty foods, such as butter and cream, make up the deficiency in calories caused by the restriction on sugars and starches. A good diabetic diet is well balanced and includes all the essential vitamins and minerals. Individuals with diabetes do not need special foods. The dishes they eat are no different from those eaten by other people, but the size of their servings of some foods may be different. They must obviously avoid rich pastries, desserts, ordinary canned fruits, and candies. Above all, they need to learn the proportions of carbohydrate, protein, and fat, as well as the number of calories in given portions of various foods. Many physicians recommend weighing foods, particularly at the beginning of treatment.

33. How is insulin taken?

Insulin can be taken only by injection under the skin with a hypodermic needle. It cannot be taken by mouth because digestive juices destroy it. Virtually all patients can learn to inject them-

[1] See answer to Question 26 of Chapter 19, page 305.

selves; even children can do it with proper instruction. With the present types of insulin, those who require it should take it every day. In most cases, a single daily injection is sufficient; but in some cases, particularly in children, more than one may be necessary. The site of injection may have to be varied systematically.

34. Is insulin habit-forming?

Insulin is not a narcotic. It is a substitute hormone for the insulin which the body would normally produce in adequate amounts or in an effective form. Even though patients take it every day, it cannot be considered habit-forming in the sense that narcotic drugs are. In fact, improvement in the patient's condition often brings reduction in the insulin dosage or, in occasional cases, eventual elimination of its use.

35. Are there substitutes for insulin in the treatment of diabetes?

In the recent decade, a number of synthetic orally administered compounds have been developed, and these are now in wide use, particularly by older patients with mild cases of the disease. These drugs are often effective in lowering blood sugar levels in diabetes when the disease had its onset in maturity. This, they apparently accomplish by stimulating the production of insulin by the islets of pancreas and in other ways. Their use should be under the supervision of a physician and go along with the usual dietary restrictions, weight control, and safe sugar levels of the blood.

36. Can diabetes be cured?

For all practical purposes, diabetes cannot be cured. In some cases, the disease may become so mild that it is well controlled by moderate dietary restrictions alone. This is particularly true for overweight individuals in middle and later life. After reducing their weight to average or less than average levels, they may show normal blood and urine tests. But even in such cases, resumption of overeating usually results in a return of the disease, sometimes in severer form than when originally discovered. For all intents and purposes, patients of this kind have diabetes which is well controlled as long as their weight is brought down and kept down. In some instances of reputed cures, the original diagnosis may have been faulty or there may have been only a temporary disruption of normal metabolism. Some difficulty in diagnosis may exist, particularly in certain conditions such as pregnancy and toxic goiter which are characterized by glandular stresses or maladjustments, either temporary or prolonged.

37. What are the major complications of diabetes?

The most serious complications in the past were diabetic coma and insulin reactions. Diabetic coma, which usually involves loss of consciousness, is brought on by taking too little insulin or too much food. It may be precipitated by an infection. If the insulin deficit is made up promptly, and the patient is properly cared for, complete recovery is the rule. Because of insulin and the early and adequate adjustment of its dosage, diabetic coma now can be virtually eliminated as a cause of death. In the large experience of the George F. Baker Clinic in Boston, only 1 percent of all the diabetic deaths are now due to coma, in contrast to 64 percent in preinsulin days.

An insulin reaction is the opposite of coma. It is caused by too much insulin or too little food, and it also may bring on unconsciousness. A blood sugar test and two urine tests can determine within a half-hour whether a patient is suffering from diabetic coma or insulin reaction. Most reactions can now be quickly cured.

The circulatory system in persons with diabetes, particularly in those who are inadequately treated, tends to degenerate earlier than in those without diabetes. Changes are found in the heart, brain, kidneys, and in the lower extremities. The most characteristic complication of this kind is probably diabetic gangrene. Before insulin was discoved, the major surgery required in cases of gangrene was so hazardous that it was not often tried. Now, not only can this surgery be done with less risk, but new methods of determining the efficiency of the circulation have removed the need for many major amputations. Even more important, better management of diabetes and careful instruction of patients on how to prevent gangrene have cut down the frequency of this complication.

Most deaths related to diabetes today result from degenerative changes in the heart, brain, and kidneys. The death rate from these conditions in diabetes mellitus is at least double that of persons of comparable age in the general population. It is not known why these ailments develop earlier in diabetic individuals, nor why they progress more rapidly in them. Intensive studies of this problem now under way may throw light on the causes which lead to the hardening of the arteries and other evidences of aging.

38. How can the major complications of diabetes be prevented?

Diabetic coma will seldom occur if a patient is under good medical supervision and follows the rules of treatment. If this complication threatens, however, it may be prevented by using insulin according to the doctor's orders. Insulin reactions are best prevented by regularity in taking meals. Patients using slow-acting insulin may need additional snacks between meals and before going to bed. Repeated reactions require that the patient's whole regimen be reviewed. The prevention of gangrene is largely a matter of meticulous care of the feet and the avoidance of any injury to the feet or the circulatory system. For example, new shoes should be fitted properly and broken in slowly, and circular elastic garters should not be used. No specific measures are known for the prevention of the other arterial complications of diabetes, but in general their progress may be slowed by careful adherence to treatment and by the maintenance of weight at or below the average level. The relatively high fat content of the diabetic diet may be harmful, and there is a tendency to reduce it.

39. Does diabetes interfere with working activity?

Well-controlled diabetic persons can generally carry on as they did before their disease began and as do people without diabetes of the same age. Consequently, most diabetics may be considered to have an unimpaired working capacity. Practical considerations, however, may sometimes make it advisable for such people to adjust the duties of their job or to change jobs. This applies specifically to types of employment in which there is a potential hazard to the diabetic individual as well as to others. For example, running a locomotive is not a desirable occupation for a person with diabetes who requires a large insulin dose to control his disease, even though many work at equally responsible jobs without harm to others.

40. What should be the policy of employers with regard to the employment of people with diabetes?

For the most part, the policy pertains to men or women who are already on the job and have seen many years' service. These people are usually valuable employees because of their age and experience. There is no question that the great majority can and should be retained in service, although as already indicated, it may be desirable in certain situations to shift them to other jobs. Individuals with diabetes seeking employment should be given every consideration, particularly those who are under good medical supervision and take good care of themselves. While selective placement in jobs is desirable, there are very few jobs in business and industry which cooperative and well-controlled diabetic persons of working age cannot fill satisfactorily, if they are otherwise qualified. Altogether, an enlightened attitude on the employment of such individuals exists in the country's leading business and industrial concerns.

41. Are persons with diabetes insurable?

Virtually all insurance companies accept such individuals if they insure categories of risks with higher than average mortality. Even so, they select carefully those that they accept and the rejection rate is high. It is important for those with diabetes who seek life insurance to know that the major considerations are the faithfulness with which they follow the prescribed treatment, the regularity of medical supervision, their habits, as well as their actual physical condition at the time they apply for the insurance.

42. Should persons with diabetes marry?

There is no reason why they should not marry, but anyone with the disease contemplating marriage should not conceal from the prospective mate either the presence of diabetes or the knowledge of any limitations imposed by the disease. It is also advisable for someone with diabetes to avoid marrying into a family where the disease exists because of the greater likelihood that offspring of such a marriage would eventually develop diabetes.

43. Should diabetic individuals have children?

Women with diabetes can now bear healthy babies safely, but it is extremely important that they get good prenatal care in early pregnancy. There may be special hazards for the baby which may be prevented or overcome by expert supervision during pregnancy and at delivery.

44. Is it safe for those with diabetes to drive cars?

Such individuals may be permitted to drive, but there are certain extra precautions that the diabetic person should take for his own sake as well as for the sake of others. If he uses insulin, he should take a snack when driving, such as a couple of crackers or an orange every hour or two in order to avoid insulin reactions. He should also have his vision tested regularly so that any changes can be corrected promptly. A person with diabetes should not drive at any time he feels ill. He must also rigidly adhere to the rule never to take alcohol before or during a drive.

45. What should you do if you suspect diabetes?

You should visit your doctor promptly so that he may determine whether or not you have the condition. If he discovers that you have diabetes, you will benefit from having it diagnosed as early as possible. If you do not have it, such reassurance will be of value.

46. What are the advantages of early diagnosis?

Early diagnosis of diabetes means prompt treatment; this is the only way to prevent serious complications from the disease. Thus, early diagnosis can mean not only better health and vitality, but also less interference with normal working capacity and other activity. The benefit of early diagnosis in diabetes is illustrated by the experience of patients of the George F. Baker clinic. Among patients who, at first visit, showed insignificant or no other impairments beside their diabetes, the death rate was less than one-third that of patients with serious impairments or diabetic complications when first seen.

47. What steps are being taken by government and voluntary health agencies to combat diabetes?

The United States Public Health Service, as part of its chronic disease program, has a separate section on diabetes and also supports research on diabetes. The Diabetes Branch conducts such activities as case-finding projects, the development of educational materials for the use of patients and physicians, demonstrations in how to teach diabetic patients, and other aspects of combating the disease. As part of its case-finding activities, it has developed new laboratory techniques that permit blood sugar tests to screen out quickly those who require further study. The Diabetes Branch works closely with local professional groups and health authorities and also with the American Diabetes Association.

The American Diabetes Association, whose membership of about 2,600 consists chiefly of physicians interested in the treatment of diabetes or in research concerning it, is the only national non-profit organization devoted to the subject. It has four major program objectives, namely, professional education, patient education, public education and detection, and research.

An important activity has been to stimulate the formation of Affiliate Diabetes Associations based on professional societies, but whenever possible including lay societies as well, throughout the nation. There are now 50 Affiliates.

The American Diabetes Association publishes a professional journal, *Diabetes,* which has become the world's foremost journal in the field. The Association also issues a bi-monthly magazine for people with diabetes and their families, *Ada Forecast.* In addition, it prepares and issues other professional and patient education materials.

The Public Education and Detection program of the American Diabetes Association, popularly known as Diabetes Detection Drive and highlighted annually by Diabetes Week is a year-round activity developed through Affiliate Diabetes Associations and County and State Medical Societies. The research program includes research fellowships and the support of an annual research symposium. This activity is expanding and recently the Association established a Research Foundation.

Many state and local health departments have established programs in diabetes prevention and control. In a few places, voluntary health agencies have extended their operations into this field. A few life insurance companies also have diabetes educational programs for patients and the general public.

48. What are the principal lines of research in Diabetes?

Diabetes research today is varied and increasingly complex. The goal of many investigators is the difficult task of finding out what causes the condition. A great deal of current research therefore deals with fundamental studies of the intricate metabolic processes. Some investigators are working with problems relating to insulin, seeking to determine more precisely its nature and its relationship to the disease and the reason why it may be inactivated in some patients. The production of insulin by synthesis in the not too distant future seems probable, and this would have great import both for research and treatment in diabetes. Still others are studying the specific mechanism of the action of the oral compounds.

A most important area of investigation is the relationship between diabetes and the development of the circulatory disorders, especially in relation to the small blood vessels, because of the proneness of the diabetic to these conditions. Diabetes research involves investigation of the entire hormonal system because of the important interrelationships in the action of hormones; one aspect of this is the relationship of pregnancy to the onset of diabetes.

The genetic aspects of the disease are also under constant study. Much attention is being paid also to the so-called prediabetic state with the hope that it may be possible to identify the diabetes long before it can be detected by present biochemical procedures.

Chapter 11

A Diminishing Burden— Pneumonia and Influenza

1. What are pneumonia and influenza, and why are they usually linked together?

Pneumonia and influenza are the only acute diseases still remaining among the major causes of sickness and death in this country. Both are highly infectious respiratory conditions with relatively sudden onset and a short severe course. Influenza is a virus infection of the upper respiratory tract. Pneumonia is an infection of the lung caused most often by bacteria, the most common being the pneumococci, of which many varieties have so far been identified. Many newly discovered viruses may also cause pneumonia. The so-called "primary atypical" pneumonia has now been shown to be due to different forms of organisms known as *pleuropneumonialike,* but generally referred to as *Eaton agents.*

These diseases are referred to jointly in medical literature be-cause they are often linked together in experience. Influenza is nor-mally much milder than pneumonia and by itself is seldom a cause of death. The greatest danger in influenza is from the bacterial com-plications, of which pneumonia is the most serious. A great many of the deaths attributed to influenza are actually the results of the secondary effects of pneumonia. To enhance comparability of their mortality over the years, these diseases are grouped together in the study of time-trends.

2. What is the annual death toll from pneumonia and influenza in the United States?

In 1962, there were 60,000 deaths from pneumonia and influ-enza, and the death rate was 32.3 per 100,000 population. This com-bination of diseases accounted for 3.4 percent of all deaths.

3. How many cases of pneumonia and influenza are there annually in this country?

Although both pneumonia and influenza are on the lists of diseases to be reported to public health authorities in most states and territories, the records of the number of cases, especially in a mild

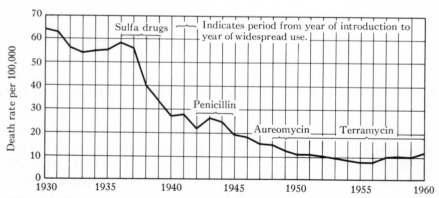

Chart 13. Standardized death rates per 100,000 from pneumonia, total per-sons ages 1–74, Metropolitan Life Insurance Company, Industrial Experience, 1930–1960.

year, are very sketchy. Influenza is usually so mild a disease and is so often confused in the public mind with the common cold that many cases do not even receive medical care. The number of cases in any year is, therefore, not known, and it would be futile to make an estimate. As regards pneumonia, it is believed that at least half a million persons a year come down with one form or another of this disease.

4. How does this country compare with others in mortality from pneumonia and influenza?

Only The Netherlands and Australia have had lower death rates in recent years from pneumonia and influenza (combined) than the United States. For a long period before World War II, many of the countries of Western Europe—England and Wales, the Scandinavian nations, Holland, France, Germany, and Switzerland—were about on a par with this country, while the Southern and Eastern European nations on the whole lagged far behind with much higher rates.

5. How do pneumonia and influenza rank among the causes of death in the United States?

Pneumonia and influenza are still among the leading causes of death in this country. In recent years, they have been outranked in mortality only by heart disease, cancer, cerebral hemorrhage, accidents, and deaths in early infancy. In 1900, however, pneumonia and influenza held the first place.

6. What has been the trend in mortality from pneumonia and influenza since 1900?

The death rate from pneumonia and influenza dropped from 202.2 per 100,000 population in 1900 to 32.3 in 1962, a decline of 84 percent. During the first quarter of the century, the fall in mortality averaged around 1 percent a year and reflected largely the general improvements in medical care and advances in the standard of living. No specially effective pneumonia treatment was then available, and none has even yet been found for influenza. In the late 1920's the antipneumonia serums (a different one for each of the major types of pneumococcus) were introduced in the United States and from 1930 to 1938 the decline in mortality from these respiratory diseases averaged 2.5 percent a year. Toward the end of the decade, sulfa treatment for pneumonia was adopted, and still later, at the end of World War II, penicillin was used; more recently, many other antibiotics have been effective against pneumonia. As a result of drug therapy, the decline in the pneumonia and influenza death rate since 1938 has been about 5 percent per year. (See Chart 13 on page 160.)

7. In terms of lives saved, what does the reduction in mortality from pneumonia and influenza mean?

Instead of about 60,000 lives lost a year now because of pneumonia and influenza, about 370,000 would be lost if the death rates of 1900 had continued. In other words, each year about 310,000 lives are being saved that might have been lost under the conditions of 60 years ago.

8. What are the different forms of pneumonia and influenza, and how do their death rates compare?

There are three clearly identified forms of influenza—types A, B, and C—distinguished by the kind of virus which causes them rather than by the symptoms of the diseases. The chief forms of pneumonia are lobar, usually a primary disease which attacks the lobes of the lungs; bronchopneumonia, more often a secondary disease attacking the lungs and bronchi of persons already weakened by other complaints; and virus pneumonia, which is a primary disease and normally much less severe than lobar or bronchopneumonia.

Ninety-five percent of the deaths from pneumonia and influenza in 1962 were pneumonia deaths, and 5 percent were influenza deaths. Almost two-thirds of the influenza deaths were in cases with respiratory complications, which usually means bronchopneumonia. Of the pneumonia deaths, bronchopneumonia accounted for slightly more than half; lobar, for about three-eighths; and the remaining forms and the unspecified types for less than one-eighth. Virus pneumonia causes only a small fraction of all pneumonia deaths, but it constitutes a much greater share of the pneumonia cases.

9. Is pneumonia a common contributory cause in deaths from other diseases?

The importance of pneumonia as a cause of death cannot be gauged alone from the cases in which it is reported as the killer. In 1962, for example, 56,564 deaths in the United States were attributed to the pneumonias, but in a large number of other deaths pneumonia was listed as an associated cause. In 1955 (the last year for which figures are available) pneumonia was officially recorded as contributing to 37,619 deaths from the cardiovascular-renal diseases, 11,783 cancer deaths, and 5,289 accidental and violent deaths.

10. Is pneumonia a contagious disease?

Not only is influenza, which so often precedes pneumonia, highly contagious, but so is pneumonia itself. It occasionally sweeps through such groups as families, children in the same school, and soldiers living in the same barracks. Studies have shown that from 80 to 90 percent of the healthy members of the population have pneumonia germs present in their mouths, but these are, as a rule, relatively non-virulent. Just how the virulent bacteria are spread is not yet clear. It is believed that they may be transmitted by "carriers," apparently healthy individuals who harbor the infecting agent. In general, it has not been possible to trace the source of infection in pneumonia outbreaks.

11. At what ages is mortality from pneumonia and influenza highest and lowest?

Pneumonia and influenza take their greatest toll in infancy and old age, particularly the latter. During childhood and early adult life, mortality from these diseases is extremely low today. The rate for children aged 5 to 14, for example, was 2.3 annual deaths per 100,000 individuals in 1960; the rate for those less than a year old was 226; and for those 75 to 84 was 297. From childhood on, the rise in death rates is only nominal until middle age; it increases rapidly only after old age is reached.

12. What ages have benefited the most from the reduction in mortality from pneumonia and influenza during the past half century?

The reductions in mortality were relatively greatest among children one to four years old and among young adults up to 35 years of age. In these groups, mortality from pneumonia and influenza was cut by more than 90 percent during the 50-year period. At the extremes of age, where mortality from these diseases has been the highest, the improvements have been less.

13. How do male and female death rates from pneumonia and influenza compare?

Males have higher death rates from these diseases than females all through life. The largest difference comes in middle age, from 40 to 64 years, when men have about double the mortality of women. The sex differential in pneumonia and influenza in adult life is partially explained by the greater exposure of men to environmental and occupational hazards that provide fruitful ground for these diseases.

14. Do pneumonia and influenza death rates vary with marital status?

The married have lower death rates from these diseases than the unmarried at practically all ages. This is true for both sexes, but married men have a greater advantage over bachelors than married women over single women. In 1960, married men from 25 to 44 years old had death rates from these diseases only half as great as single men, while married women of the same ages had rates from two-thirds to three-quarters those of single women.

15. How do the death rates from pneumonia and influenza for white and colored persons compare?

The over-all death rate from pneumonia and influenza among the colored is about twice as high as among the whites. For some age groups in early adult life, the colored rate is three to four times the white rate.

16. How sharply does pneumonia and influenza mortality fluctuate with the seasons?

Mortality in winter months has normally been at least twice that in midsummer. Although the drug treatments for pneumonia have brought down the annual mortality from these infections, these diseases are still definitely seasonal in nature.

17. Does climate make a difference in pneumonia and influenza mortality?

Within the United States, climate does not seem to make much difference, although sudden variations in weather may.

18. Are there regions within the United States which have especially high death rates from pneumonia and influenza?

The regional death rates are no longer marked. In 1960, only two regions, New England and the East South Central States, showed materially higher death rates from pneumonia and influenza than for the country as a whole. These regional variations may be due to a variety of circumstances. Local outbreaks of influenza may play an important role in some years, or especially severe winters affecting

the New England area may account for the high incidence of pneumonia in some years. In the South, the presence of a large Negro
population also tends to raise the death rate from these diseases.

19. Do cities have lower pneumonia and influenza death rates than rural areas?

The death rates from pneumonia and influenza are lower in the
urban areas than in the rural. In 1960, for example, the mortality
from these acute respiratory infections was 34.7 per 100,000 in the
former, and 43.0 per 100,000 in the latter. This difference may reflect
the fact that hospital and expert medical care are more likely to be
available in the urban centers than in the small towns and villages of
the country.

20. Do some occupations involve unusual dangers from pneumonia and influenza?[1]

21. What part do general environmental factors play in pneumonia and influenza?

Everything affecting a person's general state of health influences
his susceptibility to pneumonia or influenza. Many surveys, both here
and in England and Wales, have revealed the tendency for both incidence and mortality to rise as one approaches the lower end of the
social-economic scale. One of the ways in which a poor standard of
living affects health is through housing. In special studies of housing,
the highest pneumonia and influenza death rates were among those
living under the most crowded conditions.

22. Is pneumonia especially dangerous to alcoholics?

The case fatality rate in pneumonia is much higher for alcoholics
than for nondrinkers. In one survey, the rate for alcoholics was more
than twice as high as for nondrinkers or those who took only an occasional drink. The rate for moderate drinkers fell about halfway
between.

23. Do epidemics and pandemics of influenza recur in cycles?

Influenza, with its secondary pneumonia, has long been recur-
ring in epidemics and pandemics. The cyclical, as distinct from seasonal, nature of its outbreaks has puzzled epidemiologists, and only

[1] See answer to Question 29 of Chapter 18, page 284.

recently have theories been worked out which seem to account for most of what has happened. Today it is generally accepted that type A and type B influenza vary independently, though both may on some occasions be present in the same epidemic. Type A has a cycle of two or three years, and type B about twice as long. The interepidemic disease is believed to be basically the same as epidemic influenza but caused possibly by a less virulent strain of virus, or perhaps kept in check by a population having temporarily greater immunity. Pandemics of calamitous proportions also recur at intervals, but are much less regular in their appearance. The relation of the infecting agent in pandemic influenza to that of the nonepidemic disease is not known because there have been no pandemics since the isolation of the influenza viruses.

24. How extensive was the 1918 influenza pandemic?

The 1918 wave of influenza accompanied by secondary pneumonia killed an estimated minimum of 20 million individuals throughout the world, considerably more than the war which immediately preceded it. An estimated 200 million contracted the disease. In this country, about 20 million came down with influenza and 550,000 died. It is probable that some of the high mortality of the 1918 outbreak may be blamed on the war, which had devastated large sections of Europe and worn down millions of people with years of malnutrition and suffering. Medical literature contains stories of whole towns laid waste within a few weeks or months by the pandemic, which was as severe in some areas as the medieval plagues. The virulence and explosiveness of the outbreak have been the subject of a great deal of study because it was the only experience of its kind in modern history. The epidemics which used to ravage nations and continents occurred largely before the development of the modern science of medicine. In recent years, the outbreaks have been much more moderate, and their effect on mortality was largely concentrated in the older age groups.

25. Did the 1918 outbreak change the age and sex distribution of influenza and pneumonia deaths?

Instead of a low death rate from these diseases in early life, the 1918 pandemic had a peak in mortality among those 25 to 34 years old, which was exceeded only by that among persons 75 and over. Not only were very many young persons stricken, but in this country the healthy and vigorous seemed particularly susceptible. Although men had previously had higher mortality than women, the difference in rates was increased still more by the pandemic.

26. Did the 1918 influenza pandemic affect mortality from other diseases?

The combined mortality from all causes of death was one-third higher for 1918 than for the five preceding years. This was not only the result of the greatly swollen influenza and pneumonia toll, but also because of increased death rates from a number of other diseases, particularly the chronic and degenerative diseases. Tuberculosis, heart disease, and nephritis death rates went up during the pandemic, and then dropped sharply right afterward. The subsequent fall was temporary for heart disease and nephritis, but tuberculosis mortality continued to decline rapidly, suggesting that many active cases of tuberculosis succumbed in the epidemic and thus removed from the population many foci of infection.

Other epidemics of influenza and pneumonia have also raised the death rates of diseases outside this group, but this is not invariably the case. In the epidemic of 1928–29, most of the excess deaths were influenza and pneumonia deaths. In the epidemic of 1943–44, the excess mortality in 35 cities was found to be largely attributable to other causes. Less than one-third of the additional deaths were recorded as having been caused by influenza or pneumonia. In the recent outbreak covering 1958 to 1960, the excess mortality included many suffering from such chronic conditions as diabetes, heart disease, and nephritis.

27. How did the 1918 outbreak affect women who were pregnant?

Although in general the epidemic concentrated on men more than women, the death rates for causes connected with pregnancy rose about 40 percent. It was not the usual causes of death in pregnancy—puerperal septicemia and the toxemias—which rose, but rather the so-called accidents of pregnancy, miscarriage, and premature birth. As a matter of fact, the death rates from septicemia fell off during 1918.

28. Has there been any change recently in the frequency or severity of influenza outbreaks?

There has been little change in the frequency of influenza outbreaks since 1918, but there has been a great change in the severity. There were epidemics or at least relatively severe waves of influenza in 1923, 1926, 1931, 1933, 1937, 1939, 1941, 1944, 1946, and 1958 to 1960. As drug therapy was more widely used, the successive waves became smaller, standing out from the surrounding years but not attaining the severity of preceding periods.

Since World War II there have been a number of mild waves of influenza in this country, while in many parts of Europe there were more serious outbreaks. It is noteworthy that in this country there was a large supply of sulfa drugs and penicillin at that time, while in Europe, where mortality went up so sharply, these medicines were relatively rare.

29. Are there ways to immunize persons against influenza and pneumonia?

Vaccines for immunizing persons against both influenza and pneumonia have been increasingly employed in recent years, and apparently with considerable effect. The difficulty has been to include new strains of virus that arise from time to time. Recent experience has shown, however, that it is possible to prepare vaccines against some strains soon enough to meet the immunization needs while an epidemic is in progress.

The problems in pneumonia are similar. Vaccines have been made up with great difficulty from groups of the more common pneumococci, and in a few wartime trials they had some success. They are, however, still experimental, and their effectiveness has not been proved.

30. What preparations have been made to combat future epidemics?

After World War II, the World Health Organization set up an International Influenza Center in London. Many countries, including the United States, are cooperating by organizing their own local influenza information services to detect new outbreaks and identify the infecting virus. The idea is to determine the specific strain of influenza causing any new epidemic before the disease has had much chance to spread. It may then be possible to incorporate the newly identified strain in influenza vaccine and perhaps, by immunization, limit the extent of the epidemic. In this country a National Influenza Strain Study Center in New York City has been designated to handle the main technical work, with laboratories throughout the nation, including one each in Alaska, Hawaii, and Puerto Rico, reporting to it.

31. Are we likely to have another influenza pandemic like that of 1918?

The possibility of such a pandemic will be with us until a way is found to create general immunity to influenza and to treat the disease more effectively than at present. Many public health authorities believe influenza could again ravage this country and kill hundreds of thousands in a few months. The standards of health and living maintained here are no guarantee of protection, and the relative freedom from severe influenza that this nation has enjoyed recently means there is a large section of the population which has had no opportunity to build up a natural immunity. Influenza is no respecter of boundaries, nor have oceans in the past served as barriers to its spread. If a serious outbreak got started again, it might well travel over the entire world, as it did four decades ago.

It is true that we now have the sulfa drugs and many antibiotics to use against the secondary pneumonia in influenza outbreaks, but unfortunately, resistant strains of bacteria are known to develop when the drugs are used a great deal. A type of infection against which these drugs are of little use might conceivably be the one to cause the next epidemic. Nevertheless, we are in much better shape to combat the next severe outbreak if and when it comes.

32. At what stage in the development of pneumonia is drug treatment most effective?

The sooner treatment is begun, the greater the chance of recovery. Increasingly large sections of the lungs may become involved as pneumonia progresses. In chemotherapy it has been found that the case fatality rate was generally much lower for those treated early in the course of the disease than for those who had been sick for the greater part of a week or more. In one study of 15,000 cases, the case-fatality rate was twice as high for patients treated after the fourth day of illness as for those treated earlier.

33. Is research on pneumonia and influenza being concentrated now on immunization?

While both cure and immunization are the subjects of many current research projects, it is probably true that the emphasis has recently shifted from treatment to prevention. The antibiotics and sulfa drugs have proved so effective in the pneumonias that the most immediate need seems to be for a useful preventive vaccine. In the case of influenza, a method of effective immunization appears to be at hand, but the use is still very limited.

One field of research which is receiving special attention is that of cross immunization. Attempts are being made to find a way to build up immunity against a variety of types of bacteria or virus with serums prepared from many types. If this were possible, it might result in a single or a smaller number of vaccines which would provide immunization against all influenzas and a single or limited number effective against all pneumonias.

34. What are the chances of eventually dying from pneumonia or influenza?

The chances of a white baby eventually dying from pneumonia or influenza were about 37 in 1,000 under mortality conditions of 1960. The probability of dying from these infections was considerably greater for males than for females, and for the colored than for the white.

35. What is the outlook for improved control of pneumonia and influenza?

Barring severe epidemics, the recent sharp drops in mortality from pneumonia and influenza may be expected to continue for a time even without further medical advance. The new drugs are becoming more readily available and the rising standard of living means that these diseases are no longer being spread as easily as they once were. In the long run, however, control depends on more medical progress and on better public health work. With the medical profession of the country, as well as the health agencies of the federal, state, and local governments, alert to the dangers of pneumonia and influenza, it seems almost certain that further great scientific advances will be made in combating these two respiratory diseases.

Chapter 12

An Increasing Burden— the Circulatory Diseases

1. What are the major diseases of the circulatory system?

The major diseases of the circulatory system are the various forms of heart disease (including coronary artery disease), high blood pressure, general arteriosclerosis (hardening of the arteries), and cerebral hemorrhage (apoplexy). Cerebral thrombosis is increasingly important. The major diseases of the circulatory system are frequently studied jointly with the chronic diseases of the kidneys, although anatomically they are separate. It is convenient to consider these various conditions together since they are generally associated with the aging process; the term "diseases of the circulatory system" is used with this understanding in the rest of this chapter. With advance in age, the heart, blood vessels, and kidneys tend to lose some of their elasticity and adaptability. Since these organs are closely related, any

171

derangement in one of them may ultimately affect the others. The interrelationship of these organs in disease is also evidenced by the great frequency with which they are reported together on death certificates.

2. How does the heart do its work?

The heart is a muscle about the size of a fist. It is divided by a muscular wall down the middle into two main divisions—a right and a left. Each division has two chambers which work together as a unit. The right side of the heart receives blood from the body through two great veins and pumps it to the lungs where, first, the blood gives up the carbon dioxide (a waste gas) it collects from the cells of the body, and then accumulates oxygen to bring back to the cells. The return flow is from the lungs into the left side of the heart. From here, the contractions of the heart muscle pump the blood through a great artery (the aorta) which leads into an intricate system of lesser arteries, and tiny branches called capillaries that reach into all parts of the body. The capillaries are a particularly important part of the circulatory system since it is through them that the exchange of nutritive substances and oxygen for waste products takes place.

3. What are the major causes of heart disease?

Heart defects may be either structural or functional in nature, and have a variety of causes. A small, but important fraction of the heart diseases are congenital in nature; that is, they are defects with which some babies are born. These constitute the major cause of heart deaths up to age 20. It has recently been found that such defects may arise in cases where the mother had German measles during early pregnancy. There are a number of congenital defects of the heart and blood vessels for which surgery now offers help and, sometimes, cure. Most heart diseases found in children and the younger adults, say up to about age 40, have their origin in a childhood attack of rheumatic fever.[1] A small proportion of heart disease manifesting itself from about ages 40 to 50 and, even later, is a consequence of a syphilitic infection, usually acquired in early adult life. With newly developed treatments, syphilis can now be controlled before it has a chance to damage the heart or blood vessels. Heart disease in association with high blood pressure is most commonly found from about

[1] See answer to Question 6 of Chapter 13, page 192.

ages 40 to 60. Arteriosclerosis (the hardening of the arteries), which is often associated with high blood pressure, is by far the leading cause of heart disease from age 40 and increasingly so with each advance in age.

4. How do diseases of the coronary arteries affect the heart?

The heart receives its nourishment not from the blood in its chambers but through the coronary arteries, whose many branches form a network throughout the heart muscle. When the lumen of these blood vessels becomes narrowed because of the thickening of their walls or because of the accumulation of deposits, the blood supply to the heart is diminished. The effect of this interference may become noticeable when a person with such condition attempts any unusual physical activity. At that time, the heart works harder and it requires more blood for its nourishment. The lack of ample blood supply is made evident by sudden sharp and oppressive pains beneath the breastbone or in the left side of the chest that last just a few minutes or sometimes longer; this sensation has been called "angina pectoris." When a coronary artery is suddenly closed, the condition may be either a coronary thrombosis or a coronary embolism. Contrary to popular impression, most persons live through their first coronary attack.[2]

5. How many people suffer from the circulatory diseases?

According to a recent estimate by the United States Public Health Service, there are about 5,000,000 persons in our country with known heart disease, somewhat more with high blood pressure or arteriosclerosis, and more than half a million with kidney disease. Altogether, there are at least 12 million persons with some circulatory disease, many with more than one of these conditions. The estimates are based upon field surveys and may considerably understate the number of existing cases.

6. Does the prevalence of the circulatory diseases rise with advance in age?

According to the recent National Health Survey, about 1 percent of the people at ages under 25 years already have some circulatory disease. The proportion rises to 8.5 percent at ages 45 to 54, and to

[2] See answer to Question 25 of this chapter, page 180.

32 percent after age 75. It is interesting to note that whereas only a small fraction of those with circulatory disease at ages under 25 had little or no restriction of their usual activities, less than half of those at ages 65 and over could follow their ordinary pursuits.

7. What is the annual death toll from the circulatory diseases?

There were 968,809 deaths attributed to the cardiovascular-renal diseases in the United States and reported for 1962. This number constituted well over one-half of all deaths in that year. The heart diseases alone accounted for 688,009 deaths, or about 71 percent of the mortality from the circulatory diseases. Of these, the most important category was arteriosclerotic heart disease, including coronary disease 54.5 percent). Deaths from general arteriosclerosis and high blood pressure accounted for over 10 percent; nephritis and other renal sclerosis for 1.2 percent; rheumatic fever and chronic rheumatic heart disease for 1.8 percent; the remaining deaths under this general caption included a variety of diseases, which accounted for a small fraction of the total. Not only did the circulatory diseases as a group far outrank every other cause of death, but heart diseases alone led every other cause by a wide margin.

8. How has the proportion of deaths due to the circulatory diseases changed in recent years?

In 1900, only one-fifth of all deaths were ascribed to the circulatory conditions. The proportion rose to more than one-fourth by 1920, and to well over two-fifths by 1940. At present, the ratio is over one-half. Most of this rise in the proportion of deaths from the circulatory diseases results from the increasing proportion of older persons in the population and from the decreasing mortality from the infections.

9. How does the proportion of deaths from the circulatory diseases vary with age?

The circulatory diseases are a very minor item in the mortality of infants and children. In the age group 15 to 24 years, however, these conditions account for about one-twelfth of the deaths from all causes combined. The proportion then rises steadily with advance in age. At 25 to 44 years it amounts to over one-quarter, at 45 to 64 to one-half, and at 65 and over to two-thirds. The proportion of deaths from the circulatory diseases at the various periods of life is about the same for both sexes.

10. What has been the trend of mortality from the circulatory diseases?

Superficial examination of the figures indicates an upward trend in the mortality from the circulatory diseases in the past four decades. This rise reflects entirely the increasing proportion of older people in the population, among whom the mortality from the circulatory diseases is high. When allowance is made for the aging of the population, the mortality from these conditions is found to have declined somewhat. The reduction has been greatest at the younger ages, the rate of improvement decreasing progressively with advance in age among all but white males. The latter continued to experience high rates at middle and older ages until 1950 when these rates also began to decline a little. Of special interest is the marked reduction of mortality from circulatory diseases among white women.

11. What are the important factors in the improved mortality from the circulatory diseases?

The circulatory conditions at the younger ages are largely of infectious origin, hence most of the improvement in mortality at this stage of life stems directly from increased control gained over the infections. Very much the same can be said for reductions in early maturity and midlife, and particularly for heart disease of rheumatic origin, and later in life for chronic nephritis, which is largely a sensitivity reaction to infection. Modern treatment for syphilis has been a potent factor in lowering the mortality from syphilitic heart disease; further improvement will result from the more extensive use of penicillin and other antibiotics for early syphilis.[3] More effective treatment of hypertension has also helped. The reduced burden of childbearing has probably played a part in reducing the death rate from the circulatory diseases among women. Marked declines have also been noted in the category of hypertensive heart disease. Quite generally, there are the beneficial effects of better living and working conditions. Better and more medical care and services, improved quality and variety of food, and labor-saving machinery have lessened the strain of manual labor.

12. What have been the trends in mortality for the various circulatory conditions and how are they to be interpreted?

Although the death rate from the circulatory diseases as a group has moved downward, that for heart disease has gone up. On the other

[3] See answer to Question 33 of Chapter 19, page 308.

hand, the rates for chronic nephritis and cerebral hemorrhage have declined continuously and sharply even when adjusted to remove the effect of the aging of the population. The contrary trends for arteriosclerotic heart disease and for chronic nephritis and cerebral hemorrhage arise largely from changing diagnostic concepts. Thus, deaths which in years past would have been attributed to nephritis or cerebral hemorrhage are now being reported as due to arteriosclerotic heart disease as a result of revised concepts of the relation of high blood pressure to these conditions. Another illustration is edema (dropsy); many cases with this complication which were previously attributed to a renal condition are now ascribed to heart disease. In other words, for a proper understanding of the course of the death rates from the circulatory conditions it is necessary to search for the underlying factors that have contributed to the picture presented.

13. What is the probability of eventually dying from one of the circulatory diseases?

According to mortality conditions in the United States in 1948, the chances for white persons at age 30 were about 60 in 100. The chances increase with advance in age and are nearly 65 in 100 at age 60. The probability of eventually dying from a circulatory disease is about four times the probability of dying from cancer.

14. How does mortality from the circulatory conditions in cities compare with that for rural areas?

For the country as a whole, there is a distinct gradation from relatively low to high mortality for death rates from the circulatory diseases with increasing size of community. The differences among cities of various population sizes are not appreciable, but between the cities as a group and the rural areas the differences are rather sizable, although these differences are smaller now than they were 20 or 30 years ago, perhaps because differences between urban and rural life have been decreasing. The higher mortality from circulatory conditions in urban areas may reflect in part the effect of city life.

15. Does mortality from the circulatory diseases vary geographically within the United States?

There is a fairly definite pattern in mortality from the circulatory diseases, with the death rates highest in the Northeast, somewhat lower in the North Central states, and lowest of all in the Mountain states. The Pacific Coast states tend to fall between the high and the low areas. The somewhat higher rates in the southern region result from the large proportion of Negroes in the population, with higher mortality from diseases of the heart.

16. How does mortality from the circulatory conditions among the married compare with that among the single, widowed, or divorced?

Married men have a much lower mortality from the circulatory conditions than do the unmarried. Women show a similar experience, but the difference is not as marked as for the men. In 1959–61, the mortality from the cardiovascular-renal diseases among single men was 39 percent higher than that for the married; for the widowed the ratio was 60 percent higher, and for the divorced over 80 percent higher. In the case of women, the ratio of mortality to the married was: single, almost 10 percent higher; widowed, 50 percent higher; and divorcees over 30 percent higher.

17. What is the risk of death from the circulatory diseases among overweights?

The risk of death increases very rapidly with the degree of overweight. The recent Build and Blood Pressure Study by the Society of Actuaries showed that mortality from circulatory conditions among males 20 percent overweight is 25 percent higher and for those 30 percent overweight 42 percent higher than for those with normal weight. For women 20 percent overweight the mortality is 21 percent higher, and for those 30 percent overweight 30 percent higher. These excess mortalities increase with advance in age. In one insurance experience, it was found that mortality from circulatory conditions among males overweight from 5 to 15 percent was 44 percent higher than that for those of normal weight; those overweight by 15 to 25 percent had double the mortality of normal weights. For causes other than the circulatory diseases, the mortality ratio was 10 percent higher for the first group of overweights and 20 percent higher for the second.

18. What is the significance of the recent rise in mortality from diseases of the coronary arteries?

The recorded death rate from diseases of the coronary arteries in the United States has gone up rapidly from 7.9 per 100,000 in 1930 to 274.6 in 1961. Some of this rise is a direct consequence of the increasing proportion of older people in the population among whom this disease takes its largest toll. But by far the greatest part of the rise is due to the increased alertness of physicians to detect diseases of the coronary arteries and to record the information on the death certificate. In view of this situation, the extent of the actual rise in mortality from coronary disease—if indeed, there is any at all—cannot be ascertained.

19. What do heart murmurs signify?

To the examining physician any unusual heart sounds—that is, heart murmurs—are a signal that there may be some abnormality in that organ. However, many heart murmurs are not indicative of any significant deviation from the normal heart. The physician judges the significance of the murmur by its characteristics, such as the area of the heart where it is heard, the loudness of the murmur, whether or not it is transmitted to other areas, the phase of the heartbeat at which it is heard, the quality and constancy of the sound, and other considerations. Serious murmurs may indicate, among other things, a leakage or obstruction of a valve of the heart or of the great artery leading from the left side of the heart to the body. To make up for such deficiencies the heart must work harder, and this tends to overdevelop the heart muscle. The extent of the overdevelopment increases in time. Even where there is no increase in the size of the heart, mortality tends to be high in the presence of the more serious murmurs.

20. What effect have unusual variations in rate or rhythm of the heartbeat?

Normally, the heart of an adult male at rest beats about 72 times a minute; that of an adult female, 80 times.[4] The variations in the pulse rate about these averages may be fairly large without the presence of any physical impairment. However, where the pulse rate is extremely rapid, there may be a serious condition, such as either heart disease or hyperthyroidism. Mortality somewhat above average has been found among persons with very rapid pulse rates. Certain irregularities in the pulsation of the heart, such as skipped beats or variations in its rhythm, have also been associated with an excess in mortality.

[4] See answer to Question 29 of Chapter 22, page 363.

21. What is blood pressure?

The force with which blood is pumped by the heart into the arteries exerts a pressure against their walls, causing them to stretch. This pressure is at its peak just after the blood has left the heart and it is known as the "systolic blood pressure." The pressure thereafter diminishes to a minimum until the next surge of blood is pumped by the heart into the arteries. At this low point, we have the "diastolic blood pressure." There may be rather wide variations in both the systolic and diastolic blood pressures in healthy adults.

The average systolic blood pressure is about 115 to 120 mm for men in their twenties and rises gradually with age to about 132 to 135 mm at age 60. The average diastolic is about 75 mm at age 20 and increases to about 80 at age 60. The blood pressure of an individual, however, may differ to some extent from the average for his age and still be regarded as normal in the sense that he is able to follow his daily tasks without an appreciable degree of extra mortality. For the systolic blood pressure this variation may be as much as 15 to 20 mm above or below the average, and for the diastolic 10 to 12 mm above or below the average. The proportion of men and women with significantly higher blood pressure rises with advance in age. The frequency of such elevated blood pressure is higher for men than for women up to age 40, but after that age is higher for women.

22. What is high blood pressure and what causes it?

High blood pressure or hypertension cannot be defined exactly, and authorities disagree as to the borderline which divides normal blood pressure from high blood pressure. However, most would consider as hypertensive readings of 30 mm or more above the systolic average and 15 to 20 mm above the diastolic average.

The cause of high blood pressure in most cases is unknown, but in a sizable number the increased blood pressure is due to diseases of the kidneys and rarely to certain types of glandular disease. The blood pressure level is subject to many influences. At times it may become high temporarily, especially during excitement or under nervous strain. In this situation, nerves controlling the smaller blood vessels cause them to tighten and as a result the flow of blood into them becomes more difficult. Accordingly, the pressure in the arteries rises. In some persons, smaller blood vessels are constantly tightening up so that the blood pressure persists at a high level irrespective of the person's activity.[5]

[5] See answer to Question 35 of Chapter 22, page 365.

23. What is the effect of high blood pressure on mortality?

High blood pressure has an adverse effect on longevity, largely because the extra work placed upon the heart often brings early breakdown of that vital organ. Death rates from heart diseases and from cerebral hemorrhage are high in people with high blood pressure. Mortality from Bright's disease is also high because the kidney is primarily involved in some cases of hypertension. Among carefully selected applicants for insurance, the mortality is increased even with moderate elevation of blood pressure, and the death rate shows a steady rise with increasing elevation of the systolic or diastolic pressure. When both the systolic and diastolic pressures are elevated, the excess mortality is greatly increased. However, high blood pressure may not be inconsistent with long life and a goodly measure of activity. Many patients who follow the rules laid down by their doctors are able to carry on effectively and lead virtually normal lives. Women particularly appear to tolerate high blood pressure.

24. What is low blood pressure?

There are no universally accepted standards for low pressure. Some physicians put the dividing line between normal and low at 90 mm systolic and 55 diastolic for adults. Others use limits of 100 to 110 systolic and 60 to 70 diastolic, or may vary the limits according to age.

Low blood pressure, except when it is a manifestation of a specific disease or condition, is generally favorable to longevity. Insurance studies have shown consistently that the death rate among persons with low blood pressure is less than that of persons with average blood pressure and far below those with high blood pressure. The favorable outlook for persons with low blood pressure reflects the decreased frequency of premature breakdown of the heart, blood vessels, and kidneys.

25. How long do persons with arteriosclerotic or hypertensive heart disease live?

One study of nearly 500 patients with angina pectoris, all of whom have been followed up for at least 14 years, showed that more than one-fourth were living at the end of this period. In the longest case followed and still living, 32 years had elapsed since the attack. Another study, in which the over-all results were approximately the same, showed that the percentage surviving at the end of 15 years was approximately twice as great for females as for males. Favorable fac-

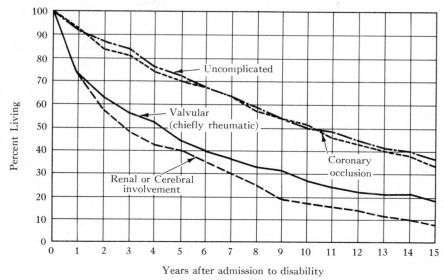

Chart 14. **Survivorship of white men disabled by heart disease. Metropolitan Life Insurance Company, Ordinary Department. Disability cases reported and/or admitted in 1934–36 and traced to anniversary 15 years later.**

tors in the outlook of cases with these conditions were normal heart size and normal blood pressure.

The record for those who suffer heart damage as a result of coronary thrombosis is not as good. Even so, many of them live for several years and frequently recover sufficiently to resume their normal activities. Much depends on the severity of the attack and the completeness of the recovery. The older the age at which the attack occurs, the more favorable the long-term outlook. Thus, in one group of patients 40 percent were living at the end of 5 years, and one-fourth at the end of 10 years. When the mortality immediately following the attack is excluded it was found that 50 percent were living at the end of 5 years and over 30 percent at the end of 10 years.

The experience of one life insurance company showed that among men so disabled by arteriosclerotic and hypertensive heart disease as to become eligible for total and permanent disability payments, 78 percent of those with uncomplicated disease lived for 5 years and 53 percent lived for 10 years. Of those who had suffered a coronary thrombosis, about 50 percent were still living 10 years later.

26. Is there any relation between heart disease mortality and occupation?

There are distinct differences in the mortality from heart disease among men in various occupations. Agricultural workers, skilled workers, and teachers, for example, have lower than average mortality from this cause. On the other hand, physicians, barbers, bartenders, and unskilled workers are at a distinct disadvantage in this respect. Differences in heart disease mortality may reflect, in part, the varying physical demands or mental stress of various types of occupations. In part, however, the differences in mortality are influenced by the fact that men with bad hearts will generally select jobs suited to their physical condition, that is, the lighter occupations. These occupations accordingly may have more than their share of cardiacs, not because they create them but because they attract them. The variations in heart disease mortality from one occupation to another may reflect also differences in economic status.

27. Do physicians have a relatively low or high heart disease death rate?

The heart disease mortality among physicians is nearly one-fifth higher than that for all white males of the same ages. If the recorded death rate from diseases of the coronary arteries is considered alone, the physicians show an excess of about 80 percent. Part of this higher mortality may simply reflect the special opportunities for expert diagnosis usually available to physicians, with the result that the disease is discovered and recorded more frequently among them. Much of the excess mortality, however, is real and appears to result from the special activities and the strains physicians undergo.

28. Should a woman with heart disease bear children?

The term "heart disease" covers a wide range of cardiac conditions, from the mildest to the most serious. Whether a woman with heart disease should bear children depends upon the extent to which the heart is impaired. Pregnancy does put an added burden on the heart, yet many women with heart disease have a normal pregnancy and delivery. Women with serious heart defects should seek expert guidance on pregnancy. The physician is in the best position to determine the risk involved in individual cases and his advice should certainly be sought. The cardiac who wishes to have children should also consider the added strain of caring for a child.

29. Does strenuous physical exercise damage the heart?

It is a common but erroneous belief that strenuous physical activity can damage the heart. The healthy heart can stand considerable physical exertion without being impaired. However, overexertion can prove fatal to the person with a diseased heart. Common examples are persons who die suddenly while playing tennis or running after a train. This is not to say that cardiacs should avoid all exercise. They are in fact encouraged to engage in regular physical activity, but they should adjust their activity according to their physical limitations.

30. Can people with heart disease work?

Most people with heart disease can work. The amount and type of activity permissible depends upon the nature and severity of the disease. Heavy manual labor would seldom be suitable for cardiac patients, although it is surprising to find that laborers engaged in such work often do very well despite serious heart defects. Young people with rheumatic heart disease need guidance and training in jobs so that they do not overtax their hearts. Middle-aged and older men and women who have angina pectoris or have recovered from a coronary thrombosis can often carry on with little difficulty in suitable jobs. In fact, one study of patients who had survived at least one year after a coronary attack and had been followed up for one to six years showed that nearly one-fourth were working full time, and a somewhat higher proportion were doing part-time or light work. The most serious deterrent to work is the fear of such patients regarding their condition. If this fear is overcome, they often do well; many are far better off being gainfully occupied.

31. How does the heart rest although it keeps beating?

The heart rests between beats. The interval is short—only a fraction of a second—but in the course of a day it adds up to a considerable length of time. If, however, the heart is burdened with an extra load, the period of rest naturally is lessened. This is why people with damaged hearts need adequate rest and should avoid prolonged physical exertion.

32. Should people with damaged hearts travel by air?

There is no definite evidence that ordinary air transportation has an adverse effect upon the heart, either healthy or impaired. Many people with heart trouble travel by plane yet death among flight passengers is very rare. The extensive experience of the United States Army Air Force in evacuating sick and wounded during World War II likewise indicates that air travel presents no special hazards to patients. While flying, cardiacs should take the precautions of not exerting themselves unduly and should, if necessary, avail themselves of the oxygen which passenger planes now carry routinely. What has been said here about air travel holds for ground travel in areas of high altitude.

33. What are "blue babies" and what can be done to remedy their condition?

Before birth, the child does not use its own lungs but receives oxygen from the mother's blood through an opening in the membrane separating the right and left sides of the child's heart. At birth, when the baby's lungs begin to function, this opening in the membrane closes in the normal child. In a number of cases, however, this does not occur, with the result that normal functioning of the circulatory system is deranged. Specifically, the blood fails to get an adequate supply of oxygen and the skin then takes on a bluish tint. Most of these defects are now readily correctable by surgery.

34. What is cerebral hemorrhage and what are its causes?

Cerebral hemorrhage, more commonly known as "stroke" or apoplexy, is the rupture of blood vessels within the skull, resulting in a free flow of blood into the surrounding area. The consequent damage to the brain may result in paralysis or even sudden death. Autopsy studies indicate that one-half or more of these fatal cases of cerebral vascular disease involve thrombosis rather than hemorrhage, with the thrombus formation usually part of the arteriosclerotic process. The causes of cerebral hemorrhage are not clearly understood. Quite frequently, the condition is associated with high blood pressure, arteriosclerosis, or other significant changes in the cardiovascular system. Deaths from cerebral hemorrhage are concentrated in the later ages of life, even more so than for heart disease. Physicians now realize that many patients suffer from minor strokes which apparently involve little or no serious permanent injury.

35. What is the structure and function of the kidneys?

The kidneys are bean-shaped organs where the waste products gathered by the blood from the cells of the body are collected and eliminated. Each of the two kidneys is made up of more than one million tubules (nephrons) where the actual work of separating the waste products from the blood is performed. Within each nephron there is a knot of capillaries called glomeruli to which blood is brought by a very small artery. As the blood circulates through this knot, it gives off some of the plasma (the liquid portion of the blood) which is filtered into a tubule leading from the knot. In the course of the flow of the plasma through the tubule, there is returned to the blood most of the water and the normal ingredients. What is left contains body wastes and drains to the bladder, from which it is eliminated.

36. What is nephritis and what are its chief causes?

Nephritis, commonly known as Bright's disease in honor of the English physician who first described it in modern terms, is the most important and frequent type of kidney disease. In acute nephritis, which occurs during some infectious conditions, the kidneys are temporarily inflamed. This inflammation may interfere with the normal function of the kidney in eliminating body wastes from the blood, and if sufficiently severe may cause death or chronic disease of the kidneys. By far the most important type of chronic nephritis is that which results from the general physical breakdown of the kidneys, particularly the hardening of the arteries of the kidneys which is associated with the process of aging. This eventually causes elevation of the blood pressure and involvement of the heart and blood vessels.

37. What is the incidence of nephritis?

Older data supplied by the National Health Survey indicated that new cases of nephritis arose annually at the rate of 1.1 per 1,000 males, and 1.3 per 1,000 females, the rates rising with advancing age. Incidence rates may now be considerably lower because of the decrease in the amount and severity of the streptococcal infections which in the past were responsible for much of the chronic nephritis.

38. What are some of the common devices used to test the functioning of the circulatory system?

There are many specialized devices to test the functioning of the heart, kidneys, and blood vessels. The stethoscope, probably the most familiar of these instruments, is used by the doctor to hear the heart sounds more easily and to judge their quality. The sphygmomanometer is also well known; it is an instrument to measure both the systolic and the diastolic blood pressure. The electrocardiograph is a machine which traces graphically on paper the variations in electric current produced by the action of the heart. Physicians trained in this technique will recognize changes from the normal pattern which are indicative of heart damage. Then there is the fluoroscope, which permits the doctor to see an x-ray image of the heart and aorta in action. For a permanent record of the size and shape of the heart, the doctor takes pictures with the x-ray machine. In connection with the x-ray, certain dyes are sometimes used to study the chambers of the heart, and the principal blood vessels of the chest and the lungs. More recently, catheterization of the heart has been used as a diagnostic procedure in congenital and rheumatic heart disease. Exercise and other tests have been devised to observe the functioning of the heart under strain. There are now routine procedures to study the chemical composition of the blood. Functional tests are also available to test the efficiency of the kidneys. Urinalyses are now routine and are used to test for nephritis, diabetes, and other conditions. Among the kidney function tests are several so-called clearance tests, used to observe the efficiency of the kidneys. In addition to these more common devices to test for disturbances in the circulatory system, there are many others used, as occasion demands, for more accurate diagnosis.

39. What are some of the outstanding recent advances in the control of the circulatory conditions?

Notable progress has been made in the control of infections which leave their mark on the circulatory system, particularly in reducing much acute and chronic nephritis. Rheumatic fever, which is the leading cause of heart disease up to about age 45, has recorded a considerable reduction both in incidence and in mortality. Repair and replacement of valves scarred by rheumatic disease is another advance. Similarly, syphilis, a major cause of heart disease in middle life, shows a declining death rate. Open heart surgery is an important technique in many heart conditions. Even for coronary disease, the prospects have become brighter in the light of recent developments, of which the use of anticoagulants is an example. The success of surgery with "blue babies" has been striking.[6] Surgery has also been successful in certain cases of high blood pressure. There has also been

---

[6] See answer to Question 33 of this Chapter, page 184.

renewed interest in special diets in hypertension. Of chief importance in this respect are the rice diet and diets that are low in sodium, a constituent of common table salt. With reference to coronary artery disease, dietary fat and a substance called cholesterol have assumed importance. For certain types of heart disease much has been accomplished with drug treatments. Among them penicillin and other antibiotics are effective against subacute bacterial endocarditis, an infectious condition.

40. What efforts are being made to rehabilitate people with heart disease?

Rehabilitation programs for cardiacs are of relatively recent origin. Sheltered workshops for persons with physical disabilities accept a limited number of cardiacs. In New York and a few other cities, clinics have been set up to study the working capacity of cardiac patients and to advise them as to the type of work within their physical capacity. During World War II, the War Manpower Commission and the United States Civil Service Commission analyzed the physical demands of various types of jobs to aid in the occupational placement of cardiacs as well as other physically handicapped persons. The Altro Workshop in New York City, which has been conducted for many years to restore ex-tuberculous patients to working capacity, has experimented with a similar program for cardiacs. The results indicate that the chief limitation in most cases is not so much the condition of the patient's heart as his attitude toward his disease. This applies to those who are able to work full time. For those with more severe limitations of cardiac capacity, there is need to work under sheltered conditions so that both the pace and the length of the working day can be accommodated to the individual.

41. What is the National Heart Institute?

The National Heart Institute is one of the National Institutes of Health within the United States Public Health Service. The National Heart Institute was established in 1948 under an act of Congress which authorized it to support and conduct a program of research in the cardiovascular diseases and also to help the individual states in their local control programs. In accordance with this direction, the National Heart Institute granted nearly $90 million in 1963 for research and for training and for fellowships in various institutions throughout the country and for training specialists. In addition, the Institute carries on its own research projects in a number of federal and nonfederal institutions under various arrangements.

42. What is the American Heart Association?

The American Heart Association is a national voluntary health agency devoted to programs of basic research, professional education, community service, and health education in heart disease. Its activities are financed by funds solicited from the public. The Association supports fundamental investigations conducted in medical schools and other institutions, helps to raise the standard of care of cardiac patients, and brings essential facts regarding heart disease to the public and the medical profession through lectures, discussions, publications, and other means. Public support is measured by a budget of $28 million in 1963.

43. What are the life insurance companies doing about the problem of the circulatory diseases?

Late in 1945, a large number of life insurance companies in the United States and Canada organized the Life Insurance Medical Research Fund for the purpose of supporting medical research on the diseases of major public health import. The fund operates by providing financial grants to institutions and fellowships to individuals engaged in important research projects. The fund has distributed over $16 million for research in the United States and Canada in the period from its organization to the middle of 1963. The results of these researches are published in medical and other professional journals. Most of the work being supported deals with high blood pressure, hardening of the arteries, heart disease, and rheumatic fever.

In addition, the life insurance companies through the Institute of Life Insurance, acting in cooperation with the National Association of Life Underwriters, have in recent years developed a public service program in which the life underwriters in the various communities engage. In 1963 close to 400 associations were involved in some type of public service in their home community, of which a large number were for the support of the local heart association.

44. What can the community do to meet the problem of the circulatory diseases?

The local community can initiate case-finding campaigns among large sections of the population and can stimulate similar efforts in industrial groups. Cases of circulatory disease discovered in this way are likely to be in the early stages, when treatment can be most effective. The community can also see to it that adequate medical, hospital, clinical, and nursing facilities and personnel are available. At the same time, the public should be educated to make full use of available facilities. The community can also support a program of rehabilitation, including vocational training.

The keynote to community action is cooperation. By a pooling of knowledge and experience and by concerted effort, the official health agencies, the local medical and nursing societies, the voluntary health agencies and civic groups, and, particularly, the local life underwriters can develop an integrated program.

45. What can the individual with circulatory disease do for himself?

Detection of the disease as early as possible is of paramount importance. This is best accomplished through an annual health checkup, but a physician should be consulted without delay for such symptoms as a pain in the chest, shortness of breath, and swelling of the feet or ankles. These symptoms, while they should be investigated, do not necessarily mean circulatory disease.

When a circulatory disease is discovered, the patient should follow the doctor's orders faithfully. In addition to taking medical treatment, the patient generally is required to live a life of moderation with respect to diet and general activity. Infections should be avoided, if possible, because they impose an added burden on the heart; when they occur, they should be treated without delay. By cooperating with his physician, the patient materially enhances his chances of survival.

Chapter 13

The Problem of

the Rheumatic

Diseases

1. What are the rheumatic diseases and why are they grouped together?

The term rheumatism covers a wide variety of diseases and disorders, namely, rheumatic fever, the various forms of joint diseases such as arthritis, and some less clearly defined disorders such as muscular rheumatism, lower back pain, bursitis, neuritis, and sciatica. These conditions are classed together because they have certain symptoms and findings in common, particularly pain, stiffness, or swelling in the joints or muscles, and because a basic pathologic relationship appears to exist between many of them.

2. How many people have rheumatism?

Rheumatism is the leading chronic disease in the United States as well as in many other countries. On the basis of the National

Health Survey, 1957–59, about 11 million persons in this country suffer from one of the many forms of the rheumatic diseases. Nearly 1,000,000 persons were reported as disabled by these conditions for a week or more during the course of a year. As measured by the amount of time lost from work, rheumatism is second in rank among the causes of illness. Of this loss, it was estimated that approximately 60,000,000 days were bed-disability days. There was a gradual increase with age in the number of bed-days per person. In spite of the huge loss of time and activity due to these conditions, very few deaths are ascribed to them.

3. What are the chief features distinguishing various conditions classified as rheumatism?

Age, type of onset, and the parts of the body affected help to differentiate the various rheumatic disorders. For example, rheumatic fever usually has its onset in childhood, and is often characterized by continued low-grade fever and by muscle aches and joint pains which move from one set of joints to others. Its most serious aspect is the involvement of the heart. Rheumatoid arthritis usually has its onset between 20 and 50 years of age and is characterized by stiffness, pain, and swelling in the joints. Many joints are usually involved, but at first only one or two may be affected. Degenerative joint disease or osteoarthritis usually has its onset in middle and later life, and a certain few joints are primarily involved. Types of rheumatic diseases involving other structures than the joints are differentiated by the site and nature of the condition.

4. What is the relative prevalence of the various rheumatic diseases?

There are no accurate data on the prevalence of the individual rheumatic diseases. It has been estimated, however, that for those who seek medical care, the approximate proportions are:

Rheumatoid arthritis	30 to 40 percent
Degenerative joint disease	25 to 30 percent
Muscular rheumatism, neuritis, sciatica, etc.	10 to 20 percent
Traumatic arthritis	7 to 10 percent
Gout	3 to 5 percent
Rheumatic fever	3 to 5 percent
Miscellaneous forms	5 to 7 percent

Many sufferers from rheumatic conditions, particularly those not affecting the joints or those with degenerative types, do not seek medical attention, and consequently the true proportions are unknown.

5. What is rheumatic fever and what causes it?

Rheumatic fever is essentially a chronic disease marked, however, by one or more acute episodes. Occasionally it begins in the preschool ages, but it usually has its onset between the ages of 5 and 10, and less commonly after 10. The cause of the disease is still uncertain. Almost uniformly there is a history of a streptococcal infection, particularly sore throat, before the onset, but the exact nature of the relationship between this infection and rheumatic fever remains obscure.

6. Why is rheumatic fever a serious condition?

The chief danger in rheumatic fever lies in the damage it often does to the heart. The disease is the principal cause of heart disease from childhood well on into middle life. The risk of permanent heart damage is increased by the severity of the first attack and of the recurrence of acute attacks, and it is for that reason that chief emphasis in the care of the disease is placed on the prevention of these recurrences.[1]

7. How does the prevalence of rheumatic fever and rheumatic heart disease vary with sex and age?

Rheumatic fever occurs somewhat more frequently among girls than boys. The rate of onset rises sharply from early childhood to a peak at around age seven; it declines slightly during the next few years to puberty, but then falls rapidly after the age of puberty. A recent survey of Chicago elementary school children showed a prevalence rate of less than 2 per 1,000.

8. How does the prevalence of the disease vary by geographic area?

Rheumatic fever is world-wide in its prevalence. The disease, however, is most widely prevalent and most severe in the temperate zones and relatively infrequent and milder in the more tropical climates. Mortality and morbidity statistics show that in the United States the prevalence of the disease is highest in the Rocky Mountain and Middle Atlantic states and lowest in the area bordering the Gulf

[1] See answer to Question 3 of Chapter 12, page 172.

of Mexico and in the Southwest. The disease generally shows a higher concentration in urban industrial than in farming areas.

9. What is the effect of social and economic conditions on rheumatic fever?

Rheumatic fever occurs more frequently in low-income families than in those which are better off economically. Crowding in homes seems to be related to the incidence of the disease and appears to be more serious if living quarters are poor and unsanitary. However, even children from well-to-do homes are not immune to the disease so that poor environmental conditions may be considered as contributory rather than causative factors in the disease.

Household crowding is less frequent in rural than in urban areas and this in part explains the lesser prevalence of rheumatic fever in the former.

10. Is rheumatic fever a communicable disease?

No. It is true that multiple cases of rheumatic fever have been recorded within a short period of time in schools, military training camps and barracks, and even in families. However, these outbreaks have generally followed epidemics of streptococcal infections, especially streptococcal sore throat. The latter are contagious, not the rheumatic fever which develops in susceptible individuals in such epidemics.

11. Is the tendency to rheumatic fever inherited?

Careful analysis of family histories of patients indicates that the number of cases found is in line with what would be expected on the basis of the Mendelian theory of inheritance of a recessive characteristic. On this basis, both parents must either have had rheumatic fever or be "carriers" (i.e. able to transmit susceptibility to the disease to their offspring). If both parents had the disease, all the children will be susceptible; if only one parent has a positive history, the other being negative but a carrier, half the children will be susceptible. However, if neither parent had rheumatic fever, but both were carriers, one-fourth of the children will be susceptible. The incidence of the disease observed in twins also is consistent with the hypothesis that heredity plays a part in rheumatic fever. Among identical twins in rheumatic families, both are usually affected, if at all; but among fraternal twins, the occurrence of the disease follows the usual pattern.

12. What has been the trend in mortality from rheumatic fever?

The death rate from acute rheumatic fever and rheumatic heart disease has been declining steadily for a long time. Since 1940, the rate for children 5 to 14 years has declined from 7.8 per 100,000 to 0.7 in 1960, or over 90 percent. In the last decade alone the rate has been cut by about 80 percent at these ages. While the reductions at the later ages of childhood and early adult life have been much less marked, they have been substantial, indicating that great advances have been made in the control of this disease. The rates are much higher for colored children than for white.

13. Does the occurrence of rheumatic fever vary according to season?

Acute episodes of rheumatic fever are least frequent in the fall of the year. They show a steady rise during the winter and spring months to a peak in April or May, and then recede gradually to the fall minimum.

14. What is the effect of rheumatic fever on the heart?

During an acute attack of rheumatic fever, there is often an inflammation of the muscle, valves, and lining of the heart. In most cases under current treatment with antibiotics, bed rest, salicylates, and, where necessary, corticosteroids, this virtually clears up with recovery, but in some cases the heart is left permanently and more or less seriously damaged. Recurrent attacks of rheumatic fever increase the likelihood of serious heart impairment. This impairment generally is due to scarring of one or more of the valves, as a result of which the heart does not function properly. This puts an extra burden of work on the heart, and may bring an increase in its size and premature breakdown. To some extent this may be averted or postponed if the individual keeps his activities within the working capacity of the heart. In spite of marked advances in the control of this disease, it is still a serious cause of illness and disability, especially in the colored population.

15. Can rheumatic fever be prevented?

Initial attacks of rheumatic fever can frequently be prevented by prompt antibiotic treatment. Moreover, recurrences can often be prevented. This depends primarily on prevention of streptococcal infections of nose and throat and maintenance of a high level of health, a good diet, and sufficient rest. It is especially important for children who have had an attack of rheumatic fever to adhere faithfully to a schedule of antibiotic prophylaxis, either sulfonamides or penicillin, under direction of a physician.

16. What are the symptoms of rheumatic fever?

The early symptoms of rheumatic fever may be very mild and not at all specific of the disease. Among such symptoms are pallor, poor appetite, and failure to gain weight. More characteristic symptoms are frequent nosebleeds, pain in the joints or muscles of the arms and legs or in the abdomen, and a persistent low-grade fever. Although the disease is called rheumatic fever, joint symptoms may be a minor feature or essentially absent. Chorea, or St. Vitus' dance, may be a symptom leading to its discovery, especially in older children.

17. How is rheumatic fever treated?

Complete bed rest is the basic element in the treatment of rheumatic fever. The aim is to lessen the work of the heart. Specific measures to combat the infection and inflammation include the antibiotics and salicylate drugs such as aspirin to reduce the fever and relieve the pains in the muscles, joints, and tendons. Sulfonamides or penicillin are used to eradicate the streptococcal infection. In cases in which the heart is severely affected, bed rest must be continued for many months. Regular medical and nursing supervision is necessary. Good nutrition is also important. Activity can be resumed gradually only on the doctor's advice. Today increased emphasis is put on measures to avoid making the child a chronic invalid. Consequently the child is encouraged to engage in simple games and hobbies which can be carried on in bed with little physical effort, and home instruction in his school work is recommended for school-age children during the period of convalescence. Cardiac clinics in the larger communities have been very useful for follow-up services to rheumatic fever children.

18. Does change of climate help victims of rheumatic fever?

Most rheumatic fever specialists now generally agree that a change of climate is neither desirable nor necessary in the care of the patient with rheumatic fever. While there may be less risk of streptococcal infections in areas with warm, dry climates, these areas may not have adequate medical facilities for the care of the patient. Moreover, if the patient returns to his original environment, he is just as likely to have a recurrence of rheumatic fever. Consequently, potential gains from seeking a more favorable climate are usually outweighed by the economic and other problems resulting from breaking up a home and settling elsewhere. Good care and proper medical supervision are much more important than climate in controlling the disease.

19. What is the effect of rheumatic fever on longevity and working capacity?

This depends greatly on the extent of heart damage during the acute episodes of rheumatic fever. This is clearly evident from a follow-up study of nearly 3,000 children and young people made by the Metropolitan Life Insurance Company. Of those under age 10 at first observation who had no reported evidence of heart damage during the attack, 90 percent were still living at the end of 19 years. For children between 10 and 20 years, 84 percent survived. However, among those with evident heart disease at first observation, the proportion surviving at the end of the nineteenth year exceeded 75 percent for all the girls under age 10, and exceeded 60 percent for the older girls and boys. Generally, the record was better for girls than boys. (See Chart 15 on page 197.)

The great majority of these young people now lead quite normal lives. Most of those who have reached adult life are working and many are married. Sizable numbers of the older boys were in military service in World War II. Many of them were in combat units, and five of them lost their lives in action.

20. Can women who have had rheumatic fever bear children safely?

Each case must be considered individually. Where no significant heart damage exists following rheumatic fever, the risk to the pregnant mother is much the same as in those who have not had the disease. There is little extra risk for women with mild rheumatic heart disease who can engage in the everyday activities of housekeeping, office work, or light factory work, without evidence of strain on the heart. Whatever added risk there is can be minimized by good medical care from the beginning of pregnancy. In the follow-up study by the Metropolitan Life Insurance Company of children with rheu-

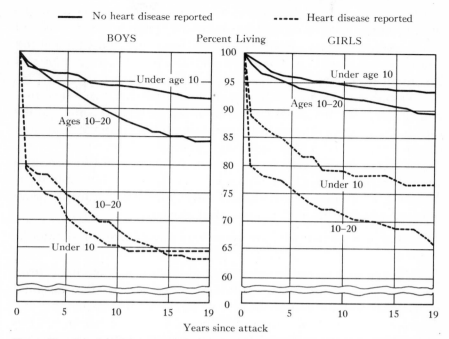

—— No heart disease reported   ----- Heart disease reported

BOYS   Percent Living   GIRLS

Years since attack

Chart 15. **Survivorship of children with rheumatic fever, Metropolitan Life Insurance Company, Industrial Department, who received nursing care during 1936–38, traced to anniversary of discharge from care in 1955. By sex, age, and cardiac status at first observation.**

matic fever it was learned that many of the girls became mothers, not a few having had a number of children.

21. What public health measures are effective in controlling rheumatic fever?

Measures which lead to prompt treatment of "strep" infections and to early detection of cases of rheumatic fever have been most effective. These comprise periodic examination of children in rheumatic families, school health examinations, follow-up of children who are under par or who have chronic infections, and careful observation of such cases by teachers in the public schools. Heart sounds screening (phonocardiography) is an important method of detection of unknown cases. These measures are also valuable in the early detection of recurrences.

Educational programs are also of value. These extend to various groups in the community: to physicians in order to help them improve their knowledge of the disease, and to parents and teachers so that they may bring children with signs and symptoms of the disease to medical attention. Education has also been important in creating a more hopeful attitude toward the outlook in rheumatic fever and rheumatic heart disease.

Because of the chronic nature of the disease and the cost of prolonged care, public provision of hospital, laboratory, and public nursing facilities is important. In addition, public-supported research of many types has yielded knowledge of value in the control of the disease. In the same general way, the many public health measures which have contributed to a high level of child health have raised the resistance of children to rheumatic fever and have indirectly contributed to its declining incidence and mortality.

22. What special facilities are needed in the control of rheumatic fever?

The special facilities useful in the control of rheumatic fever are child cardiac clinics and consultation services, separate hospital wards or hospitals, public health nursing, home instruction, and vocational training and guidance. The cardiac consultation services and clinics are often needed for diagnosis; the latter also provide supervision and follow-up of children with rheumatic heart disease. The special wards or hospitals are needed to furnish adequate care over long periods for the many children with rheumatic fever who cannot get this care at home. The children can get their schooling during their convalescence in these hospitals. The special hospitals provide invaluable opportunities for research in rheumatic fever. Public health nurses and visiting teachers serve the children receiving care at home.

In the Crippled Children's Program, which is operated in individual states with financial support of the federal government, a comprehensive service is provided for children with rheumatic fever.

The special facilities needed for rheumatic fever control are scarcely adequate anywhere. This is particularly true regarding long-range needs such as rehabilitation and job placement of the patients.

23. How can the schools contribute to the control of rheumatic fever?

The schools occupy a unique and important position in relation to rheumatic fever control. The disease usually begins at the lower elementary school ages, and recurrences are most common while the children are still of elementary or high-school age. Teachers and others in daily contact with school children can be taught the early signs and symptoms that may mean rheumatic fever, and the types of children among whom the disease is most likely to develop. This is useful in the early detection of recurrent as well as new cases. School nurses also can contribute to the early detection of cases and also to adequate follow-up in order to keep known cases under medical supervision. School health examinations may reveal unknown cases or changes in the cardiac condition of children who have had rheumatic fever.

24. What is rheumatoid arthritis and what causes it?

Rheumatoid arthritis is a chronic disease affecting chiefly the joints and adjacent muscles. It is not an infectious disease although in many cases it has the characteristics of an infection. Sometimes the inflammation of the joints resembles rheumatic fever. It is a systemic disease, i.e., not localized. In the late stages, rheumatoid arthritis is marked by deformity and immobility of the joints, with changes in joint and bone structure and atrophy of the adjacent muscles.

The cause of this disease is still unknown. There appeared to be a hereditary factor, but some workers have questioned this recently. A small percentage of the cases report other members of the family to be affected.

25. What are the major features of the onset and course of rheumatoid arthritis?

The onset of this disease is usually insidious. It may be rather difficult to determine just when the illness begins because the early symptoms may not be specific. For example, these may be simple fatigue, muscular stiffness, loss of weight, and general debility. Among the factors which may precipitate symptoms are lowered physical resistance, exposure to damp and cold, chronic infections, emotional stress, and injuries. Usually the first joints affected are those of the fingers and then other joints in the wrists, arms, legs, feet, and spine gradually may become involved. There is characteristic swelling of certain joints. Pain occurs with movement of the affected parts and increases in severity as the disease progresses. The early course of the disease is marked by remissions and relapses.

If the disease progresses, both symptoms and changes in the affected joints become more marked. In the advanced cases, there may be severe crippling, fusion (ankylosis) of some joints and contractures of affected limbs. These effects are sometimes so severe that the patient may become chair- or bed-ridden.

26. Why is the rheumatoid form of arthritis of particular importance as a cause of disability?

Rheumatoid arthritis holds first place among the chronic diseases as a cause of disability and crippling at the working ages. It is estimated that in 80 percent of the cases onset occurs between ages 20 and 50. The disease is also of major medical, economic, and social importance because of its severity and the prolonged disability and loss of working capacity resulting from it. About two to three times more women than men are affected by the disease.

27. How is rheumatoid arthritis treated?

There is no specific cure for rheumatoid arthritis at the present time although it is possible in many cases to control the disease or delay its progress. The measures of proved therapeutic value are for the most part directed toward improving the general health of the patient. Rest for the body as a whole and for the inflamed joints is probably the most important single measure in the treatment of acute phases of the disease. Great emphasis is placed on prevention of deformities of the joints by the use of splints, proper exercises, and physical therapy. In view of the frequency of emotional distress as a factor in the disease, psychotherapy is of value for many patients.

Few drugs have had any proved effect on the disease. Gold compounds have been used increasingly in recent years, but because they have potential toxic effects, they can be most safely prescribed only by physicians experienced in their use and familiar with the early signs of toxic reactions.

New promise of effective drug treatment of the disease was given by adrenocorticotropic hormone (ACTH) and corticosteroids, which have produced dramatic remissions of the disease in some cases. There are, however, serious drawbacks to their use.

The observation that remission of rheumatoid arthritis often occurs in pregnancy has also suggested the existence of an endocrine factor in this disease. In the past, various attempts have been made to treat the disease with various placental products or even by transfusions from pregnant women, but without any definite benefit. Trials with plasma taken from mothers shortly after childbirth and with the hormone pregnenolone have proven to be of no value. Recently, antimalarial drugs (chloroquine and hydroxychloroquine) have been found to be moderately effective in the treatment of rheumatoid arthritis.

28. What is the prognosis in rheumatoid arthritis?

The outlook for persons with this disease is extremely variable and it is, therefore, difficult to predict what it will be for the individual patient. However, the widespread feeling of pessimism regarding its prognosis is far from justified. The disease is subject to remission and with good care the periods of remission can be greatly lengthened; at the same time, much can be done to give the patient relief. The experience of specialists in the field shows that about one-fourth recover completely, and that about one-half have periods of freedom of varying length. Up to recent years, the remainder of the cases, about one-fourth of the total, seemed to suffer progression of the condition no matter what was done for them. It is for these cases particularly that the corrective exercise and splinting, gold compounds, antimalarial drugs, and corticosteroids hold out the greatest hope.

29. What is osteoarthritis and what causes it?

Osteoarthritis, or degenerative joint disease, is a chronic disease characterized by degeneration and enlargement of cartilage and bone. Pain occurs generally upon use of the affected joints. Unlike rheumatoid arthritis it is usually localized, affecting chiefly the weight-bearing joints and those of the ends of the fingers. The disease is for the most part a consequence of wear and tear on the joints with advancing years, coupled with injuries to these structures.

30. How does the prevalence of osteoarthritis vary with sex and age?

This degenerative type of joint disease is the most common. Some evidence of the joint changes characteristic of this condition can be found in most persons over 40. However, clinical manifestations rarely occur until much later in life; they reach their peak of frequency in elderly people. There is no marked sex difference in the prevalence of the disease affecting the larger joints, particularly if allowance is made for the fact that at the ages at which it usually occurs women in the general population considerably outnumber men. There is a distinct predominance of osteoarthritis of the terminal finger joints (Heberden's nodes) among women.

31. What are the chief characteristics of osteoarthritis?

In the very nature of the disease the onset is not clearly defined. Rather marked degrees of degenerative changes in the joints may be found on x-ray even though the individual has no complaint or discomfort. A frequent early sign of degenerative joint disease is a tingling sensation in the fingertips. Other symptoms which become more prominent with progression of the disease are stiffness and pain on motion. This is increased with activity. As time goes on, deformities in the affected areas occur. A characteristic deformity in advanced stages of the disease is the bony enlargement around the last joint of the fingers so frequently seen in older people. Generally they develop gradually, but occasionally rapidly.

The joints of the knee are a frequent site of degenerative changes. These may occur relatively early because of excessive strain on these joints or injury to them. Obesity is also a factor in many cases. The joints in other areas may also be affected. The most severe cases are those involving the hip joints and the spine. The extent of crippling in osteoarthritis is sometimes very great, and, as in rheumatoid arthritis, may cause invalidism.

32. How is osteoarthritis treated?

This disorder cannot be cured, but the pain and discomfort it causes can be relieved to a very great extent and the degenerative process retarded. Resting the affected joints is perhaps the most important measure in treatment. Where necessary, further relief can be obtained by supporting the affected parts by orthopedic appliances such as splints, strapping, and braces, or in the spinal forms of the disease by use of a corset. Where obesity is a causative factor, weight reduction is of value in cutting down the strain on the weight-bearing joints. Physical therapy such as heat and massage is valuable in treating the disease, and the salicylate drugs (aspirin, etc.), when given regularly and in adequate quantities, give considerable relief.

33. What is gout and what causes it?

Gout in its classical form is perhaps the easiest to recognize of the diseases affecting the joints. In the great majority of cases gout is a result of an inborn error of metabolism, which consists largely of an overproduction or increased synthesis of uric acid from simple biological compounds found in the body. Hence patients with gout have excessive amounts of uric acid in their blood, urine, other body fluids, and tissues. Uric acid crystals are deposited in the joints and other tissues. This gives rise to the characteristic swellings (gouty tophi) of the toes, fingers, and wrists, and nodulelike deposits in or on the ears. Usually the disease is recognized by an acute attack which has a sudden onset with typical symptoms.

The cause of the disease is unknown. Heredity is a distinctive factor. Overindulgence in food and alcohol has long been associated with the disease, and although the nature of the relationship is obscure, they are provocative factors in acute attacks. However, the disease occurs in total abstainers from alcohol.

34. How prevalent is gout?

Gout is one of the less frequent of the diseases affecting the joints, at least in its clinically recognizable form. The number of cases in this country is estimated to be about 350,000. These are, with few exceptions, persons past 30, and the peak of the disease appears to be between 40 and 50. More than 90 percent of the victims of gout are men. So far as is known, no racial group is free from the disease, and cases occur in persons of every social-economic level.

Gout has been known from ancient times. It is, however, much less prevalent today than ever before. Possibly the better diets of today act to prevent its clinical appearance in a substantial proportion of the cases. The disease appears to be less common in this country than in certain areas of Western and Southern Europe, but reliable statistics on its prevalence do not exist to back up this impression.

35. What are the chief features of the onset of gout?

The onset of gout is usually sudden and gives no warning symptoms, although some experts in the field assert that a symptomless phase is common before the acute phase which leads to the diagnosis of the disease. The rapid and acute onset of gout is often a good clue to the diagnosis. Typically, there is acute swelling of a single joint, which within the space of a few hours becomes hot, red, and very tender. The joints of one of the big toes is most commonly affected.

Other frequent early sites are the leg, the ankle, the heel, and the knee. Any joint may be affected, but usually those of the lower extremities. The initial attack may last a few days, but sometimes as long as a fortnight. In the first attack the symptoms usually clear up and complete restoration of normal function of the joints occurs.

36. What is the course and prognosis of gout?

The course of the disease is quite variable. A considerable length of time—sometimes many years—may elapse before a recurrence, and in fact further attacks may be warded off for even longer periods if the patient sticks faithfully to treatment. When the disease recurs the joints affected may not be the same as in the initial or previous attacks. Eventually the characteristic deposits of urate crystals occur. Usually this happens only 10 years or more after the initial attack. From one-fifth to one-half of the chronic cases show these deposits, according to different reports. The deposits vary in size from a small fraction of an inch to as much as two or three inches. If gout is inadequately treated and controlled, attacks occur with increasing frequency; there is less freedom from pain between attacks; and characteristic joint deformities develop. In some cases the high concentration of uric acid in the blood leads to the formation of kidney stones and eventually failure of the kidneys may occur. This is a major cause of death among persons with chronic gout.

37. How is gout treated?

During the acute attack, the patient is kept at complete rest and where possible the affected part is elevated. Because of the extreme tenderness of the part, even the weight of the bed clothes may cause discomfort and provision is made to protect it from contact or pressure. A simple diet with abundant liquids is prescribed in the acute attack. A drug called colchicine is commonly used to stop an acute attack and to prevent recurrences. This drug should be administered by a physician. Recently effective drugs have been developed which reduce excessive uric acid in the body to usual levels.

Since the disease is essentially a chronic condition with periods of remission, treatment must be on a long-range basis and attention given to the correction or management of complications and deformities. Diet plays a moderately important role in the long-term plan of treatment. This diet is low in those foods which are considered to cause excessive uric acid in the blood. These are meats, fish, seafood, and the leguminous vegetables—beans, peas, and lentils. Certain foods such as liver, kidneys, anchovies, and sardines, as well as alcoholic beverages, are entirely forbidden. The main content of the diet includes eggs, vegetables, milk, cheese, and fruits. The patient may also have to use the drug colchicine for extended periods. For victims of gout who are overweight, a weight reduction diet is usually beneficial.

38. What are the major types of nonarticular rheumatism and how prevalent are they?

These types of rheumatism cover a variety of disorders, most of them related, and involve many body structures. Heading the list in importance are those forms which are now grouped under the heading of fibrositis. These include muscular rheumatism, bursitis, lumbago, involvement of the joint capsules, and the areas around the large nerves such as the sciatic nerve. Fibrositis in its various forms is the most common of all the rheumatic diseases, and in the medical experience of the British Army accounted for the majority of admissions to hospitals for rheumatism. Fibrositis may occur as a primary or a secondary disorder. It is frequently associated with infections, with the articular forms of rheumatism, and with postural and structural defects. It is highly important as an occupational disorder, either as a result of injury or physical strain involved in the job. It is frequently brought on by exposure to cold, sudden changes in temperature, or fatigue.

The symptoms of fibrositis are pain, stiffness, or soreness of the involved structures. Specific physical changes are negligible. In a high proportion of cases, emotional stress is an important factor in causing the disease. Some physicians, in fact, consider fibrositis one of the most common of the psychosomatic disorders.

Fibrositis is distinguished from rheumatoid arthritis largely by the absence of such symptoms as joint pain and swelling, muscular atrophy, weight loss, and bone changes. Characteristic of fibrositis are a normal temperature and prompt response to treatment.

Often included with the rheumatic disorders are many conditions such as neuritis and back and foot pains which are essentially of an orthopedic character but in which there are secondary rheumatic manifestations.

39. What is the treatment and prognosis in nonarticular rheumatism?

The treatment of muscular rheumatism and fibrositis is relatively simple. In the acute stage, protection from cold and relief from pain are most important. Aspirin and similar drugs generally suffice to relieve pain, but where indicated injections of suitable local anesthetics are used. In low back pain and sciatica, most frequently due to a slipped disk in the spine, the patient should rest flat on his back and the mattress should be firm or boards placed under it.

When the acute attack of fibrositis subsides, physical therapy of various kinds is useful. These include heat, massage, mild exercise, hot baths, and sometimes diathermy. In many cases it is necessary to teach the patients to correct their bad postural habits and to take off excessive weight.

In cases where rheumatic conditions are secondary to other disorders, the patient obviously needs careful examination to determine the underlying cause, if unknown, and suitable treatment for the primary disorder.

The outlook in uncomplicated nonarticular rheumatism is excellent if the patient fully cooperates in treatment. Symptoms may be quickly relieved. However, emotional disturbances and long-established defects in posture and living habits are likely to prolong disability or lead to recurrences. Even in such cases, uncomplicated disorders of this character are seldom if ever fatal and are without any effect on longevity.

40. What organized attack is there against the rheumatic diseases?

The American Rheumatism Association, consisting of physicians interested in the disease, has carried on a limited program of professional education. It has made available to physicians summaries of the enormous literature on rheumatic diseases, and has organized national and international conferences on the subject. The few local societies of the association and individual members have encouraged local communities to provide better facilities, especially clinics, for victims of rheumatic diseases. The association sponsors the Arthritis and Rheumatism Foundation to raise funds for a program of professional and lay education in these diseases and for support of research, fellowships, and care of patients.

Organized activity by voluntary lay agencies against rheumatic fever has developed as an integral part of the campaign against heart disease under the auspices of the American Heart Association and local heart societies. To implement its rheumatic fever program, this association has formed a Council on Rheumatic Fever and Congenital Heart Disease, which is composed of interested medical and allied professional as well as lay members. The Council carries on a program of popular and professional education on the disease, stimulates improved treatment and increased facilities for its victims, helps community organization against the disease, and sponsors and finances research. The Life Insurance Medical Research Fund, the Helen Hay Whitney Foundation, and the Masons in New York State are also giving generous support to fundamental research in rheumatic fever.

The activities of governmental agencies include the National Institute of Arthritis and Metabolic Diseases of the Public Health Service, which abundantly supports research, graduate training, and fellowships in rheumatic diseases. For many years, now, a joint federal-state program has been in operation on behalf of children with rheumatic fever[2] and the funds and facilities of the National Heart Institute support research in the disease.

41. What needs exist in the field of the rheumatic diseases?

In view of the widespread prevalence of these diseases and the comparative neglect of the field, the needs are great and varied. First, there is room for great expansion of hospital and clinic facilities. Special rheumatic clinics exist in a few cities, but even there they are inadequate in number and equipment. More beds are required for hospital care of cases and for clinical studies in these diseases. A few special hospitals for those with crippling disease would be of value. These institutions could combine care and treatment with rehabilitation and vocational training when necessary. It has also been suggested that some of the government-supported hospitals for the care of the tuberculous may be readily converted to provide care for patients with chronic rheumatism and other degenerative diseases. Such hospitals are often well equipped for this type of care and for the effective rehabilitation of their charges.

There is need for more fundamental research in various phases of the rheumatic diseases. Up to about 1954 the amount of money available has been quite meager. Fortunately, through the National

[2] See Question 23 of this chapter, page 198.

Institute of Arthritis and Metabolic Diseases research funds have been enormously increased.

Another important need is a thoroughgoing program of professional education in diagnosis and treatment of these conditions. This would bring to general practitioners, who treat most of these cases, the latest knowledge about these diseases and their management.

Chapter 14

The Hazards
of Infancy
and Childhood

1. How many infants are there in the United States?

At the beginning of 1963 there were about 4,160,000 infants, that is, children less than one year old. They comprise 2.2 percent of our population—a small but very important section. Not only do they appeal naturally to our emotions, but they also attract our attention and interest because they are the start of a new generation.

2. Is infancy a healthy period?

Infants can take a surprising amount of hardship and still survive, much more than their helplessness and small size indicate. Nevertheless, there are great dangers to health in the first year of life. Disease and defect cause proportionately more deaths in the year of infancy than in any other year before advanced old age.

3. What is the infant mortality rate in the United States?

The infant mortality rate is usually expressed as the ratio of the deaths under one year of age during a calendar year to the number of live births within that period; this ratio is generally multiplied by 1,000. Thus, the infant mortality rate in the country today is about 25 per 1,000 live births, or 2.5 percent. This is less than half of what it was 30 years ago.

4. How does infant mortality in the United States compare with that in other countries?

The infant mortality record for the United States is among the best in the world. Lower rates are found in a few countries, including New Zealand, Australia, the Scandinavian countries, The Netherlands, England and Wales, and Switzerland. It should be pointed out, however, that some of these differences in the rates may result from differences in the definitions of what is a live birth. Many European countries do not consider a birth live unless the infant *both* breathes and has a detectable pulse. In the United States *any* evidence of life denotes a "live birth" even though survival may be measured in minutes. Nevertheless, some European countries would have lower infant mortality rates even if a similar statistical system were used.

Infant mortality is a good index of the general level of health in a country and also of the state of public health work. Infant mortality is generally highest in Asia and Latin America. For example, Chile in 1961 reported an infant mortality rate of 116 per 1,000 live births, or more than four times the rate prevailing in the United States.

5. What has been the trend in infant mortality since 1915?

In 1915, when the annual collection of birth statistics from registration records was started by the Bureau of the Census, only the New England states, New York, Pennsylvania, Michigan, Minnesota, and the District of Columbia reported. The infant mortality for these states as a whole was then 100 deaths per 1,000 live births. This was probably lower than the rate for the entire country.

By 1930, when all but South Dakota and Texas had joined the birth registration area, the rate had been cut to 65 per 1,000 live births. The infant mortality rate for 1950, covering the whole country, was 29 per 1,000. Now it is only 25 per 1,000.

6. How many lives have been saved by the reduction in infant mortality in the two decades since 1940?

In 1961 alone, there would have been over 90,000 more deaths of children under one year of age if the infant mortality of 1940 had continued unchanged. In all, the steady improvement in infant health since 1940 has resulted in saving the lives of about a million babies during the years following.

7. Which regions within the United States have high and which have low infant mortality rates?

The rates are lowest in the North Central and New England states and are followed closely by the Pacific Coast states. The rates are appreciably higher in the South Atlantic and South Central states. Mississippi, Alaska, and the District of Columbia have the least favorable records of all, reflecting the unsatisfactory conditions prevailing in a large proportion of the nonwhite population which they contain.

8. Which season is safest for newborn babies?

Summer is the safest season for babies. In the warm months infant mortality is low—the rate for June being about 15 percent below the December figures. The principal communicable diseases of childhood and the acute respiratory infections are less prevalent then. Because the environment seems to be more favorable in summer, it is also a good time for babies to be born. If they have the summer months to gain strength, they are better able to resist the annual winter bouts with contagion.

9. What changes have taken place in the seasonal fluctuations of infant mortality?

At the turn of the century, summer was by far the most hazardous time of year for babies, with a mortality rate twice as high as in winter. Diarrhea and enteritis were then the chief fatal diseases of infancy, caused largely by unclean and improper food and contaminated milk and water. By about 1925, the standards of sanitation had improved and the respiratory diseases had replaced diarrhea and enteritis as the principal cause of illness in infancy, thus reversing the seasonal pattern. Summer then became the safest season, and it has remained so ever since. However, with the advances in health and medicine, the extent of the seasonal fluctuation in infant mortality has steadily been reduced.

10. To what extent are infant deaths concentrated in the very first days of life?

Mortality in the first year of life is highest at the very beginning and decreases steadily as the year advances. In 1960, for example, there were 13 infant deaths per 1,000 live births on the first day of life. In fact, if the death rate of the first day had continued for 100 days, not a single baby would have survived. One-half of infant deaths fall within the first day of life and close to three-quarters within the first month. The concentration of infant deaths in the early period has resulted largely from the reduction in the toll of the infections, thus increasing the relative importance of prematurity, birth injuries, and congenital difficulties.

11. What are the chief causes of death in the first month of life?

Nearly half of all deaths within the first month of life are caused by prematurity, with and without mention of other conditions. Injury at birth accounts for almost one-sixth of these deaths, and congenital malformations for more than one-eighth. Asphyxia, pneumonia and influenza, and diarrhea and enteritis combined make up about one-ninth of the total.

12. What are the chief causes of death in infancy after the first month of life?

Pneumonia and influenza are the leading causes of infant death after the first month, accounting for close to one-third of the total. Congenital malformations rank second, with about one-sixth of the deaths; accidents come third with one-tenth; diarrhea and enteritis fourth with one-twelfth.[1]

13. Are there differences in infant mortality according to race and sex?

In 1962, the infant mortality rate for nonwhites (mostly Negroes) was 41.4 per 1,000 live births, or close to double that for whites. The mortality rate in infancy for male babies is about a third above the rate for female babies.

[1] See answers to Questions 11 and 19 of Chapter 16, pages 245 and 247.

14. What are the most frequent types of fatal congenital malformation?

The most common of all fatal congenital malformations are those of the heart, followed by those of the digestive system. Also not infrequently fatal are congenital hydrocephaly, and spinal and central nervous system defects. Although most deaths caused by congenital malformations occur very early, occasionally an individual with a serious congenital defect will survive infancy and die from a malformation sometimes many years later.

15. Does weight at birth affect the baby's chance of survival?

A baby's chances of successfully passing through the hazardous first month of life are greatly influenced by its weight at birth The mortality rate is exceedingly high for the smallest babies, but it drops sharply with increase in birth weight up to about $5\frac{1}{2}$ pounds.

16. What is the outlook for further improvement in infant mortality?

The steady reductions in infant mortality in recent decades can be expected to continue, but at a reduced scale. Not only is the practice of having births in hospitals being extended, but prenatal and postnatal care is also spreading. Public health facilities are being expanded in small towns and rural areas, where the birth rate and the infant mortality rate have been highest.

In the last half century, the advances have been made largely against the infectious diseases which caused infant deaths. Today, however, prematurity and malformation are the principal problems. Research on the effect of the nutrition of the mother and other aspects of maternal health, including the Rh blood factor on the constitution of babies, should help reduce infant deaths from nondisease causes. Altogether, it is to be expected that the infant mortality rate in our country will be brought down to about 20 per 1,000 live births during the next decade—a rate already achieved by a number of countries.

17. How many children are there in the United States?

In 1960, there were all told more than 64 million children in the United States, counting all under 18 years old. Normally, for health purposes, only those through the age of 14 are considered children;

the others, in their late teens, are usually either considered separately
or with young adults.

There were 16 million children more than a year old but less
than 5; over 18.7 million between 5 and 10; and somewhat less than
17 million aged 10 to 14. The combined groups, aged from 1 to 14,
inclusive, number more than 51 million, or over one-quarter of the
entire population of the country. If the two highest "teen" ages, 18
and 19, are added, the number of children and youth totaled 73
million in mid-1962 or about two-fifths of the entire population.

**18. What has been the trend in childhood mortality in the last half
century?**

The reduction in mortality among children since 1900 has been
spectacular. In fact, a good part of the total reduction in the national
death rate has resulted from the gains made among children. From
1900 to 1962, the death rate for the population at all ages was reduced
by more than 40 percent. However, at ages 1 to 4, it was cut by 95
percent, and at ages 5 to 14 by about 90 percent. At the turn of the
century deaths in childhood (not counting infancy) comprised almost
one-seventh of the annual deaths in the country; but in recent years
childhood deaths accounted for only about one-fortieth of the total.

The remarkable record of improvement in child health has been
the result of a threefold advance; in sanitation, in medicine, and in
the standard of living in American families.

**19. How many children are saved annually by the reduction in mor-
tality since 1900?**

Today, for every school child who dies, 10 would have died if
the conditions of 1900 had continued to the present. For every preschool child who dies, 20 would have died but for the improvement
since 1900. This comes to an annual saving of the lives of more than
400,000 children.

20. What are the safest years of life?

The chances of surviving from one year to the next are greatest
at ages 9, 10, and 11. These are the safest years of life in terms of
mortality. After infancy, the death rate drops to a low around the end
of the first decade of life and then increases gradually to the end of
childhood. After age 14, the rate continues up slowly until midlife

when it begins rising more steeply. In old age, the increase in mortality with each year of life is extremely rapid.

21. What are the leading causes of death among children today, and how do they compare with years ago?

Currently, accidents account for one-third of all deaths at ages 1 to 14 years. Cancer ranks second, with about one-eighth of all deaths at these ages, followed by influenza and pneumonia and congenital malformations, which causes account for approximately 10 percent each of all deaths. In contrast to this present-day picture, in 1910, when death rates in childhood were much higher, one-sixth of the deaths were from pneumonia and influenza, one-seventh from diarrhea and enteritis, and one-ninth from diphtheria. About one-twelfth of all childhood deaths were then from tuberculosis. In this early mortality picture, which was heavily weighted with infectious disease, only one-tenth of all deaths among white males at ages 1 to 14 years were from accidents.[2]

22. What are the principal communicable diseases of childhood?

The principal communicable diseases of childhood are diphtheria, measles, scarlet fever, and whooping cough. Fifty years ago, these infections together accounted for one-quarter of all childhood deaths. Today, they account for less than 1 percent of all deaths at ages 1 to 14.

23. How many children are killed in accidents?

About 5,000 children aged 1 to 4 die every year from accidents of all kinds, and about 7,000 between the ages of 5 and 14.

24. What are the most frequent types of fatal accidents in childhood?

Motor vehicle accidents are the most frequent type of fatal accident in childhood. Burns, fires, and explosions also take a large toll, especially among girls; drownings are also an important factor, particularly among boys. Serious falls are all too frequent among boys and girls, and firearm accidents are not uncommon among school-age boys. Railroads take the lives of numerous school-age boys, as the tracks and yards are favorite places to congregate and play.

[2] See answer to Question 11 of Chapter 16, page 245.

In general, boys are more often involved in outdoor accidents than girls, but a great many fatal accidents to boys as well as girls occur in or around their homes. An appreciable number of small children are run over in their own yards and driveways.

25. How do the diseases of childhood differ from those of the other periods of life?

The leading diseases of childhood, with the exception of cancer, are infectious diseases, and most of them are acute rather than chronic. They come on quickly, often cause extremely high fevers, and usually are relatively short-lasting. In contrast, the major health problems of adult life are more and more becoming the chronic and degenerative diseases with gradual and uncertain onset, long course, and too often a fatal termination. Against many of the childhood diseases, either immunization or drug therapy can be used; against the chronic and degenerative diseases of later life, prevention appears at present to be the most effective weapon.

26. How frequent is illness in childhood?

According to the National Health Survey (1959–61), in the course of a year there was an average of close to four illnesses from acute conditions per child, and one-half of these cases were caused by acute respiratory diseases and more than one-tenth by injuries. Boys and girls had about the same average number of acute illnesses per year. Children under 5 averaged 13 days per year of restricted activity; those 5 to 14, 16 days, of which about half were bed-disability days.

27. What are the causes of most school absences?

The same National Health Survey reported that children 6 to 16 years of age lost an average of 8.4 school days during the year. Acute respiratory conditions were by far the most common, accounting for about 70 percent of the cases. Infectious, parasitic diseases were responsible for 15 percent, and injuries for about 5 percent of the cases.

Boys and girls, 6 to 16 years of age, missed about the same number of days from school because of illness and injury. Urban children missed a greater number of days than either rural nonfarm or rural farm children and, finally, children in families with incomes under

$4,000 per year had about the same average number of days lost from school as did children from higher income families.[3]

28. How much has childhood mortality from tuberculosis been improved?

Tuberculosis was one of the most common causes of death in childhood at the turn of the century. Children in families having other tuberculous members usually contracted the disease very easily and succumbed quickly, often to miliary or generalized tuberculosis infections. From 1900 to 1960 the tuberculosis death rate per 100,000 among children aged 1 to 4 was cut from 102 to 0.6, and among those aged 5 to 14 from 36 to 0.10. Although tuberculosis is still an important cause of death in childhood among the colored in certain areas, it is no longer a noteworthy health problem among white children in the United States.

29. How successful has the campaign against diphtheria been?

The campaign has been a highly successful one because ways of controlling the infection and immunization procedures were discovered early and were quickly put into use through widespread public health efforts. In the period 1911 to 1960, the death rates at ages 1 to 14 among children dropped to the vanishing point. Shortly before World War I, immunization of school children in large cities was begun, and by about 1934 the program had spread so widely that in New York City, for example, about half of the preschool children had been immunized. Many American cities have reported no deaths from diphtheria for at least five years. In 1962, only 33 deaths from diphtheria were reported among children under age 14 in the entire country.

30. What has been accomplished against measles?

The childhood death rate from measles has also been cut spectacularly. This disease which in earlier decades was a serious menace to young children has, like diphtheria, been virtually eliminated as a factor in mortality in the United States. It still plays an important role as a cause of disability; but here, too, much progress will be made as the newer methods of passive and active immunization against the disease are more generally applied.

[3] See answer to Question 15 of Chapter 19, page 300.

The disease is still an important cause of sickness and death in the less developed countries of the world.

31. What progress has been made against whooping cough?

Whooping cough mortality has long been declining, and in recent years has been cut about as sharply as that from diptheria and measles. Whooping cough is particularly hazardous to infants. In fact, the death rate from whooping cough in the first year of life is greater than for measles, scarlet fever, and diphtheria combined. It is a much more serious disease among the colored than among the white infants. Much of the credit for the drop goes to immunization, especially in infancy, but a great deal is also the result of better infant care.

32. What gains have been made against scarlet fever?

The reduction in mortality from scarlet fever has been greater than for any of the three other principal communicable diseases of childhood. Formerly responsible for thousands of childhood deaths each year, scarlet fever was reported as the cause of death of only 36 children in the whole country in 1962. The death rate among children aged 1 to 14 has actually dropped more than 99 percent. The relatively recent introduction of sulfa drugs and penicillin therapy for streptococcus infections has helped to speed the decline in scarlet fever mortality.

33. What has been the recent trend in acute poliomyelitis?

The recent trend in acute poliomyelitis is an extraordinary example of the effectiveness of modern preventive medicine. Only 15 years ago this disease seemed beyond control. While its causative viruses had been identified, there appeared to be no way then known by which pure cultures of the organisms could be obtained and grown in sufficient quantities to produce an effective immunizing agent. Then came the epoch-making discovery by Enders that the polio viruses could readily be grown in pure culture. This made it possible for Salk to produce his vaccine which, when widely applied to children, resulted in an immediate and marked reduction in the number of new cases and deaths. At the same time, a number of workers and, more particularly, Sabin, developed an attenuated live virus vaccine which taken orally confers an even more durable resistance to poliomyelitis infection.

The general adoption of these vaccines by health authorities throughout the world has brought about results nothing short of amazing. In 1962, the death rate from this condition dropped to 0.0 per 100,000 from 1.3 10 years earlier. The number of cases tell an equally dramatic story. In 1962 they had been reduced to 910. Only seven years earlier the number was 29,000, and in the pre-Salk period of 1950–54, the annual number of cases averaged close to 39,000.

34. How important is cancer in childhood?

Cancer, including leukemia and Hodgkin's disease, is now the second-ranking cause of death at ages 1 to 14. About 4,500 children under 15 years now die from these conditions each year in the general population of the United States. In 1960 the rate was about 11 deaths per 100,000 children at ages 1 to 4 years; it was 7 at ages 5 to 9, and about 6 at ages 10 to 14. The long-term increase in cancer deaths among children reflects in large part more accurate diagnosis, rather than a true increase in the incidence of the disease.

35. What are the common causes of physical handicaps in childhood?

It has been estimated that about 400,000 persons less than 21 years old are listed in the state registers of crippled children, and that a great many additional children are partially or totally crippled but not registered.

The leading cause of physical handicaps at the younger ages is poliomyelitis. Second is cerebral palsy, a condition which until recently has received little public attention, although it is not uncommon and those suffering from it can be greatly helped by proper care. Injuries also cause a number of orthopedic impairments. Clubfoot is not too infrequent as an impairment. Rickets, once a common complaint and the cause for much crippling, is now relatively rare because of improvements in knowledge about nutrition and advances in the standard of living.

36. What proportion of school children have health defects of any kind?

As already pointed out in the National Health Survey of 1959–61, there is a large problem of illness among children resulting from the high prevalence of the acute diseases and accidents among them. The report also showed high prevalence of the chronic infections and physical defects. Thus, it was found that 18 percent of the

children under 18 had at least one chronic condition and this is probably an understatement of the true situation. The most important of
these conditions were hay fever, asthma, and all the allergies (74.3
per 1,000) and sinusitis, bronchitis, and other respiratory diseases
(34.2 per 1,000). These two account for about one-half of all chronic
conditions reported. Other conditions include paralysis and orthopedic impairments, 26.3 per 1,000, ear impairments 6.5, speech defects 8.8, and heart disease 4.2.

These findings of the National Health Survey are confirmed by

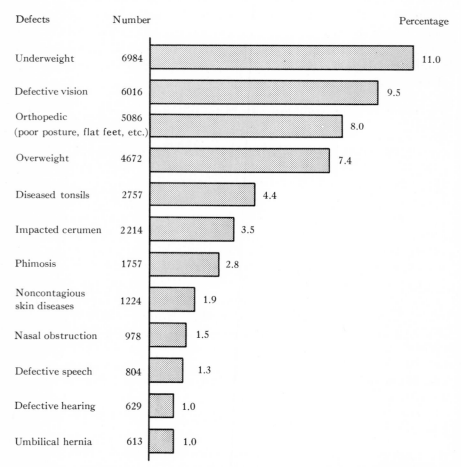

Defects	Number		Percentage
Underweight	6984		11.0
Defective vision	6016		9.5
Orthopedic (poor posture, flat feet, etc.)	5086		8.0
Overweight	4672		7.4
Diseased tonsils	2757		4.4
Impacted cerumen	2214		3.5
Phimosis	1757		2.8
Noncontagious skin diseases	1224		1.9
Nasal obstruction	978		1.5
Defective speech	804		1.3
Defective hearing	629		1.0
Umbilical hernia	613		1.0

Chart 16. **Leading causes of impairments among children in Philadelphia,
Penn., 1962–63.**

other reports on defects found in routine health examinations of school children in a number of cities. In Philadelphia, Penn., for example, where such examinations have been conducted for many years, the most recent report for the year 1962–63 showed that about 40 percent of the children have physical defects important enough to require prompt medical treatment. Aside from tooth, sight, and hearing defects, which might normally be expected to occur rather frequently, there were a large number of other more serious defects. Over 18 percent of the children were not at their proper weight with underweights greatly outnumbering the overweights. Poor posture, flat feet, and curvature of the spine were found in 8 percent of the children. Over 4 percent had diseased tonsils and a long list of other defects were recorded in decreasing proportions. (See Chart 16.)

37. How common are sight, hearing, and speech defects among school children?

In the Philadelphia report, referred to above, about one out of every nine children was found to have defective vision in one or both eyes. From other recent surveys much higher figures are reported. Hearing defects are much less common. In the regular physical examinations in Philadelphia, only about one out of every one-hundredth child was found to have hearing problems, although a special audiometer test showed much higher proportions. Speech problems were found in about 1 out of 100 school children.

38. Do most school children have a complete set of healthy teeth?

The condition of the teeth of our school children is definitely unsatisfactory even in high-income families. More than 95 percent of the children reaching the age of 15 have already experienced some decay in their permanent teeth. Moreover, these defects are not receiving the required attention. It has been estimated that the necessary dental work was being done at only about one-sixth the rate at which the defects occurred.

39. Has the stature of school children increased in the last generation or two?

Both boys and girls are now at least a couple of inches taller than they were at the end of the last century. As might be expected, today's taller children also weigh more.

40. What are the national organizations in the field of child health and welfare?

The principal professional organization whose specific interest is in child health is the American Academy of Pediatrics. A number of other professional health organizations have sections or standing committees concerned with various aspects of child health. These include the American Academy of General Practice, American Dental Association, American Medical Association, American Public Health Association, American Pediatrics Association, and the American Red Cross. The American School Health Association is the professional society of school doctors, nurses, and hygienists.

In addition, a number of lay organizations play an important role in various child health and welfare activities. Among these are the National Society for Crippled Children, the National Foundation, the Children's Welfare League of America, which emphasizes the institutional aspects of child care; the Family Welfare Association of America; the National Association for Retarded Children, and the National Child Welfare Division of the American Legion.

The voluntary lay organizations have been actively stressing the educational and emotional problems of childhood. The National Congress of Parents and Teachers has been prominent in the first area, and Child Study Association of America in the second. The latter publishes many books and pamphlets on child problems, and organizes counseling services, lectures, and study groups. Within communities there are, of course, dozens of local organizations whose primary concern is the welfare of children.

41. What are the government agencies in the field of child health and welfare?

The federal, state, and local governments all have agencies concerned with child health and welfare. Our Social Security Act has for nearly 20 years provided a program for aid to dependent children and also for money grants through the Children's Bureau to states for the improvement of their child health plans. The Children's Bureau studies child health and welfare, publishes reports, and suggests standards for child care. The school lunch program has become an important contribution to child health. In December 1960, the sixth White House conference on Children and Youth provided the occasion for a large gathering of those interested in child health and welfare to discuss various problems and to make recommendations for bettering the life of children. The United States Office of Education and the Public Health Service are also greatly concerned with child health. The Public Health Service has, in fact, adopted a very active role in the areas of children and school health. It has established a separate school health section in the division of Community Health Services with responsibility for research, consultation, and technical assistance, as well as certain aspects of health education. It has also established a new Institute of Child Health and Human Development to foster basic bio-medical research in the child health field.

Every state has a department of welfare, health, and education and most of these have special divisions devoted to children. Local city and town governments have a great variety of institutions dealing directly with children. The responsibility of the public for the health and well-being of children has become well established in law, even to the point where the state can take children away from their parents if it is thought necessary.

42. How extensive is the Government program for the protection of Infancy and Childhood?

In 1962, close to 3,000,000 children received assistance under the Aid to Families with Dependent Children Program. Federal aid to families with dependent children *alone* was over $1.33 billion. Federal expenditures for surplus food (much of which goes to children) was $226,900,000 in 1962. The school luncheon program served millions of children at a cost of over $300 million in federal funds. This hardly exhausts federal welfare payments and does not take into account any state or local monies. It is difficult to estimate the total federal child welfare expenditures as they are scattered through several departments. Certainly they must aggregate in excess of $2 billion annually.

43. What can schools do to improve the health of school children?

The nutrition, dental care, mental health, sight, and hearing of children require more attention. In this regard, teachers are in a particularly good position because of their close daily contact with children. Coordination between doctors, nurses, and teachers, and careful physical and dental examinations in schools can catch many health deficiencies before they develop too far. Teaching programs among the children can also promote a sense of responsibility for their own health and encourage good health habits.

Chapter 15

Our Old
People

1. Who are our old people?

The old are usually considered to be those who have reached or passed the age of 65. This is arbitrary. The changes in people's lives are continuous and progressive. No one wakes up on his sixty-fifth birthday to find himself completely different in mental and physical health from the day before, and no two people age in precisely the same way. Many are still fully capable of vigorous mental and physical activity until well into their seventies or eighties. Some show signs of aging and deterioration while still in their fifties. It is only for convenience and for statistical purposes that the period from 65 to the end of life is called old age. Too often it is a difficult time, but it can be an active and productive one with a quality all its own.

2. What is meant by "aging"?

In general, aging is change. It begins with life itself and is arrested only by death. In a more limited sense, *aging* may be considered as the physical and mental changes that take place in the years past the prime of life. There are a number of familiar signs of the aging process—the thinning and graying of the hair, and the drying and wrinkling of the skin. As people grow older, their vision and hearing decrease in acuity. At the same time, the functional efficiency of the body becomes diminished. The thickening and hardening of the arteries impede the circulation of blood and diminish nutrition to the vital organs. The heart, the blood vessels, and the kidneys gradually lose their elasticity and their ability to adapt themselves to the changing needs of the body, to withstand the stresses of living. The digestive tract and other systems of the body likewise show increasing degenerative changes.

The way in which any individual grows old is determined by the constitution he inherited and the accumulated experience he has had, including what Dr. Stieglitz called the "innumerable chemical, psychologic, and physical insults to which we are all subjected." Aging undoubtedly brings a blunting of many human faculties, but it is not necessarily a process of decline. Many of the decreased abilities are counterbalanced by gains in other fields. A loss in memory for detail, for example, may be accompanied by an improved ability to see the relationships between ideas. Aging is unavoidable, but instead of being feared it can be enjoyed, and often is.

3. How many old persons are there in the United States and what proportion of the population do they constitute?

According to the census of 1960, there were 16.6 million persons in the United States who were 65 years old or more. They made up a little over 9 percent of the total population. Of the old, more than six million were between 65 and 69 years of age; over four and one-half million between 70 and 74; and the remainder, more than five and one-third million were 75 or over. In 1964, as this is being written, there are about 18 million Americans in this age bracket of life.

4. Do we have proportionately more of the old than most countries?

The answer is yes. It is partly the proud result of the high standards of living and of health in the United States. The countries of Western Europe and the nations of the British Commonwealth also have fairly high proportions of their populations in the older age groups, while the opposite is the case in most of Asia, Africa, and South America. In parts of Europe, where the population has been growing very slowly (France is a good example), the proportion of aged is even higher than in the United States, about 12 percent.

5. In what sections of the country do most old people live?

There are striking differences in the concentration of old persons in different sections of the country. The old form the highest proportion of the total population in such long-settled New England states as Maine, New Hampshire, and Vermont, where one out of every nine persons is now at least 65. The lowest proportion is found in North and South Carolina and New Mexico. Our two newest states, Alaska and Hawaii, have minimal proportions of old people— 2.4 and 4.6 percent respectively. Both are rapidly growing areas, with a preponderance of young families. Southern California and Florida, partly because of their climate, have become favorites with the old and retired. In some places they have colonies heavily weighted with persons in their sixties, seventies, and eighties. In general, however, the South has relatively fewer elderly persons than any other part of the country. Small towns are popular with the aged, possibly because living costs there are comparatively low and because they provide the quiet atmosphere older persons need and deserve. On the whole, rural farm areas have the smallest proportion of the old, with a higher proportion in the cities and urban areas. There are exceptions, however. Iowa, Missouri, Nebraska, and Kansas have high proportions of the aged in spite of their extensive rural areas.

6. Is the proportion of old persons growing?

The aging of the population has been accelerated in the last few decades. The number of old people doubled in the last quarter century and is now increasing by about 500,000 a year. In 1900, those 65 years old and over constituted only about 4 percent of the population. By 1960, the figure was over 9 percent, at which level it appears to be stabilized.

7. What are the political and social implications of this progressive aging of our population?

The cost of providing for the retired, the chronically ill, or the just plain old will be an increasing burden for the country to bear as the proportion of old persons rises. The gap between what is done and what ought to be done will provide an obvious appeal for politicians and political parties. The more old there are, the more old voters there are, particularly more old women, to back up special welfare plans and to change the whole political outlook of the nation. The immediacy of this danger can be seen in the experience of California and some other states where the old have already made themselves a leading political force by organizing according to age instead of according to party or political lines. A sound and continuing effort on the part of present political groups to help meet the pressing needs of the old would unquestionably reduce the propaganda value of the extravagant old-age bonus schemes.

8. What are the principal factors responsible for the increase in the proportion of older people?

First is the extraordinary advance of medicine and public health work in the United States, cutting down mortality at the younger ages of life. The children's diseases have been largely eliminated as causes of death. Typhoid fever and, more recently, tuberculosis have practically been wiped out as factors in mortality. Even the pneumonia death rate has been reduced to a small fraction of what it was 50 years ago. The effect of these savings in lives has been to bring more and more people into the older age brackets.

Another factor has been the marked decline in the birth rate; between 1900 and 1960 it fell by one-third. It is true that we experienced an upswing in births in the war and postwar decade of the 1940's, but even at its recent peak the birth rate did not reach the level of before the first World War. A reduction in the relative number of children automatically means an increase in the relative size of the old-age group.

Finally, the drastic cut in immigration since 1924 has had a twofold effect on the proportion of our population who have reached old age. It not only did away with a major source of young adults but also added to the drop in the birth rate, because immigrants had formerly tended to raise large families.

As a combined result, therefore, of the control of disease, the decline in birth rate, and the cut in immigration, there has been a decided shift in the age distribution of the population. The proportion of young persons has diminished, and the proportion of the old has increased.

9. What proportion of the newborn may expect to reach old age?

Under present conditions of mortality, close to three-quarters of the newborn babies should live to their sixty-fifth birthday. With mortality conditions prevailing at the beginning of the century, only two-fifths of the newborn babies could have been expected to survive that long.

10. To how many additional years of life may persons aged 65 look forward?

The average number of years of life remaining for white men 65 years old is 13, and for white women of the same age it is 16. The more vigorous will probably live much longer than the average, and the average itself may increase as advances are made in medicine and public health. Old age is no brief period but one of considerable duration. It is a period which, because of its length, requires consideration in substantial and constructive terms.

11. Is the human life span increasing?

The outside limit to human life is uncertain, but authenticated cases of persons exceeding 100 years are extremely rare. The social and scientific forces which have increased the proportion of aged have not pushed back this rough limit of 100 years but have increased the number who more nearly approach it.[1] Many of the asserted centenarians, especially the extreme cases, have proved on careful examination to be spurious. The goal of geriatric medicine is not basically the extension of the human life span, but rather the improvement of health during life. Drs. G. M. Piersol and E. L. Bortz have expressed it well: "The society which fosters research to save human life cannot escape responsibility for the life thus extended. It is for science not only to add years to life, but more important, to add life to the years."

12. Has there been progress recently in reducing the mortality of the old?

There has been progress in reducing mortality even among persons 75 years old and over, but it has been much less spectacular than the gains made among the younger persons. Within the first half of this century, the mortality of those 75 and over has been cut by about

[1] See answer to Question 1 of Chapter 24, page 391.

one-fifth, but among those aged 5 to 14, the death rate has been reduced by more than four-fifths. Nonetheless, the decrease at the higher ages is a remarkable achievement.

13. What is the sex ratio among the old?

Old women outnumber old men. Even in 1870 there were more women aged 75 or over than there were men, although it was not until the census of 1940 that women outnumbered men at ages 65 to 74. The preponderance of women among the old is a result of the lower mortality of women than of men at every age. According to the 1960 census of the population, there were only 872 men for every 1,000 women aged 65 to 69; 848 men for every 1,000 women from 70 to 74; and 744 men for every 1,000 women aged 75 or more.

14. What are the main sources of income of the old?

The old receive their incomes in a variety of ways. Almost one-fourth receive their income from current employment, either as earners or wives of earners. About 60 percent receive an income under the old-age, survivors and disability program of our Social Security laws or under the Railroad Retirement scheme also operated by the government. The proportions with income under our veterans' program, Federal Civil Service Retirement, and other forms of federal benefits are relatively small. About one-seventh are being supported by public welfare funds. At present, pensions from private industry are providing some income to about 11 percent of the aged. To the sources of support just enumerated should be added such items as bank savings, life insurance benefits, government savings bonds, and various forms of current investment income.

15. What is the income of the aged?

In 1962 one-half of the married couples with one or both members aged 65 and over received an income of $2,875 or more. The corresponding figures for nonmarried men and women were $1,365 and $1,015. For those living in rural communities, the average money income was less. However, among the latter, income received in kind, such as farm products, may be an important source of support.

Payments under the old-age, survivors, and disability insurance program still are at a rather low average level, about $82 a month for a retired male worker with no dependents, about $63 for a retired female worker, and $129 for a retired worker and his aged wife.

16. What are the insurance benefits payable to the aged under the revised Social Security Act, and how are the amounts computed?

Monthly old-age insurance benefits are payable at age 62 to a retired insured worker and to the wife or dependent husband of the retired worker. Survivor benefits are paid at age 62 to a widow, dependent widower, and dependent parent. Benefits are also paid to a wife or widow at any age if she is caring for a child who is entitled to child's benefits, and to the worker's unmarried child under age 18 (or over 18 if the child was permanently and totally disabled before 18).

Full monthly benefits are payable in the case of widows, widowers, and dependent parents age 62 or over, but benefits to retired workers, wives, or dependent husbands are in actuarially reduced amounts if paid before age 65.

To qualify for benefit payments for himself and his dependents or survivors, a worker must have a specified amount of work in employment or self-employment covered by Social Security. The primary insurance benefit amount is based on the worker's average monthly earnings. A table in the law specifies a primary insurance amount for each average monthly earnings amount. For most workers the average monthly earnings are computed by adding up the worker's total covered earnings in a number of years specified in the law (generally from 1951 up to age 65 or 62 for women) and dividing by the number of months in those years. In computing this average, the five years of lowest earnings are omitted. The primary insurance amount is approximately 59 percent of the first $110 of average earnings and 21.4 percent of the next $290.

Benefits for dependents and survivors are figured as a percentage of the insured person's primary insurance amount. A wife, dependent husband, or child each receives 50 percent of the primary insurance amount; a widow, widower, or a single parent receives 82.5 percent. If two dependent parents are entitled to benefits they each receive 75 percent. A widow under age 62 who is caring for the worker's child and each surviving child receives 75 percent. The ceiling on total benefits payable to a family is $254 or 80 percent of the average monthly wage whichever is less. In no case, though, is the total family benefit less than one and one-half times the primary insurance amount.

The law provides that a person receiving benefits who has substantial amounts of earnings from work will have some or all of his and his dependents benefits withheld, depending on the amount of his earnings and how many months he works. However benefits are payable to persons age 72 or over regardless of their earnings.

Nearly 113 million persons had earnings credits at the beginning of 1963, of whom 91 million had worked long enough to be insured. In December 1963 about 62 million people (including members of the armed forces and railroad workers) were employed in covered jobs. Excluded from coverage were about four million federal, state, and municipal employees who have not been brought under OASDI but who had their own public retirement programs. In addition, it is estimated that at the beginning of 1964, nearly 24 million persons were covered by private retirement plans.

17. What is the nature of the old-age assistance plans under the Social Security Act?

Under the Social Security Act, federal funds are available to states to help them give assistance benefits to indigent persons aged 65 or older. Although the state assistance plans must meet certain federal requirements in order to receive social security grants, the states fundamentally control their own programs. There is a wide variation in the average benefit paid. In December 1963, the average monthly old-age assistance payments ranged from $112 in Minnesota to $39 in Mississippi. About 2.2 million persons received such assistance in December 1963.

18. What does the support and care of the elderly now cost the country each year?

The figure runs well up into the billions of dollars annually. In fiscal year 1963 payments under federal programs of benefits and services for persons 65 and over amounted to about $17 billion; over $13 billion from federal trust funds and $3.75 billion from federal general revenues to finance income-maintenance payments and medical care services.

There are, furthermore, the public assistance expenditures for the aged by the states and local jurisdictions (almost $1 billion in addition to federal grants) and their outlays for the care of the aged in hospitals, homes for the aged, and other institutions.

19. What are the benefits under the disability feature of the Social Security Act?

Under the disability provisions of the Social Security Act, an individual who is unable to work because of a physical or mental impairment that is expected to last indefinitely, or result in death, may receive a disability insurance benefit equal to the amount he would receive as an old-age benefit on retirement at 65. In addition, benefits are provided for dependents of the disabled as they are of the old-age beneficiaries.

In January 1964, a total of 1,456,000 persons (827,000 disabled workers and their dependents) were receiving benefits under this provision. The average monthly benefit paid to a disabled worker was about $91.

20. How are the aged housed?

In 1960, over 93 percent of the aged lived in households, either alone or with some other person, related or not. Almost four-fifths had some family life, in that they were living with someone related either by blood or marriage. Well over half were household heads.

Few communities have made even a beginning in providing the kind of housing old people require. For the most part, they are left to their own devices and they do not have the funds to meet the cost of the same. Many need special accommodations, and in a few large cities private philanthropy has led the way by making available apartment buildings designed specifically for the old. Quarters in these are supplied both for couples and single persons, who have privacy in their own apartments and social contacts with others of their own age in the dining and recreation rooms. There is a trained social worker at the apartment house, and medical and nursing care is provided when needed. Many of the old pay their own way, but those who can contribute only part or even nothing at all are on an equal footing with the paying residents. Unfortunately, few of these houses are in existence and the waiting lists are long.

21. What facilities are there for the care of the elderly disabled?

The old make up the largest group of patients in hospitals for the mentally ill and for those with chronic disease. Even among the patients in general and tuberculosis hospitals they constitute a much larger share than in the population as a whole. The shortage of hospital beds of all kinds in the country for the care of the aged sick is severe. At the beginning of 1960, there were only about 200,000 acceptable beds available in the United States for chronic patients (not counting tuberculosis and mental patients), according to reports received by the Public Health Service. At that time it was estimated that an additional 500,000 beds were needed. The shortage in facilities for care of the mentally ill was equally severe.

In the face of such a lack of institutional facilities, the largest measure of care for the old must obviously remain in the hands of the private physician. An important part can also be left to local voluntary health agencies working in cooperation with the medical professions. Experience indicates that a special type of institution is needed for the old and chronically ill, differing both from the custodial home and from the expensive general hospital. An interesting experiment conducted at Montefiore Hospital in New York indicates that many old persons who are ill and disabled can be well taken care of in their own homes and at less cost than in the hospital. This scheme requires an organized service of physicians, visiting nurses, housekeepers, and social workers. Although such home-care plans might help relieve some of the hospital bed shortage and cut down the waiting time for those who do require hospitalization, they do not change the general picture of an overwhelming shortage of facilities to care for those who are old and sick.

22. What is the frequency of invalidity and disability among the aged?

Invalidism and disability increase rapidly with age. The National Health Survey, 1959–60, showed that while 21 percent at ages 55 to 64 were unable to carry on their usual activity, the percentage increased to 36 at ages 65 to 74 and to 55 percent at ages 75 and over. Disabling sickness also lasts longer among the aged. The average number of bed-disability days per person was 6.7 at all ages combined, but 10.8 days for those 65 to 74 years, and 18.6 days for those 75 years and over.

23. What are the leading causes of death among the old?

Diseases of the heart are by far the most important and together account for over 46 percent of all deaths among those 65 and over.

Cerebral hemorrhage, with over 15 percent is second, and cancer is third as a cause of death, accounting for 14 percent of the total. Then follow accidents with 2.5 percent, and nephritis with 0.6 percent. These five causes account for practically four-fifths of the deaths among the aged.

24. What are the principal illnesses among the aged?

In a family survey, it was observed that over 30 percent of the aged suffered for a day or more from a respiratory condition in the course of a year. Almost 25 percent had a degenerative disease causing illness for at least one day and about 12.5 percent were sick at some time from a digestive condition. Six percent suffered from a rheumatic or related condition, almost 3 percent from a skin disease, and 2 percent from a nervous disease. Over 8 percent were ill a day or more because of accidental injuries. It is worth noting that many of these common illnesses among the aged are not prominent as causes of death.

25. How does illness in the old differ from that in the young?

In youth, most diseases are sudden in onset and short in duration. They are most often ascribable to some specific cause, such as bacteria or virus, ordinarily introduced from outside the body. And in a great many cases, the course of disease in the young might be compared to the outline of a mountain, rising to a peak and then falling off again rapidly. Many of the diseases of youth are limited by the immunization which the body automatically builds up against them.

In old age, disease is likely to be very different in many respects. Most ailments in later life are long drawn out; they come on slowly and gradually; their cause is often obscure. Frequently, ailments in old age are the result of a number of hidden factors which produce great individual variation in the symptoms and in the course of the disease. Instead of building to a peak and then falling off, illness in later life is more likely to be unnoticed at onset, very gradual in progression, and to be of such a nature that the body cannot build up an immunity to it.

26. Do the diseases of old age have their origin in earlier periods of life?

According to Dr. Edward J. Stieglitz, "All these disorders begin silently. . . . They exist, frequently, for years, before they are grossly detectable. Though the incidence of *discovered* cases of vascular diseases rises sharply after forty years of age, the changes started years earlier. These are fifth column diseases, silent saboteurs. To be discovered early, they must be searched for."

27. Can the disabilities of the aged be postponed or controlled?

Many of them can. Diabetes, for example, when diagnosed early and treated properly, results in practically no disability, and the onset of complications may be postponed. Likewise, some of the other chronic diseases can be controlled if detected soon enough, although few of them can be cured. Even high blood pressure, hardening of the arteries, and arthritis can be arrested if they are discovered in time and are properly taken care of. Control of chronic disease often requires adjustments in the living habits of the individual; it is not merely a matter of taking medicine.

28. How important to the health of older people is the maintenance of proper weight?

Probably no other physical factor is more important in controlling the chronic diseases of old age as maintenance of proper weight. Contrary to common belief, it is not normal to continue to gain weight steadily throughout life. At age 25, structural growth has usually ceased. After that, putting on weight above the level required for a person's particular body build is likely to impair health and even to shorten life. Diabetes and many of the circulatory diseases are much more frequent among overweights than among persons of proper weight. Habit may keep old persons eating the same size meals they needed when young, despite the fact that age has reduced their activities and therefore their food and energy requirements. The old saying that many people dig their graves with their teeth has a lot of truth in it.

29. Is mental disease found more frequently among the aged than the young?

Mental disease is much more common among the old than among those at other periods of life, but it is not true that all mental diseases increase in incidence with age. Senile psychosis and psychosis from cerebral arteriosclerosis are by nature primarily diseases of later life. On the other hand, schizophrenia, the most common form of functional psychosis (as distinguished from psychosis having organic cause), has its peak of onset in early adult life. Manic-depressive psychosis may come on at almost any age, but particularly between 20 and 60. The highest rate of first admissions to mental hospitals is among the old. Practically no young children are hospitalized for mental illness. This does not mean that children are immune to mental disease, but rather that the diseases are usually not diagnosed until later, and also that young children are normally more easily treated and can frequently be cared for without hospitalization.

30. What are the common emotional problems of the elderly?

A lonesome and unwanted feeling is the most common emotional problem of the elderly. As one gets older, the circle of friends and associates is reduced by death and the normal changes of residence typical of our time, and activities are of necessity curtailed. Modern industry and business have a tendency to retire the old worker. The modern family, especially in the city, also has little room for the older generation. Statistics cannot measure the meaning of aging in these terms, but the unhappiness brought on by feeling rejected is certainly a fundamental aspect of all the problems of old age. It is difficult even to save the life of a sick old man who would just as soon die as not. No government can make up for the feeling of having been left behind by life. It is the common fact of rejection by business and by family which so often and so seriously affects the old.

31. Are the old often unjustifiably placed in mental institutions?

Almost one-quarter of the patients admitted for the first time to mental institutions are suffering from senile psychosis or psychosis resulting from arteriosclerosis. Since these diseases are largely incurable, these patients are seldom discharged. Many of these older inmates of mental hospitals are not insane but are rather forgetful, irresponsible, and often unable to take care of themselves. Most general hospitals will not accept such patients, and the private nursing homes which do are beyond the financial means of the majority of the old and of their families. Keeping a senile person in a small household is a chore and a responsibility not many families wish to undertake. As a result, the senile are too frequently committed to mental institutions because there is no other place for them to go. There is great need for a new type of institution for the care of such old and senile patients. These would be well served in smaller nursing home type of establishments where they could be cared for

by kindly disposed but not necessarily professionally trained personnel, more like practical nurses with good professional nursing and
medical supervision.

32. Do many of the older workers do well?

In one survey of industrial concerns, three-quarters said that
older workers produced as much as younger workers, and in another
study the majority of companies said the older workers turned out a
better quality of work. One precision instrument firm in New York
State, for example, has a policy of hiring older men and even trains
them for new jobs. A gun company headed by a president past 75
also makes a practice of employing older people. Most firms, whether
or not they do have large groups of old men and women working
for them, concede that the old are more loyal than the young. In
general, they are also likely to be more thorough and careful, and
often have knowledge and skill that only many years of experience
can build. What they have lost in speed they have made up in accuracy of performance.

That age does not necessarily put an abrupt stop to usefulness is
illustrated by the lives of innumerable famous men and women who
have made important contributions to society after passing 65. Scientists like Bertrand Russell and Linus Pauling, the Nobel Prize
winners, statesmen like Harry Truman, and Gen. Eisenhower; and
many of the current leaders in all fields are old men chronologically
but still young productively.

33. Do older workers have more accidents than younger ones?

Contrary to the general impression, old workers are not more
likely to have accidents than their younger associates. A study by
the Bureau of Labor Statistics showed that the industrial accident
rates for the old were below those for the working population as a
whole, and that the average length of disability from industrial accidents was nearly the same for older workers as for all workers. The
worst accident records were made by young workers still in their
teens or early twenties.[2]

34. Are absences because of illness more common among the old than the young?

The U.S. National Health Survey, 1959–60, indicates that the
average number of work-loss days per person per year increases with

[2] See answer to Question 12 of Chapter 16, page 245.

age for both male and female workers. The annual number of days lost per person for medical reasons increases sharply with age. With their greater burden of illness, the aged have fewer resources to fall back upon. Their smaller incomes cannot in general provide for the medical and hospital care they need. This is why medical aid for the aged is so pressing a problem for solution.

35. How are current pension plans both an aid and a threat to the elderly?

Pensions provided by industrial retirement plans are an important aid to the old. However, the requirement written into so many plans that workers quit at the age of 65 may be a handicap to the elderly who seek employment. Finding work is hard enough in normal times, even for younger persons, but the man past 65 often faces strong prejudice against him. In fact, many surveys show that the age prejudice begins to be important around 40. Such prejudice could be mitigated if arrangement could be made for insured workers to carry with them into their new jobs the value of the pension accrued in their previous jobs. The loss of useful activity is a threat not only to a person's morale but also to his mental and physical health.

36. How widespread are private pension and retirement plans in American industry?

About 26,000,000 of the working population of the country are covered by some pension plan, either insured or uninsured, and there are about 23,000 such private retirement plans. There is no question that retirement plans are growing at a tremendous pace and that, properly set up, they are a boon to the welfare of the aged.

37. What can be done to stimulate employment of the elderly?

The biggest part of the job is in public relations. Business does not hire out of charity. It must be convinced that it will be able to operate profitably with a greater proportion of older workers. This requires surveys of the available skills and aptitudes of old workers, and also of the jobs in different industries for which the old are best suited. Small scale demonstrations with old workers have proved valuable. Every old and still useful man who leaves work reduces the nation's productivity and at the same time requires added work on the part of others for his support.

38. What can the community do about the old?

The first and basic step toward helping the old is to take an interest in them. This is where the local community has its chance. Many of the old are self-reliant, and others are well cared for by their families. Some may need special attention. All, however, would gain by having the town or city where they live concerned with their welfare.

Care for the old requires, of course, an organization or perhaps a number of them. Use of the skills and advice of the old will usually result in many improvements in the community, so that helping to solve the problems of old age will not be a one-way affair.

39. What part can health officers play in serving the older population?

The local health officer is the logical coordinator of the activities of voluntary health groups, the medical professions, and the various federal and state health agencies. The chief causes of death today are the conditions affecting middle and old age. In working with the old, therefore, the health officer will also be dealing with some of his major health problems.

One of the most urgently needed steps is to set up a system for early diagnosis of the chronic diseases before they result in serious disability. In some places (Massachusetts and New York City, for example) a start in this direction has already been made in cooperation with the Public Health Service. Large-scale detection drives probably require the help of the state health bodies, but the local health officer is the one who will have the responsibility for most of the chronic cases which are discovered. With the progressive aging of the population, the health problems of the old will inevitably take a larger share of the work of the local health department.

40. Can the individual better prepare himself for old age?

The individual himself can help avoid many of the troubles of old age by preparation in advance. Regular medical examination through the adult years of life could mean that chronic disease, if it developed, would be lessened in amount and in severity. Planned savings to supplement Social Security benefits and pensions could bring financial self-sufficiency. The development, during earlier life, of interests and hobbies could make the period of old age not only busy but also useful and satisfying.

The personnel departments of industry could help older workers in preparing for retirement. The larger companies might even have old-age counselors to arrange classes for those in their sixties or earlier. Clubs might be organized for the development of hobbies and special skills. Communities might also provide old-age counseling as part of their welfare and recreational services. Some have already proved the value of such efforts.

41. Have the old at times been discarded as well as looked up to?

In different civilizations old age has been reviled or revered, and the old eaten or made rulers. Primitive cultures have often found that death was the quickest solution to the problem of persons too old to work or fight. Eating the aged was even said at times to prove reverence for them. The Fiji Islanders, afraid of losing their physical strength, used to commit suicide when they thought old age was creeping up. In the Gran Chaco there once was a custom requiring the son to strike down his father before the father became weak.

Greece and Rome were divided on the subject of the old. Some poets wrote of the fear of aging and the worthlessness of life in old age. Solon, on the other hand, said (when over 60) that life ought to continue until 80. In Sparta and Athens the old were given positions of great esteem and importance. In Rome for a while there was a saying, "To the bridge with the men of 60," meaning dispose of the worthless old men. In contrast, however, was the Roman senate, a body of old men supposedly picked for their wisdom.

Certainly in this country the aged have often been looked up to. Seven presidents were past their sixtieth birthday when they took office, and two score Supreme Court Justices have been appointed when at least that old.

42. Why are the old important to society?

The importance of the old is not be measured by their numbers. Their experience and wisdom can help stabilize the social order. Naturally conservative, they balance the venturesome spirit of youth. Their accumulated knowledge can provide guidance for the state. They can be a uniting and strengthening force in family life, adding continuity and the feeling of being rooted. The way in which a society treats its old is a good indicator of its sense of responsibility and its breadth of vision.

Chapter 16

The Accident
Toll

1. What do accidents cost the nation in life, limb, and money?

Accidents take an appalling toll of life, limb, and money in the United States. In 1963, more than 100,000 persons were killed and about 10 million injured seriously enough to become disabled for one day or more. Not far from two million of the injured required hospitalization. It is a sobering thought that every three seconds somewhere in the United States someone is injured more or less seriously, and every five minutes someone is killed in an accident. The money cost has been estimated at more than $16 billion annually. This includes loss in wages, medical expense, overhead cost of insurance, property damage in motor vehicle accidents, fire losses, and other direct and indirect costs.

241

2. Is life safer today than it was a generation ago?

In spite of the large losses from accidents recorded annually, life in our country is safer now than it was a generation ago. In relation to the size of our growing population, the number of deaths from accidents has been declining. The death rate from this cause in 1963 was about 52 per 100,000 population. Around 1910, the accident death rate averaged about 80 per 100,000. If the situation of 1910 had continued without change, accidents would currently claim over 50,000 additional lives each year among the American people.

3. What proportion of all deaths are due to accidents?

Accidents account for 5.5 percent of the total deaths in the United States each year. Of the 1,756,729 deaths from all causes in 1962, 97,139 were due to accidents of all kinds.

4. How does mortality from accidents compare with that from the natural causes?

Accidents rank fourth among the leading causes of death. Only diseases of the heart, cancer and other malignant tumors, and cerebral hemorrhage take a greater number of lives. Ranking below accidents are such major causes of death as diseases of early infancy, pneumonia and influenza, arteriosclerosis, and diabetes mellitus.

5. Where do most accidents occur?

Home accidents cause by far the largest number of nonfatal injuries. More than two-fifths of the 10 million disabling injuries and one-fourth of the fatalities due to accidents are caused by mishaps in and around the home.

6. What types of accidents cause the greatest number of fatalities?

Motor vehicles cause over two-fifths of all accidental fatalities. Falls are second in importance, accounting for another one-fifth of the total. Burns, which rank third, are the cause in about 1 in 12 accidental fatalities. Next in order of importance are drownings.

The causes of nonfatal accidents for the country are not fully known. A recent National Health Survey of comparatively serious nonfatal injuries showed that falls accounted for over one-quarter and motor vehicle accidents for about 7 percent of all injuries. Cutting and piercing instruments and burns are also responsible for relatively large numbers of serious injuries.

7. Are more males than females killed in accidents?

The adventuresome male has more than twice the chances of the female of being killed by accident. In 1962, the accident death rates for males and females were 72.3 and 32.9 per 100,000, respectively. Few causes of death record as wide a difference in the death rates for the two sexes. Moreover, the mortality rate from accidents is higher among males than among females at each age period from birth up to 85 years; after that, the situation is reversed. The difference is greatest at ages 15 to 24, where the accident death rate for males is five times that for females. The greatest excess male mortality, as

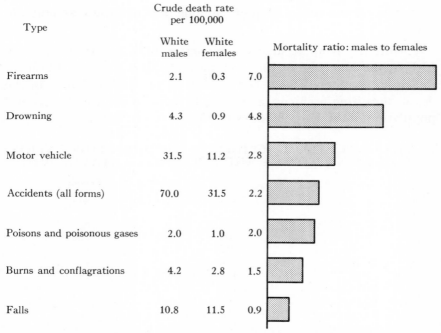

Type	Crude death rate per 100,000			Mortality ratio: males to females
	White males	White females		
Firearms	2.1	0.3	7.0	
Drowning	4.3	0.9	4.8	
Motor vehicle	31.5	11.2	2.8	
Accidents (all forms)	70.0	31.5	2.2	
Poisons and poisonous gases	2.0	1.0	2.0	
Burns and conflagrations	4.2	2.8	1.5	
Falls	10.8	11.5	0.9	

Chart 17. **Sex ratio of mortality from specified types of accidents, white persons, United States, 1962.**

one would expect, is found in mishaps which arise largely out of occupational activities and is most marked in mining, agriculture, air and railroad transportation accidents. The types of accidents associated in large part with sports and recreational activities are also much more common among males than among females. This is particularly true of firearms accidents and drownings. Of all the main types of accidents, falls alone show a lower death rate for males than for females, but the difference is not marked. (See Chart 17.)

8. Are more males than females injured in accidents?

Accidental injuries disabling for a day or more are one and one-half times as frequent among males as among females, according to the findings of the National Health Survey of the U.S., July 1959–June 1961. Disabling injuries occurred at the rate of 301 per 1,000 males and 212 per 1,000 females. However, the male excess was found only at ages under 65. It was most marked at ages 15 to 24 years, when the male rate was two and one-half times the female rate. At ages 65 and over, the rate for females exceeded that for males by about 20 percent.

9. Are accidents more frequent among the old than among the young?

Mortality from accidents is highest in old age. It is also very high in the first year of life. Among males and females, the death rate from accidents is lowest at ages 10 to 14. The variation in the death rates from accidents according to age and sex for the general population of the United States in 1960 is shown below.

DEATH RATES FROM ACCIDENTS PER 100,000 POPULATION, ACCORDING TO AGE AND SEX, UNITED STATES, 1960

Age	Total	Male	Female
All ages	52.3	72.8	32.4
Under 1 year	93.2	103.0	83.0
1–4	31.6	35.9	27.2
5–14	19.3	26.6	11.7
15–24	56.0	93.0	19.7
25–34	43.0	72.0	15.1
35–44	40.9	65.8	17.2
45–54	49.8	77.6	22.7
55–64	59.0	88.2	31.5
65–74	88.1	119.8	60.6
75–84	214.5	236.4	197.5
85 years and over	624.7	581.9	652.1

In the above study of nonfatal accidental injuries disabling for a day or more, the frequency of injuries was highest among males at ages 17 to 24. Among females there was a peak at ages 6 to 16, but the rate was highest at age 0 to 5.

10. What age is the safest from fatal accidents?

Among members of insured wage earners' families, most of whom live in urban areas, accident fatality rates are at a minimum at ages 8 to 12 years. At age 11 the chance of sustaining a fatal accidental injury is less than at any other time of life.

11. What types of accidents are most frequent in childhood?

Among infants, two types of fatal accidents are of particular importance—mechanical suffocation by bed clothes, pillows, etc., and obstruction, suffocation, or puncture by ingested objects. These two causes account for two-thirds of all accidental deaths among the children under one. At ages one to four, when youngsters begin to play in and around the home, the pattern of fatal accidents changes. Among these preschool children, motor vehicle mishaps outnumber all other types of fatal accidents and account for close to one-third of the total. Burns and scalds contribute about one-fifth and drownings one-seventh of the deaths.

Within the school ages 5 to 14 years, motor vehicle accidents contribute about two-fifths of the accidental deaths and drownings about one-fifth. Injuries by firearms, burns and conflagrations are other significant types of accidents among these youngsters. At ages 15 to 24, motor vehicle fatalities account for more than half the total number of accidental deaths; drownings, next in importance, make up one-ninth of the total. Firearm accidents are also an important element in the accident mortality at these ages.[1]

12. What types of accidents are most frequent in early maturity, in midlife, and in old age?

In early maturity (ages 25 to 44), motor vehicle accidents cause over one-half of all accident fatalities. Other important types of accidents are drowning, air transportation, falls, burns, railroad accidents, and firearms. At ages 45 to 64, motor vehicle accidents account for more than two-fifths of all accidental deaths, and falls for about one-sixth. Burns, drownings, and railroad accidents are also significant causes of death at these ages.

In old age, ages 65 and over, falls are by far the leading cause of accidental death, accounting for about 55 percent of all such fatalities. Motor vehicle accidents cause 30 percent of such deaths.

13. Are fatal accidents more frequent in summer than in winter?

The summer season is consistently the most hazardous time of the year. In 1962, a typical year, there was a daily average of 284 accidental deaths during the months of June, July, and August. In

[1] See answer to Question 24 of Chapter 14, page 215.

the spring months the average daily death toll was at a minimum, 252 per day. The averages for fall and winter were 269 and 261 deaths per day, respectively.

14. Are fatal accidents more frequent in urban than in rural areas?

Our information on this score for the country as a whole is very unreliable because of the recent change in the definition of "urban" and "rural." Older data suggested that urban areas had higher accidental death rates than rural. The indications are that this condition has persisted and has, in fact, become even more pronounced.

15. What part of the country has the highest mortality from accidents?

Accident prevention is an important public health problem everywhere in the United States. The most populous states, as might be expected, are the heaviest contributors to the national toll of about 100,000 lives taken annually by accident, and, from that point of view, have the greatest problem. Many of the smaller states, however, contribute far more heavily in proportion to their population than do the larger ones. Nevada, a state with one of the smallest populations, oddly enough, has by far the highest accident fatality rate, whereas New York State has one of the lowest.

The Mountain states have consistently recorded the highest accidental death rates. For the most part, the states with the lowest rates lie along the northern part of the Atlantic seaboard.

16. What do home accidents cost the nation?

Accidents in and about the home in 1963 claimed about 29,000 lives. It is estimated, moreover, that injuries in or about the home account for close to half of the approximately 10,000,000 persons who are more or less seriously injured in accidents each year. Wage loss, medical expense, and overhead costs of insurance attributed to home accidents amount to about $1,150,000,000 annually.

17. What types of fatal home accidents are most frequent among men and women?

Falls are by far the leading cause of fatal injury among both males and females, according to a survey of fatal home accidents in a limited area of the country. About 70 percent of the accidental deaths among females and 45 percent of the accidental deaths among males resulted from falls. Fire accounted for 12 percent of the deaths among females and for 15 percent of the deaths among males. Suffocation and strangulation was the third largest cause of accidental death for both sexes, accounting for 8 percent of the female deaths, and for 13 percent of male deaths. The fourth most important cause of accidental death among females was poisoning. Among males, firearm accidents in the home were fourth but closely following were gas poisoning fatalities.

18. Are more women than men killed in home accidents?

Surprising as it may seem, the death rate from accidents occurring in and around the home is higher among men aged 15 to 64 years than among women of these ages. In fact, the male death rate at these ages was higher by about 50 percent according to a study of home accident fatalities among insured members of wage earners' families. After age 65 women have much the higher home accident death rate.

19. What types of fatal home accidents are most frequent among children of preschool age and of school age?

Among children under five years, the most common cause of fatal accidents in the home is mechanical suffocation, with the injury being ascribed usually to pillows or bedclothes or to overlaying. In 1962, about 6,000 preschool children were killed in home accidents, and about 1,300 of them, virtually all less than one year old, died as a result of mechanical suffocation. However, in the opinion of some medical investigators, unrecognized respiratory conditions underlie a large number of deaths that are certified as due to mechanical suffocation. Not far behind in number are deaths from burns and scalds; conflagrations and scalding due to upsetting or falling into hot liquids cause most of these deaths. Falls, drownings, and ingestion of poison-containing compounds are also responsible for a large number of home accident deaths among young children.

At the school ages from 5 to 14 years, burns and conflagrations head the list of causes of accidental death in the home. These two types of accidents together account for about 650 of the approximately 1,400 fatal home injuries among school children. Firearm accidents and falls are also important causes of death at that period of life.[2]

[2] See answers to questions 12, and 24 of Chapter 14, pages 212 and 215.

20. In what part of the home do most fatal accidents occur?

More persons are fatally injured in the bedroom than in any other part of the house. According to one study which covered only a limited area of the country, 32 percent of all accidental deaths in the home occurred in the bedroom, 14 percent in the yard, 13 percent on stairs, 12 percent in the kitchen, and 7 percent in the living room. The bathroom, the dining room, and the porch each was the scene of 4 percent of the injuries.

Another study, based on the mortality of a group of industrial insurance policyholders aged 15 to 69 years, showed that one-fourth of those who lost their lives in home accidents were killed in the bedroom. Half of the fatal injuries in the bedroom were caused by poisonous gases and conflagrations often originating in other areas of the house, including the kitchen. Among women, the kitchen was the scene of the second largest number of fatal injuries, accounting for about one-fifth of their home accidents. Only a slightly smaller proportion of insured women were fatally injured on stairs and steps.

Among insured men, second in importance as the scene of fatal home accidents are the stairs or steps, where more than 20 percent of the total occurred. Accidents in areas around the house—the backyard, the garden, and the driveway—accounted for 15 percent of the deaths among men; and accidents in the kitchen for 10 percent.

21. What object or agency causes the greatest number of falls in the home?

More than one-third of all falls in home accidents occurred on stairs or steps, according to one study. About 15 percent of the falls took place on floors, while falls on walks or on the ground outside the house contributed almost as much. Next in importance were falls over objects—chairs, toys, loose boards, etc., not on stairs—and falls from chairs or tables.

22. What agency causes the greatest number of burns in the home?

Steam, hot water, and other hot liquids are the most important causes of serious accidental burns in the home. According to a study of hospitalized cases, about two out of every five burns sustained in home accidents result from scalding. Burns of this type are especially common among children under five.

Burns by gasoline or other flammable liquids are second in importance, one-sixth being so classified. Most of these accidents occurred among adults who used gasoline for cleaning purposes, or used kerosene to hasten a fire in the stove.

Burns resulting from contact with stoves, pipes, or radiators made up 8 percent of the total; matches 7 percent; and lye and other chemicals 5 percent.

Virtually all the victims of burns due to matches were children under 15 years of age.

23. What poisons most frequently cause death?

In 1963 alone, about 2,000 people lost their lives as a result of accidental poisoning by solids or liquids ingested in the home or elsewhere. The leading poison was barbituric acid and its derivatives. Wood and denatured alcohol, which three decades ago caused more deaths than any other poison, is now second in importance. Lye and potash ranked third, followed by arsenic and its compounds. Nux vomica and strychnine, which as recently as the late 1930's were the cause of 100 deaths annually, are now of minor importance.

Among very young children, oil of wintergreen (methyl salicylate), a liniment used in many American homes, and kerosene are relatively important causes of fatal accidental poisoning.

24. What do motor vehicle accidents cost the nation?

In recent years, motor vehicle accidents have killed well over 40,000 persons and injured about 1,500,000 seriously enough to disable them for a day or more. Over 40 percent suffered bed-disabling injuries, some of which are completely crippling. The estimated annual money cost of motor vehicle accidents is in the neighborhood of $7.5 billion. This includes well over $2.6 billion in property damage.

As many as 9.5 million motor vehicle accidents involve property damage only each year.

25. Is the motor vehicle toll increasing?

There are many indications that the intensive campaign to control the heavy loss of life from motor vehicle accidents is meeting with a small measure of success. Between 1950 and 1963, the traffic death rate dropped for a number of years and, more recently, returned to about the earlier level. On the basis of miles traveled, however, there is a more favorable picture, the rates per 100,000,000 vehicle miles having declined from 7.6 deaths in 1950 to 5.3 in 1962. The national toll of over 40,000 lives a year is about the same as in 1941, despite the marked increase both in population and in vehicle mileage.

26. Are more pedestrians than riders killed in motor vehicle accidents?

Each year, about one-fifth of those killed in motor vehicle accidents are pedestrians or cyclists; the rest are drivers and the passengers they carry in their cars at the time of the accident.

27. Of the pedestrians killed in motor vehicle accidents, what proportion are old people?

About one-third of all pedestrians who lose their lives in motor vehicle accidents are 65 years of age or over, although they account for only 9 percent of the population.

28. Of the riders killed in motor vehicle accidents, what age group contributes the largest proportion of deaths?

One-fifth of the drivers killed in motor vehicle accidents are between ages 20 and 24 years. These are also the ages with the largest proportion of passenger deaths, but the age group 15 to 19 years is not far behind.

29. Are there more motor vehicle fatalities in urban than in rural areas?

More than two and one-half times as many people are killed in motor vehicle traffic accidents in rural areas than in urban areas, despite the fact that traffic volume is estimated to be approximately the same for both. Four-fifths of the drivers and passengers killed in motor vehicle accidents meet death in rural areas. On the other hand, less than half of the pedestrian fatalities occur in rural areas, that is, in places having fewer than 2,500 inhabitants.

30. At what season of the year are deaths from motor vehicle accidents most frequent?

Quite consistently, the death toll from motor vehicle accidents is highest in late fall and early winter. In recent years, August has been the heaviest month for these fatal accidents with close to 10 percent of the annual toll. October, November, and December approach closely the record for August.

31. On which day of the week and on what holidays do most motor vehicle accident fatalities occur?

Motor vehicle accident deaths are most frequent on Saturday, with Sunday running a close second. These two days together contribute approximately two-fifths of the accidents with fatal outcome. Holidays also are marked by a high toll of motor vehicle fatalities. Christmas Day, or one of the two days preceding it, usually is found to have the worst record for the year. New Year's Day also ranks high.

32. Do young drivers have the worst motor vehicle accident record?

The available estimates indicate that drivers under age 25 have by far the highest rate of involvement in motor vehicle accidents. These estimates, however, do not take account of the amount and kinds of driving done by persons at different ages.

33. Are men safer drivers than women?

There is no satisfactory answer to this question, since available statistical information is very limited. It is true enough that 8 out of 10 drivers involved in motor vehicle accidents are men, but men also spend a far greater time in driving. Besides, the kinds of driving are radically different for men and women. These and other factors must be taken into account before it can be said with any assurance which one of the sexes makes the better driver.

34. How many persons are killed and injured in occupational accidents each year?

The accident toll in industry in 1963 was around 14,000 killed and nearly 2,000,000 injured. Of these injured, 1,750,000 required bed care. About 80,000 of the nonfatal injuries each year result in permanent impairments, and about 1,900 of these are totally disabling.

35. How many working days are lost to industry each year because of occupational accidents?

The actual time lost by workers injured in occupational accidents each year totals about 40,000,000 days. In addition, about 195,-000,000 man-days are lost because of accidents by workers other than those injured. This figure includes such items as time lost by those who help the injured person, or who stop to discuss the accident, temporary reduction in the efficiency of persons witnessing serious accidents, and suspension of work caused by damaged equipment. These figures alone do not measure the entire cost to the economy in lost production due to occupational accidents in one year. Allowance should also be made for the effects on future production of the years of working life lost by men killed in occupational accidents and for the diminished working capacity of those who suffer permanent disabling injuries. The production time lost each year because of fatal and permanently disabling occupational injuries is around 8,000,000 man-days.

The money cost of occupational injuries to the nation in one year is estimated at more than $5 billion by the National Safety Council.

36. What are the most hazardous industries?

The very highest recorded mortality rates among the common occupations are found where there is a combination of a high probability of accidents and exposure to dusts which contain a very large percentage of free silica. This situation is found in some hard-rock mining, such as gold, silver, copper, and especially lead and zinc mining. American insurance company studies indicate that the mortality in these occupations is more than three times that of white-collar workers.

37. Are more workers killed on the job than off the job?

On the average, one worker is fatally injured at work for more than two killed off the job. In 1962, about 13,700 workers were killed in accidents on the job and about 30,000 in accidents off the job.

38. What are the chief types of occupational accidents?

Falling, sliding, or moving objects are the most common cause of injury in industry. Accidents of this type caused more than one-quarter of all occupational injuries according to one study of occupational injuries made by the National Health Survey, 1959–61. The type of accident in which workers are caught in, on, or between machines or objects accounted for 13.5 percent of all injuries; slips and overexertion for 15.8 percent.

39. Do impaired workers have more accidents than unimpaired workers?

If placed intelligently, the impaired are no more likely to experience disabling work injuries than the unimpaired, according to the statistical findings of a recent study. According to this survey, the injury frequency per million exposure hours was 8.9 for the impaired workers, compared with 9.5 for unimpaired workers exposed to the same hazards.

The study also showed that the average time lost as the result of disabling injuries was somewhat less among the impaired than among their unimpaired co-workers. Further, it was noted that there was a very marked similarity in the kinds of injuries experienced in the two groups. The injuries experienced were related to the hazards of the particular job, not to a proneness on the part of the impaired person to certain kinds of injury.[3]

40. Has the safety movement in industry been successful?

The safety movement in industry has been remarkably successful. Particularly noteworthy are the achievements of the railroads and the iron and steel companies in cutting down the accident toll among their employees. In 1889, 1 railroad employee in every 357 was killed in an accident arising out of his work; in 1949, the figure had dropped to 1 in every 2,776 employees, in 1962, only 1 in every 3,503 employees. In a select group of iron and steel establishments which had consistently carried on a positive safety program, the accident frequency rate declined over 92 percent between 1913 and 1940, and another two-thirds between 1940 and 1961.

Among employees of companies in a wide variety of industries reporting to the National Safety Council, the accident frequency rate declined 53 percent and the severity rate 55 percent between a base period 1935–39 and 1962.

Some individual companies have achieved amazing accident records. An electrical equipment plant of Western Electric Company worked without disabling injury for more than 32 million man-hours and a chemical plant of E. I. Du Pont de Nemours more than 31 million man-hours.

41. How large is the accident toll among farm residents?

According to an estimate by the National Safety Council, the 1962 toll of farm residents was 8,700 killed and 800,000 injured. Of

[3] See answer to Question 38 of Chapter 18, page 287.

those fatally injured, 2,100 were killed in home accidents, 3,700 in motor vehicle accidents, and 2,500 in occupational accidents.

42. Where do most accidental injuries occur on farms, and what are the main types of accidents?

Three sample surveys conducted in a cross section of the country showed that, of all accidents to farm residents, 16 percent occurred in the home, 22 percent in the barn, 34 percent elsewhere on the farm, and 11 percent on roads or streets. The remainder occurred in other or unknown places. Falls were the leading type of accidents, contributing 25 percent of the injuries; next in order were machinery accidents with 13 percent, and then injuries by animals with 12 percent. Other important types were motor vehicle accidents, mishaps in handling objects, use of hand tools, and stepping on or striking against objects.

43. Which is the safest mode of travel—by railroad, airplane, bus, or private automobile?

In the three-year period 1960–62, according to one study by the National Safety Council, the safest modes of travel were by railroad and bus. The passenger death rate per 100,000,000 passenger-miles traveled by railroad was 0.13, by bus 0.16, in scheduled air transport plane 0.57, and in passenger automobile or taxicab 2.2.

44. What are the main causes of fatal falls on streets and sidewalks?

Injuries sustained by slips on ice and snow accounted for well over one-third of the fatal falls on streets and sidewalks, according to one life insurance study of persons of ages 15 and over. Intoxication was a factor in one-fifth of the fatal falls studied. Another fifth was due to infirmities of age, fainting, epileptic seizures, or to other effects of disease. Among the other causes of fatal falls were tripping on broken or uneven sidewalks, over various small objects, elevated manholes, protruding cellar doors, or slipping on greasy sidewalks, pools of water, and small pieces of fruit. About 5 percent were fatally injured when they made a misstep while stepping up or down the curb, and 3 percent were felled by others.

45. Who are the principal victims of drownings?

The death rate from drowning for white males in 1962 (4.7 per 100,000) was five times that for females. Among males, drownings are comparatively frequent at all ages, but the chief victims are teen-age boys. Drownings are negligible among females past the teen ages.

46. How many persons are killed in firearm accidents each year?

Firearm accidents claim more than 2,200 lives annually in the United States, and rank sixth on the list of causes of accidental death. Males are the chief victims, especially at ages 15 to 19 years. The rate of fatal injury for males is seven times that for females.

47. What part does hunting play in the toll of firearm accidents?

One-quarter of the total of firearm accidents occurred while hunting, according to a life insurance study of experience among industrial policyholders, mostly urban dwellers. However, twice as many were killed in firearm accidents in the home as in hunting accidents. Firearm accidents in public places, exclusive of those occurring in hunting, accounted for almost one-quarter of the total.

48. What are the chances of being struck by lightning?

Lightning killed 153 persons in 1962 in the United States. The probability of being fatally injured by lightning, however, is far greater in rural than in urban areas. About 9 out of every 10 fatalities from this cause occur in places with 2,500 or fewer inhabitants, although these areas have only 30 percent of the total population.

49. What do fires cost the nation in property damage each year?

Property valued around $1,265,000,000 was destroyed in fires in 1962, according to an estimate of the National Board of Fire Underwriters. Approximately 562,000 private dwellings were destroyed by fire.

50. What are the chief causes of fires in buildings?

Careless smoking and the careless use of matches cause the largest number of fires in buildings. Other important causes of fire included defective electrical fixtures, wiring, and appliances; defective or overheated heating equipment; faulty chimneys; rubbish; and lightning.

51. How does the frequency of school accidents vary by grade?

According to one study, injuries to students occurred at the rate of 11.8 for boys and 5.8 for girls per 100,000 student-days, counting only absences of one-half day or more because of accidents in the school building, on school grounds, or while going to or from school. The injury rate rose fairly steadily from 3.6 for girls in the kindergarten to 23.5 for boys in grades 10 to 12.

52. How many are killed annually while riding bicycles?

Approximately 500 bicyclists are killed each year in collisions in which motor vehicles are involved. An additional 70 deaths result from falls off bicycles, and from collisions with railroad trains or street cars, or from running into curbs, trees, or other fixed objects.

53. How many persons are killed by electricity each year?

Electricity kills approximately 1,000 persons each year, most of whom are adult males. As might be expected from the preponderance of deaths among men, the majority of fatalities are sustained in the course of employment.

54. What is meant by a catastrophe?

An accident is generally considered a catastrophe when five or more persons are killed.

55. Are catastrophes a major factor in the annual accident toll?

Accident catastrophes in recent years have accounted for about 1,500 lives, or around 1.5 percent of all deaths from accidents in the United States. However, there have been years in our history when a single great disaster made catastrophe a much more important item in the total accident death record. Our most devastating catastrophe, the Galveston tidal wave in 1900, alone claimed 6,000 lives.

56. What types of catastrophic accidents have caused the greatest number of deaths?

In 1963, there were eight major catastrophes, each of which took more than 25 lives. The worst of these disasters occurred when a scheduled plane fell near Elkton, Maryland, killing 81 persons. Another scheduled plane crashed in Florida, causing 43 deaths. Three other major catastrophes involved fires and explosions. One of these an explosion and fire in the state fairground coliseum in Indianapolis accounted for 73 lives. Other disasters were associated with bus transportation and the sinking of a tanker.

In general, accidents involving motor vehicles are responsible for about two-fifths of the loss of life in all accidents causing five or more deaths. Fires and explosions, largely in homes and apartments, account for about one-third, and civil aviation for an additional one-seventh of the fatalities and catastrophes. Water transportation, mine accidents, natural catastrophes, and military aviation cause most of the remainder.

Chapter 17

Suicide
and Homicide

NOTE: Suicide and homicide have been brought together in this chapter because they are two forms of violence. They have in fact much in common in causation and in other characteristics. They both reflect extreme forms of aggressive behavior; the one to the self, and the other to other persons. Both are reactions to frustrations generated sometimes by economic, sometimes by social forces, and often by forces within the individual himself. These phenomena are thus closely responsive to similar environmental as well as psychic factors. The reactions to these factors are, however, frequently in opposite directions as when suicide varies negatively and homicide positively with economic levels of well being and with the strength of external restraints over personal behavior. But these very differences throw an additional light on the basic similarities of the two.

Suicide

1. How many suicides occur in the United States each year?

About 19,000 people are officially recorded each year as having put an end to their lives. In 1962, this corresponded to a rate of

10.4 suicides for each 100,000 of population. Because self-destruction still carries a stigma, many self-inflicted deaths are not recorded as such. Recent studies have indicated that in addition to the officially recognized suicides, as many as 30 percent are now classified in the official records as due to accidents or other causes. This would make a total number of about 25,000 suicides in the country each year.

2. Are there many unsuccessful attempts at suicide?

Added to the probably 25,000 people who end their own lives, there are seven to eight times as many more who find life so difficult that they make an attempt to end it.

This suggests that from 175,000 to 200,000 additional persons in the United States each year attempt to kill themselves. In view of the fact that these unsuccessful attempts are for the most part by younger people their numbers accumulate over the years. It is estimated that in all probability there are about two million people alive in the United States who have a history of one or more attempts at self-destruction. They constitute a pool from which many completed suicides of succeeding years are largely drawn. The record shows that a sizable fraction of completed suicides had made previous unsuccessful attempts.

3. How does the suicide rate in the United States compare with that of other countries?

The countries of the world differ greatly in the prevalence of self-destruction in accordance with their traditions and customs, religious convictions, social viewpoints, climatic conditions, and other factors influencing human conduct. Suicide is a serious problem among both the Japanese and the Germans, two peoples widely separated in geographic location, social tradition, and religious belief.

The highest suicide rates in 1960 among the highly developed and organized countries were in Hungary (24.9 per 100,000 of population), Austria (23.0), Japan (21.3), Switzerland (19.0), and Germany (18.8). The rate for the Federal Republic of Germany in 1959 was 18.7, while West Berlin recorded a rate of 34.0 in that year, doubtless reflecting the turbulent conditions in that city. The lowest rates were recorded in the Irish Free State (3.0) and in Spain (5.2). In the Western Hemisphere extremely low rates of under 3 per 100,000 were recorded for Colombia and Costa Rica. Here, as in Ireland and Spain, the rate evidences the influence of the Catholic religion.

The English-speaking countries record rates roughly corresponding to those for the United States. In the Orient, suicide is not looked upon with disfavor as in the West, which explains the relatively high mortality from suicide which is recorded for Japan and other Eastern countries.

4. Is suicide more frequent among men than among women?

Men are much more likely to kill themselves than are women. In the United States, male suicides have usually outnumbered female suicides by more than three to one. The excess of male suicides is found among both the white and colored races and prevails in most countries. At the advanced ages, the sex ratio often rises to about 10 to 1.

5. Is suicide attempted by more men than women?

Women attempt suicide much more often than men, but they are less frequently successful. These failures may be largely the result of their choice of less violent and disfiguring methods, which are also less apt to prove fatal. It is an open question whether women choose less effective methods because they are not so determined to die, or because they are more accessible, or perhaps because they involve less violence. Also, many women who attempt suicide may not be entirely sincere in their purpose; very frequently their suicidal arrangements seem so planned that rescue is not only possible but even probable. They often call for help in distress.

6. How do the suicide rates of whites and nonwhites compare?

For the country as a whole, the rate among white persons is three times that of Negroes. In the Northern states, where both Negro and white rates are higher than in the South, the difference is somewhat less than the average for the country.

The suicide rates for the Japanese and Chinese in this country have in past decades ranged from two to three times that of whites. In recent years, their rates have approximated those of the white population. American Indians have somewhat higher rates.

7. At which ages is suicide most frequent?

The frequency of suicide increases rapidly with age, particularly among men. More than half of the women who commit suicide and nearly two-thirds of the men are 45 years of age and over.

Children rarely kill themselves. After the period of adolescence, when the suicide rate is below 1 per 100,000 for either sex, the rate for white men rises steadily to a peak at ages 75 and over. Colored men show a less distinct pattern, with the rates at a considerably lower level. Among white women, the frequency of suicide is highest at ages 45 to 64, after which age the rate declines.

The age pattern of unsuccessful suicides is considerably different. Special studies show that more than half of the women, and a quarter of the men who make ineffective attempts to kill themselves are under 30 years of age. In each sex, the chance that an attempt at suicide may end fatally increases with age.

8. How does suicide among the married compare with the unmarried?

Married people, and especially those with children, are less inclined toward suicide than either those who have never married or those who are widowed or divorced. The latest available data for 1959 show that single men have a suicide rate one and two-thirds times that for the married, while the widowers have a ratio two times that for the married, and the divorced four times. Among females, the corresponding ratios of suicide are at a lower level; for the single the ratio is about one and one-third times the married, for widows one and two-third times, and for the divorced about four.

9. Is suicide more frequent in some parts of the country than in others?

Although the rate for the country as a whole was 10.6 per 100,000 in 1960, the regions had rates ranging from 8.6 in the East South Central states to 15.2 in the Pacific Coast states.

10. What are the chances of death from suicide?

According to the current situation, it is estimated that 15 white males and 4 white females out of every 1,000 born will eventually take their own lives; for the nonwhites, the corresponding figures are much lower.

11. What is the effect of war on the suicide rate?

Practically every belligerent country, and in some instances the neighboring neutral countries as well, experiences declines in suicide during wartime. In the United States, the suicide rate dropped by one-third from 1915 to 1920, the period of World War I, and it dropped again by one-third in World War II years 1943 and 1944, compared with the three years preceding Pearl Harbor.

It is commonly thought that this wartime drop in suicides lies in the tendency for personal worries and discouragements to be pushed into the background during such periods of national stress. The needs of the country become paramount. People live for the present and worry less about the future, especially as new channels of activity are opened to them because of demands for both military and industrial personnel and also because of the spurt in the money income of many people.

12. What are some of the principal motives for suicide?

There are many motives for suicide, but they are often very difficult to unravel. The reasons most often indicated by the person who commits suicide or by the family are ill health, economic distress, the loss of a loved one, and domestic discord. Behind all these immediate considerations are found almost invariably certain emotional attitudes: fears and anxieties, a sense of inferiority or insecurity, hatred, aggressiveness, guilt, frustration, or revenge. In many instances, particularly in the unsuccessful attempts at suicide, the driving force is a desire for help. The final circumstances leading to a suicide come usually at the end of a long chain of contributory events and may in themselves not be closely related to the underlying cause for the individual's attitude.

13. Are the suicide motives of men different from those of women?

Ill health is most frequently given as the motive by men, with domestic difficulties second. Among women the order is reversed. Together, these two reasons are estimated to account for almost three out of every four suicides. Unrequited love or other frustrated love affairs are relatively rare as the stated cause of suicide—in only 1 in 10 attempts by women and in only a negligible proportion of the attempts by men. But the indications are that these frustrations play a much larger role than is admitted by both sexes.

14. What are the most common methods of suicide?

Close to 90 percent of those who die by their own hand use one of three methods—shooting, hanging, or poisoning or asphyxiation by gas. Although this percentage has remained practically unchanged in the past quarter century, there have been changes in the relative importance of the individual means, with shooting and hanging on the increase, and poisoning on the decrease.

There is a marked difference in the relative frequency of the methods used by the two sexes. Among white men, firearms continued as the most frequent means throughout the last quarter century, accounting currently for over one-half of all suicides. Hanging, ranking second, is now used in about one-fifth of the deaths; poisoning and asphyxiation by gas follow with nearly one-sixth of the total. Among white females, the methods, in order of frequency, are poisoning and asphyxiation by gas, firearms, and hanging. The use of firearms has increased in frequency in recent years. Women are, to an increasing extent, choosing the more violent and disfiguring means of suicide.

15. Is suicide more frequent in urban than in rural areas?

Suicide has always been more common in cities than in the country in the United States and in most of Europe. This finding parallels the fact that mental disease and divorce are also more frequently reported in urban centers than in rural communities. The latest available data for 1960 show that the highest rates are in the largest cities and decline with the size to the smallest. It should be noted, however, that the greatest decline in the rate in the last 30 years has been in the largest cities, and that the gap in the rate between urban and rural has been markedly reduced.

16. What is the effect of social disorganization on suicide?

The suicide rate varies directly with the extent of social disorganization. This is best illustrated by the high rate found to exist in certain run-down areas of large cities, particularly those near railroad stations which attract transients, those living on the fringe of society, with no family or friends to tie them into the social organization.

17. How important is mental illness as a factor in suicide?

A number of prominent physicians and psychiatrists have stated that all suicides are psychotic and that no normal persons, or even those relatively neurotic, actually carry out intentions they may have expressed to do away with themselves. However, other skilled observers are more cautious in discussing the etiology of suicide. In part, this difference is based on the problem of defining what is normal. The absence of a diagnosis of mental illness in the medical history of a person who committed suicide does not rule out the possibility of an unrecognized psychosis. A variety of studies have reported that from one-fifth to one-half of the suicides were suffering from a recognized mental disorder.

18. What are some of the preliminary signs of suicidal action?

In addition to recent suicide attempts, self-destructive threats and fantasies, complaints of pain, suffering, hopelessness, and physical symptoms such as sleeplessness, loss of weight, and anorexia may be considered indications of impending suicidal acts. In such situations, even minor and accidental environmental influences may trigger the fatal act.

19. In which season is suicide most common?

There are more suicides in spring and early summer and fewer in winter. This finding holds for both rural and urban areas, and for both North and South. Attempts to explain this phenomenon in terms of cosmic forces or as the result of changes in temperature have proved unconvincing. Suicide is obviously not a reaction to seasonal severity for it has a high incidence in springtime, the pleasantest period of the year. It is significant that in the Southern Hemisphere the heaviest incidence is six months later.

20. Is the frequency of suicide related to religious affiliation?

The influence of religion helps to explain some of the differences in the suicide rate among nations. Most of the countries with low suicide rates are those in which the Roman Catholic faith predominates. On the other hand, most Protestant countries record high rates. Needless to say there are several exceptions to these generalizations. Austria, which is predominantly Catholic, and France, likewise, have much higher suicide mortality than Protestant Northern Ireland or Norway and The Netherlands. In general, suicide is rare where the authority of religion is unquestionably accepted.

21. What has been the trend of suicide in the United States since 1900?

The over-all picture shows practically no change since the turn of the century. The rate for the five-year period 1955–60, for example, is approximately 11 suicides annually per 100,000 population, and for the five years, 1900–04, it was 10.9. However, within this period, the fluctuations in the rate have corresponded to the changes in the economy. The high point during the last half century came in 1932, at the bottom of the Depression, when the suicide rate reached 17.4. The low point, 10.0 per 100,000 occurred in 1944, in the midst of World War II. It would appear then that the changes in the 60-year period are most closely linked with changes in the economy and with the effects of the country's participation in the two world wars.

22. Is suicide related in any way to social status?

Recent studies, both in the United States and Great Britain, indicate a definite correlation between social status and the incidence of suicide. The highest rates are found among those in the professions and the highest ranks of business life. On the other hand, those at the bottom of the scale, with rare exceptions, have the lowest rates.

23. Which occupations are most prone to suicide?

High suicide mortality has been found to occur among physicians and dentists. Rates greatly above the average are also recorded for those engaged in the liquor trade. On the other hand, other professional workers, such as teachers and clergymen, have uniformly very low suicide rates. Skilled workers and agricultural laborers have the lowest rates. A high incidence also appears in the group of unskilled laborers.

24. Do economic conditions influence the suicide rate?

The suicide rate tends to rise during hard times and to fall when production and employment are high and also in wartime. The lowest suicide rates of the last half century were found either during or right after wars, while the highest rates occurred during the panics preceding World War I and the Depression of the 1930's. The effect of changes in business conditions is particularly noticeable in the fluctuations of the suicide rate among older men.

25. Does suicide occur among primitive people?

It has often been asserted that suicide is a disease of civilization and that primitive people do not kill themselves. Recent investigation, however, has shown that suicide is not at all uncommon among various primitive peoples, whether among Indians in North or South

America, among the aboriginal tribes in Central India, or the many groups across the equatorial belt of Africa. It is apparently an old-established custom and represents traditions which often have the sanction of religion. Among many primitive groups it has its roots as a ritual or a ceremony connected with major events in the life of the tribe. It has been found that suicide is a world-wide phenomenon, common among primitive stocks as among the more civilized peoples. The motivations for suicide among these tribes are very much the same as are found in our own society.

26. What specific agencies have been launched to help prevent suicide?

In the United States, the most effective agency is the Suicide Prevention Center in Los Angeles. Established in 1958 with the encouragement and support of the National Institute of Mental Health of the U.S. Public Health Service, it has offered professional help to an increasing number of patients. Its staff includes psychiatrists, clinical and research psychologists, psychiatric social workers, public health nurses, and clerical personnel. More recently it has added a number of semiprofessional workers. Patients can contact the center by telephone at any hour of day or night and receive immediate help.

The center has achieved a measure of success not only in saving certain individuals in their distress but has demonstrated how to organize an effective prevention center along broad lines. It has shown how potential suicides can be distinguished from the large number of disturbed persons who are in no immediate danger but are seeking help for some personal problem. It has published a large body of significant research and is serving as a center of instruction for those in other cities seeking to set up similar projects.

27. What other centers for suicide prevention exist in the United States, in England, and the European continent?

The psychiatric clinic of the Massachusetts General Hospital in Boston is doing effective work along professional lines. "Rescue, Inc." in Boston, under Catholic church auspices, and the "Friends" of Miami, Florida, under lay direction, have rendered useful service and may develop into effective centers for their communities when they succeed in receiving fuller support from other interested professional and lay groups in their area.

In Great Britain, the most promising suicide prevention service is conducted by "The Samaritans" and has developed during the last 10 years 22 branches in England and Scotland. The distinguishing mark of this operation is its emphasis on the efficacy of the lay volunteer. A consulting psychiatrist and lay therapists are called in when necessary. The movement is a growing one in Britain.

On the continent, a suicide prevention center is doing an effective job in West Berlin, but the most outstanding operation is the "Lebensmuedenfuersorge" of Vienna, a preventive agency of the Catholic welfare organization of that city. This is a well-established professional organization and includes a wide variety of workers with a large clientele who apparently are benefited by the help they receive there, in a city with a high suicide rate.

28. How successful have such preventive measures been in controlling suicide?

It is difficult to say how much has been accomplished to date because most agencies in the field are of recent origin, are often ill equipped to render technically efficient service and to follow up their clients for a sufficiently long period. The record keeping of these agencies has been, with few exceptions, far from adequate. Nevertheless, they have rendered valuable aid to those they have served even if they have touched only a small fraction of the problem to date.

29. What does a successful campaign against suicide call for?

Since the motives behind suicide are varied and complex, a many-sided attack on the problem is called for in each center of population. The contributions must come from teachers, the clergy, physicians (including psychiatrists) and particularly from our social workers who are our first line of defense in all cases of maladjustment and distress. When all these professional groups are alerted to this problem and will report their emotionally disturbed contacts to the central mental health clinic for service, much could be accomplished. With more concentrated attention on early evidence of depression and mental illness, there will be fewer who turn their thoughts to self-destruction.

30. Who are the key persons to advance the suicide prevention movement throughout the United States?

They are the health officers who are charged by law with the responsibility for protecting and advancing the public health. Suicide is an important public health problem and it is preventable. The health officer, because of his central position in the community, can best take the initiative to expand the work of the mental health centers, where they already exist, or establish one where needed, bring together the necessary professional skills and develop a well-coordinated and organized working plan such as has been demonstrated in Los Angeles and in a few other places. The important point is to have the support of all the medical and social service agencies of the community, and no one can do that better than the health officer.

31. Are persons who have made an attempt at self-destruction likely to repeat it?

Even the most expert preventive services will not always serve to preclude an eventual termination by suicide. It is a characteristic of the suicidal persons that they will make repeated efforts until they finally succeed. This is indicated by many case histories of individuals who show a recovery from their condition after long treatment but, upon finding their way back into society, will use the first opportunity to put an end to themselves. Thus, among the successful suicides, we find between 5 and 10 percent who have a history of previous attempts at suicide.

Homicide

32. What is homicide?

Homicide is a general term used to denote the killing of one human being by another. There are, however, differences in concepts between the meaning of homicide in mortality and in criminal statistics. This is important because mortality statistics supply most of the information on the victims of homicide while criminal statistics are the source of facts about the slayers. Homicide is not always unlawful; it may be excusable or justifiable and therefore within the law, as when an officer of the law, while discharging his duties, kills someone, or when one man kills another in self-defense. Such persons are not regarded as guilty of any crime and are not reported in crime statistics. Mortality statistics list such deaths as homicide. On the other hand, mortality statistics exclude accidental deaths due to criminal negligence, which are classed as homicides in crime statistics.

33. How many homicides occur each year?

About 9,000 homicides have been reported annually in the mortality statistics records of the country in recent years.

The Department of Justice, on the other hand, reported 7,375 criminal homicides in 1960, including 4,389 murders or nonnegligent manslaughters, and 2,986 manslaughters by negligence. The reason for this difference of about 2,500 homicides between mortality and criminal statistics was discussed in the previous question.

34. What has been the trend in homicide in the United States?

The homicide rate rose quite steadily from 1.2 per 100,000 in the beginning of the century to 9.7 in 1933. From that time until the latter part of World War II, the homicide rate fell gradually to a level˜of 4.9 per 100,000 in 1944. After the war it again increased slightly, reaching 5.8 per 100,000 in 1948 and has fallen since to 4.9 in 1963.

35. How does the homicide rate in the United States compare with that of other countries?

Homicide in the United States ranks high compared with other countries. Prior to World War II, our rate was 15 to 20 times that of The Netherlands, or of England and Wales, and well above that for Finland, which had the highest rate in Europe. Recently, more homicides have been recorded annually in the city of Chicago, alone, than in the entire United Kingdom. Wartime and postwar disturbances were reflected in homicide rates that were higher than normal in many countries of Europe, but Italy and Finland have been the only European countries rivaling our record.

36. Are men more often involved in homicide than women?

The victims in homicide cases are predominantly male. Among white persons, the homicide rate of men in 1963 was close to two times that of women—3.0 compared with 1.6 per 100,000 population. The ratio is four to one among the colored, 35.6 for the men and 8.9 for women.

Men comprise an even larger proportion of the slayers. In 1962 there were five times as many men as women arrested in the United States for criminal homicide. According to one study, men tend to kill members of their own sex, but the contrary is true for women.

37. How do the homicide rates of the white and colored populations compare?

The homicide rate among the colored is eight times the white rate. In 1962, the rates were 21.8 for the colored and 2.7 for the whites. Among males at ages 25 to 34, the ratio of colored to white homicide rates was more than 11 to 1, but the ratio decreased with advancing age.

38. At what age is homicide most frequent?

Age, as well as color and sex, is an important factor in the frequency of homicide. The highest rates are found in early adult life. At ages under 15, homicide rates are relatively low, and about the same for both sexes. After age 15, however, the rate for white males rises to a high point at about ages 25 to 34, where the frequency of homicide averaged close to 7 slayings per 100,000 in 1962. Among colored men, the rise in adolescence and early adult life is extremely rapid. The peak rate of 85.5 per 100,000 was found at ages 25 to 34 in 1962, after which the rates declined. The highest death rate from homicide among white females is in the first year of life (4.1 in 1962) while among colored females the highest rates were recorded from ages 25 to 34. A similar age pattern in arrests for criminal homicide is reported by the Department of Justice.

39. How does the homicide rate vary from state to state?

There are large variations in regional homicide rates. The lowest are found in New England and the highest in the South. The states regularly reporting the highest rates are Alabama, Georgia, Florida, South Carolina, and Mississippi. In these states the rates range from 6 to 20 times as high as those of some Northern ones, such as most of New England, Minnesota, Iowa, Wisconsin, and North Dakota.

40. Is homicide more frequent in cities than in rural areas?

Homicide rates, when adjusted for age and color variations in our population, were somewhat higher in small cities of 2,500 to 10,000 persons in 1960 than in larger urban centers or in rural areas. The differences were not great among white persons, but were important among the colored.

41. Which cities in the United States report the highest homicide rates?

Certain cities in the Southern section of the country report very high homicide rates each year. Among them are: Huntsville,

Alabama; Little Rock, Arkansas; Macon, Georgia; Charlotte and Durham, North Carolina; Chattanooga, Tennessee; Midland and San Angelo, Texas; and Texarkana. In these cities homicide is responsible for more deaths than most of the infectious diseases.

42. What are the leading causes of homicide?

A review by the Metropolitan Life Insurance Company of 500 homicides highlights the striking fact that a huge fraction of all killings occur under the stress of emotions. Petty quarrels and disputes are the antecedent condition of half the homicides. Also, in almost half of the 250 killings arising from quarrels, either the slayer, the victim, or both had been drinking.

Jealousy or thwarted love accounted for 17.6 percent of the homicides. In killings motivated by jealousy or thwarted love, the loved one, and not the rival, is the usual victim. Killings arising from or committed during a crime of violence accounted for 16 percent. Among the latter, officers of the law and law-abiding citizens are unfortunately the victims more often than the criminals. Spectacular murders by gangsters constituted a surprisingly low percentage of the total —less than 3 percent. These findings are supported in the main by information from the Department of Justice which indicates that only about 45 percent of those imprisoned for homicide had previous criminal records or had their fingerprints on file. In recent years, the proportion of persons imprisoned for homicide who had previous criminal records has been rising.

43. In what season of the year are homicides most frequent?

Conditions vary according to areas but, in general, the greatest number of homicides is recorded in the summer. The difference between seasons, however, is not great.

44. How frequent is infanticide in our country?

Although the homicide rate of white females is highest in infancy, the slaying of children less than one year of age is now a small factor in the total in the United States. In slightly more than 2 percent of the 9,013 homicides recorded in 1962 were the victims under one year old. The infanticide record of the United States is much more favorable than that of many other countries, including those with low homicide rates. In the Orient infanticide has long been relatively common.

45. What are the chief means used in homicides?

Firearms, the principal means of homicide in the United States, are used in over half of all cases. Both sexes among the white and colored have this tendency, but the proportion of killings involving firearms is somewhat higher for males than for females. Knives and other cutting and piercing instruments account for slightly less than one-quarter of all homicides. The use of firearms in committing homicide in this country has become less common in the last quarter of a century. In 1922, three-quarters of all homicides were caused by firearms; by 1948, the proportion was less than three-fifths; now it is slightly over 50 percent.

46. Is homicide more common among the foreign-born than among natives in this country?

The Wickersham Commission, after a careful study of the available information, concluded that: "In proportion to their respective numbers, the foreign-born commit considerably fewer crimes than the native-born . . . (but) approach the record of the native white most closely in the commission of crimes involving personal violence." The statistics advanced in proof of that statement showed that the homicide record of native white males is higher than that of foreign-born males. It is also pertinent that the highest homicide rates among white persons are recorded in those states where the foreign-born are a negligible proportion of the population.

47. What proportion of homicides results in prosecution and punishment of the culprit?

Reports of the Department of Justice for 1963 indicate that arrests were made in more than three-quarters of the cases of murder and nonnegligent manslaughter known to the police. Some of the persons apprehended were released for lack of evidence or for other reasons and never brought to trial. There were convictions in somewhat less than one-half of the cases known to the police authorities. Some of these convictions, however, were for less serious offenses than charged.

48. How many legal executions are there each year?

In the period from 1950 to 1962, there was an average of about 67 executions a year. Eight states—Maine, Michigan, Minnesota, North Dakota, Rhode Island, Wisconsin, Alaska, and Hawaii—do not have the death penalty. California had the largest number of executions, followed by Texas and Georgia.

Not all of these legal executions were for murder, however. A few states in the South have retained the death penalty for other crimes, such as rape and armed robbery, and occasionally impose it. From 1950 through 1962, there were 862 legal executions reported in this country; 719 were for murder, 122 for rape, and the rest for a variety of offenses.

Chapter 18

The Labor Force
and the Hazards
of Occupation

1. How large is our labor force?

The total labor force, broadly defined as those 14 years of age or older with a job or seeking employment, averaged 75.7 million persons in 1963. The labor force is usually at a peak during the summer months because of increased farm employment and jobs sought by school children on vacation. In June, July, and August, 1963 the total labor force averaged 77.7 million. The civilian labor force (total labor force minus the men and women in the armed services) averaged 73.0 million persons during 1963. The table on the following page shows the distribution of the total labor force according to class of worker.

2. How rapidly has the labor force grown in the last 60 years?

The total labor force is at persent almost three times as large as 60 years ago. It had only about 28 million persons in 1900 compared with an average of 75.7 in 1963. The total labor force grew to record size during World War II when the men and women who entered the military services were replaced in industry by housewives, elderly men, and school-age children. In 1944, the total labor force averaged 66 million. With the end of hostilities, the figure dropped to a little less than 61 million in 1946. Since then, there has been a rise every year. The present average civilian labor force is the largest in our country's history and is still growing.

CLASS OF WORKERS IN THE LABOR FORCE IN 1963

Class of Workers	Number in Millions (Annual Average)	Percent Distribution
Labor force, total	75.7	100.0
Employed, total (civilian)	68.8	90.9
Farming or other agricultural pursuits—	4.9	6.5
Wage or salary workers	1.7	2.2
Self-employed workers	2.4	3.2
Unpaid family workers	0.8	1.1
Non-agricultural pursuits	63.9	84.4
Wage or salary workers	57.1	75.4
In domestic service	2.6	3.4
Federal, state and local government	9.1	12.0
Other wage and salary workers	45.4	60.0
Self-employed workers	6.2	8.2
Unpaid family workers	0.6	0.8
Military services	2.7	3.6
Unemployed	4.2	5.5

3. What proportion of the labor force is unemployed?

The number of persons unemployed in 1963 averaged about 4.2 million, or 5.5 percent of the total labor force. The size of the unemployed contingent of the working population has fluctuated within the past three decades between about 25 percent of the labor force in the Depression year 1933, when nearly 13 million persons were out of work; just a little over 1 per cent in 1944, when wartime demands created many local labor shortages; and currently, when about 5.5 percent are out of work.

4. What proportion of the labor force prefers or is available for only part-time employment?

Among the 60.5 million civilians at work in nonagricultural industries in 1963, close to one-fifth worked only part time, i.e., less than 35 hours during the week. Of this group of 11.9 million part-time workers about one-fifth were so engaged for economic reasons.

As a result, the labor force time lost through unemployment and part-time work was 6.4 percent in 1963.

5. Has the labor force grown in proportion to the nation's population?

In 1950, about 58.4 percent of the country's noninstitutional population 14 years of age and over was in the total labor force; at the end of 1963, it was about 57.3 percent. During the past 60 years, the proportion of the total male population, 14 years of age and over, in the labor force fluctuated around 80 percent, but the corresponding proportion for females has risen from 20 in 1900 to about 37 percent in 1963.

6. How many gainful workers are there on the average in each family?

There was an average of about 1.5 employees per family in 1962; 21.1 million of the 47.0 million families, however, have only one worker. In about one out of every three couples, both husband and wife are in the labor force.

7. Do women constitute a growing share of the labor force?

Since 1900, the number of women workers has increased from 5 million, or about 18 percent of the total labor force, to over 25 million in 1963, or 33 percent of the total labor force. In the war year of 1943, female workers numbered almost 19 million, or 29 percent of the total labor force. Although there was a decline after the war, the 1963 figure was greater than ever before. Many women who joined the labor force to take the places of men in World War II years have remained in it.

8. What restrictions have been placed on the employment of women?

Many states prohibit the employment of women in certain hazardous occupations, place limits on their daily and weekly hours of work in some industries, prohibit their employment for more than six days a week in some fields, and either limit the hours of employment of women at night or allow them no nightwork in certain occupations. Other measures to protect the health of women in industry are concerned with the employment of women before and after childbirth, industrial homework, the lifting of heavy weights, the provision of chairs or stools for women to sit on, rest periods, etc. Employers themselves in some instances have set up restrictions on the employment of women and union contracts sometimes make provisions for their protection.

9. How many persons under 18 are in the labor force, and how many over age 65?

In 1960, there were over three million young people under the age of 18 in the total labor force, or over 4 percent of the total. Nearly one million of these were only 14 and 15 years old.

Persons aged 65 years and over in the labor force in 1962 numbered 3.2 million, or 4.2 percent of the labor force; there were 2.2 million men and a little more than 900,000 women.

10. What has been the trend in the employment of children and of old persons?

Great gains have been made in controlling the employment of youngsters. The ages at which children were employed and the conditions under which they were exploited in factories, mills, and mines in the early years of the century now seem incredible. It has been estimated that even as late as 1890 children aged 10 to 13 made up 6.4 percent of the labor force. Only a negligible percentage of children of these ages are employed today. It has also been estimated that the average age at which boys entered the labor force in 1900 was about 15; by 1960 it had risen three years to 18. In 1900 about 1.75 million children 10 to 15 years of age, or 18.2 percent of all children of those ages, were reported in the census as "gainfully occupied;" in 1960, a total of 182,648 boys and 70,321 girls at age 14 were reported as employed, and of them only 15,000 boys and 7,000 girls were at work full time.

The proportion of men over 65 who are still in the labor force has decreased gradually from a little more than three-fifths in 1900 to around 30 percent in recent years. While there has been a growing tendency for older men to retire, it is also possible that the movement from farms, increasing mechanization, and other factors have made it difficult for older men to secure employment in recent years, and that many, therefore, have withdrawn from the labor force. The operations of private pension plans and of old-age social insurance have, likewise, encouraged earlier retirement.[1]

11. What restrictions have been placed on the employment of children?

The states and the federal government have legislated restrictions on the employment of children. In general, the aims are to keep children in school, to limit their working in dangerous occupations, or under conditions or at hours which would injure their health and development.

The Federal Fair Labor Standards Act establishes a minimum age of 16 for most jobs in interstate commerce, of 18 for particularly hazardous jobs, and of 14 for work in a few nonmanufacturing and nonmining occupations outside school hours and with specified safeguards. Work as an actor or performer in the entertainment industry, as a newsboy, and most types of work for the child's own parents or guardians are exempted. The jobs classified as hazardous and in which children may not be hired until they are over 18 include many in the explosives and small-arms ammunition plants, in mining, logging, sawmilling, and in industries using radioactive materials. Also considered dangerous are the operation of cold-metal working machines, driving motor vehicles or acting as a driver's helper, and operating elevators, power hoists, or wood-working machinery.

The state laws in general set minimum ages for employment and for leaving school, require work permits for those under age, place limits on the hours of work and on night work, impose additional restrictions on dangerous occupations, and provide special benefits for children who are injured in occupational accidents while illegally employed. In 1963, the Department of Labor found 10,348 minors working illegally in nonagricultural establishments. Of these, 4,400, or 43 percent, were under 16 years of age, and 4,764, or 46 percent, were 16 to 17 years old and employed in hazardous occupations.

12. Does marital status affect the proportion of men and women who work?

About 9 out of 10 married men work, but far fewer of the single men of the same ages are in the labor force. A relatively large number of the single men are still quite young, and many are still in school.

As one might expect, proportionately far fewer women than men

[1] See Question 35 of Chapter 15, page 238.

work. Two out of every five single women aged 14 and over are in the labor force; close to one out of every three married women; two out of seven widows; and seven out of ten divorcees.

13. At what ages are the most men and the most women in the labor force?

Participation of men in the labor force is at a peak at ages 30 to 44, when about 97 percent have jobs or are looking for jobs. About 80 percent of the single women aged 25 to 44 are in the labor force, and about 35 percent of the married women at these ages.

14. Are there more unskilled than semiskilled, skilled, or clerical workers?

Semiskilled blue-collar workers made up the largest single group of labor force members in 1963, totaling 12.5 million persons or 18 percent of all workers. Other large major occupation groups were professional and technical workers (12 percent), managers, officials, and proprietors (11 percent), clerical workers (15 percent), skilled craftsmen (13 percent), and service workers (13 percent). The smallest groups were composed of sales workers (6 percent), nonfarm laborers (5 percent), and farm workers (7 percent).

This breakdown of the labor force according to social-economic status is different for men and women. Clerks and service workers make up the largest group of women workers.

15. What are the most common occupations of men?

Of the hundreds of distinct male occupations listed by the Bureau of the Census, the following list represents the major occupation groups as estimated by the Bureau of Labor Statistics in 1963.

Occupation (males)	Number (1,000)	Percent
Professional, technical, and kindred workers	5,311	11.7
Farmers and farm managers	2,265	5.0
Managers, officials, and proprietors except farm	6,180	13.6
Clerical and kindred workers	3,128	6.9
Sales workers	2,642	5.8
Craftsmen, foremen, and kindred workers	8,683	19.2
Operatives and kindred workers	9,011	19.9
Private household workers	60	.1
Service workers, except private household	3,105	6.9
Farm laborers and foremen	1,486	3.3
Laborers, except farm and mine	3,457	7.6

16. What are the most common occupations of women?

Clerical, secretarial, and other office jobs are the most common occupations of women; service workers rank next in number, as may be seen in the following table for 1963, as estimated by the Bureau of Labor Statistics:

Occupation (females)	Number (1,000)	Percent
Professional, technical, and kindred workers	2,951	12.6
Farmers and farm managers	131	.6
Managers, officials, and proprietors except farm	1,113	4.7
Clerical and kindred workers	7,142	30.4
Sales workers	1,714	7.3
Craftsmen, foremen, and kindred workers	241	1.0
Operatives and kindred workers	3,496	14.9
Private household workers	2,246	9.6
Service workers, except private household	3,621	15.4
Farm laborers and foremen	733	3.1
Laborers, except farm and mine	94	.4

17. Has there been a trend away from unskilled labor?

During the present century, there has been a steady movement from unskilled work into semiskilled and white-collar work. Ordinary laborers, as a group (not counting farm hands), have not only decreased as a proportion of the total working population, but there are actually fewer individuals so occupied today than in 1910. The semiskilled trades and the clerical occupations have both expanded rapidly. Even the category of proprietors, managers, and officials (excluding farmers and farm managers) has increased both absolutely and in proportion to the size of the labor force. The number of skilled workers or craftsmen and foremen has roughly kept pace with the growth of the labor force.

18. How great has been the decline in the proportion of workers engaged as farmers and farm workers?

In 1870, about seven million persons—more than half of the gainful workers in the country—were in agriculture. Since then, there has been a progressive decline in the proportion engaged in farming, until by 1910 it was less than one-third of all workers. At present only about five million—approximately one-fourteenth of the civilian labor force—are employed in agriculture.

19. How rapidly have the professional classes grown?

There has been a great expansion in the professional classes in the last 90 years, especially among women. Today there are approximately 5.3 million men in professional, technical, and kindred work, and 3.0 million women. The proportion of men in the professional classes in the male civilian labor force has risen from less than one-fortieth in 1870 to about one-ninth today. Many fields have become numerically important only in the last few decades. In 1870 there were fewer than 8,000 chemists, metallurgists, and engineers; there are now over 100 times as many.

Among women workers, the professional classes have always made up a larger proportion than among men, growing from one-twentieth of the female labor force in 1870 to about one-ninth at present. Teachers and nurses together number around two-thirds of all professional women, but there are also many types of professional work into which women have only recently gone. The whole field of social work, for example, is largely a development of the present century. Ninety years ago there was only a handful of women doctors, lawyers, reporters, and editors; these groups now total in the many thousands.

20. How do the occupations rank according to income level?

Proprietors, managers, and officials share with professional workers in heading the list of occupations with the highest incomes, according to data compiled for 1959 by the Bureau of the Census. Not only was the median income[2] of proprietors, managers, and officials the highest for male workers, but it was about one and one-half times that of operatives and kindred workers (roughly the semiskilled), who make up the largest single nonagricultural occupation group. The table on page 282 shows the median income and percentage of workers in each group with incomes of more than $10,000. Craftsmen and foremen have a comparatively high income, well above that for all employed civilian males. The farm groups rank at the bottom of the list, but the money income of farmers is not strictly comparable to that of other workers. Farm families normally have a good deal of nonmoney income; farm owners usually raise a large share of their own food, and farm hands are usually given their room and board.

[2] One-half earned less and one-half earned more than "median" income.

INCOME LEVEL FOR VARIOUS CIVILIAN MALE OCCUPATION GROUPS COUNTING TOTAL MONEY INCOME RECEIVED IN 1959

Occupations	Median Income for Persons with Income	Percent with $10,000 and Over
All employed civilians	$4,621	7.1
Proprietors, managers, and officials	6,664	25.1
Professional workers	6,619	20.4
Craftsmen, foremen, etc.	5,240	3.4
Salesmen	4,987	12.3
Clerical and kindred workers	4,785	2.4
Operatives and kindred workers	4,299	1.2
Service workers (excluding domestics)	3,310	1.1
Laborers (other than farm and mine)	2,948	0.5
Farmers, farm managers	2,169	4.4
Farm laborers and foremen	1,066	0.3

21. How do the income levels of men and women compare?

Judging by the figures for 1959 shown below, not only is the median income of women workers below that of men, but women usually earn a great deal less than men in the same field. The median income was $4,621 for all employed civilian males in 1959, while the figures for women came to only $2,257. The proportion of women earning above $10,000 a year was largest for the occupation group consisting of proprietors, managers, and officials; there the figure was only 4 percent compared with 25.1 percent for men.

	Median Income	
Occupation	Men	Women
All employed civilians	4,621	2,257
Proprietors, managers, officials	6,664	3,355
Professional workers	6,619	3,625
Clerical and kindred workers	4,785	3,017
Sales	4,987	1,498
Operatives and kindred workers	4,299	2,319
Service workers (excluding domestics)	3,310	1,385

22. How many years may a worker expect to remain in the labor force?

With mortality conditions and labor force participation existing in 1960, it has been estimated that a working man aged 20 might expect to spend another 42.6 years in the labor force, and a man of 40, another 24.1 years.

23. How do some occupations affect health?

The effects of occupations on health are both direct and indirect. Specific hazards, such as exposure to accidents and to dust, directly influence the morbidity and mortality of workers in many jobs. The environment produced by small earnings in certain kinds of work, particularly unskilled labor, may also contribute to ill health and curtail longevity. Low pay imposes a relatively low standard of living which may be marked by inadequate food and clothing, crowded and unsanitary living quarters, the need to stay on the job when ill, and other handicaps to health. Mortality studies show that the death rate for workers and their wives increases as the economic scale is descended.

24. What are the common occupational hazards?

Industrial accidents take the largest toll, killing annually about 14,000 and causing two million nonfatal injuries. Dusts take fewer lives, but are a serious hazard in a number of industries. Not all industrial dusts are dangerous, but silica and asbestos particles are especially damaging to lung tissue.

Among the industrial poisons which are most common are carbon monoxide, benzol, and compounds of lead, mercury, chromium, and arsenic. New substances are continually being brought into use in industry, and many of them may be dangerous. The introduction of a large number of volatile solvents has increased the list of industrial poisons considerably. Beryllium compounds have also been found to cause severe lung affections and a high mortality from cancer of the lung has been reported among men employed in the chromate-producing industry.

Dermatitis due to contact with acids, alkalis, or other irritant substances is a frequent cause of disability. Overexposure to x-rays, radium, the radioactivity associated with nuclear fission, as well as to ultraviolet and infrared rays is also a potential hazard.

Aside from the specific hazards mentioned above, many jobs involve such potentially harmful conditions as excessive heat, sudden variations in temperature, dampness, compressed air, decreased atmospheric pressure, poor illumination, long-continued repetitive motion, constant pressure on a part of the body, or repeated shocks.

25. What occupations have the highest total mortality?

The very highest recorded mortality rates among the common occupations are found where there is a combination of a high probability of accidents and exposure to dusts which contain a very large percentage of free silica. This situation is found in some hard-rock mining, such as gold, silver, copper, and especially lead and zinc mining. American insurance company studies indicate that the mortality in these occupations is more than three times that of whitecollar workers.

26. What occupation groups have the lowest total mortality?

Among the occupation groups with low mortality are farmers, professional and clerical workers, and business proprietors and officials. Clergymen, notably Anglican clergymen, have one of the lowest death rates.[3]

27. What occupations have the highest mortality from tuberculosis?

Among workers who are exposed to large quantities of silica dust, the tuberculosis mortality rate is much higher than the average for men employed in nonhazardous occupations. Metal miners, granite cutters, chippers of metal, sandblasters, sandstone wheel grinders, and anthracite coal miners also have higher death rates from tuberculosis.

28. What is silicosis and how is it related to tuberculosis?

Silicosis is a disease of the lungs caused by breathing air containing large amounts of very fine free silica dust (silicon dioxide). In the lungs, silica produces nodules which have a characteristic appearance on the x-ray film. Another effect of silica is to stimulate tubercle infection; severe cases of silicosis often terminate in tuberculosis. Silica is found pure, as quartz, in many rocks and sands. A silicosis hazard is present in occupations concerned with mining; quarrying; rock crushing, grinding, or drilling; stonecutting; and other industrial work where silica dust is generated.

29. What occupations have the highest mortality from pneumonia?

The death rate from pneumonia is highest among unskilled workers and lowest among professional workers, business proprietors, and officials. Clerks, farmers, and skilled workers also have below average mortality from pneumonia. Apart from the social-economic influences affecting the death rate from this cause, workers appear to be made more susceptible to pneumonia where there are specific

[3] See answer to Question 30 of Chapter 24, page 405.

occupational hazards such as fatigue from strenuous labor, inhalation of irritating gases and dust, heat accompanied by sudden variations in temperature, and exposure to inclement weather. Mortality from pneumonia is high among welders, iron and steel foundry and mill-workers, underground metal miners, anthracite coal miners, metal buffers and polishers, and among the proprietors of drinking establishments and bartenders.

30. What occupations have the highest mortality from cancer?

Cancer mortality increases as the social-economic scale is descended from the highest to the lowest class. Specific occupational cancers have also been recognized, among which are the scrotal cancers of chimney sweeps and mule spinners, cancer of the fingers and hands of radiologists, osteogenic sarcoma of radium dial painters, cancer of the skin of oil and paraffin workers, cancer of nasal sinuses and lungs of nickel refinery workers, lung cancer of chromate workers and cancer of the bladder of dye workers.[4]

31. How common are the occupational skin diseases?

Occupational skin diseases are more common than all other types of occupational disease combined. About 1 percent of the industrial workers in the country, it has been estimated, are annually affected by occupational dermatoses, and in some fields the incidence is as high as 1 out of every 13 workers. In a Public Health Service survey of 12 different industries, it was found that the synthetic resin and chemical and dye industries had the highest frequency of occupational skin disease. In general, the most common causes of such complaints in industry are petroleum products and greases. This is not because they are the most powerful skin irritants, but because more workers are exposed to their action than to any other class of irritant chemicals. Next in frequency as causes of skin difficulties are the alkalis, solvents, plants and woods, and the materials used in metal plating.

32. Do many occupations leave noticeable marks or signs on workers?

The number of occupational signs or marks is considerable. Although such distinguishing marks were once more common than they now are, the development of industrial medicine and safety

[4] See answers to Questions 18, and 19 of Chapter 9, page 131.

engineering has by no means eliminated them entirely. The physical signs of work may range all the way from superficial calluses or skin irritations to alteration of both appearance and personality. A few examples are: calluses on the back of the left little finger among stone cutters (from holding the chisel in a particular way) and on the center of the shins among the house painters (from leaning against ladder rungs). The fingertips on the left hands of bricklayers are often so abraded that fingerprinting is almost impossible. Workers exposed to certain chemicals used in munitions manufacturing occasionally have their skin discolored yellow or orange. A peculiar leaning, accelerated way of walking known as "rooster gait" may be the result of manganese poisoning, and an exaggerated high-stepping gait may come from lead or arsenic poisoning. Mercury poisoning, once not infrequent among felt hat workers, may even lead to extreme shyness and timidity.

33. What occupations have the highest mortality from accidents?

Data relating to fatal accidents while at work are limited to broad industrial groups and therefore conceal the very high rates for certain individual occupations. The highest death rate recorded is for the extractive industries—mining, quarrying, and the oil and gas well industries. As a group, workers in these fields have an occupational accident rate much higher than that of workers in general. Very high rates are recorded also for the construction workers, agricultural workers, and transportation workers.

Life insurance studies of general mortality show a high total accident death rate, occupational and nonoccupational combined, for building wreckers, electric light and power linemen, fishermen, long-shoremen, lumbermen, miners, motorcycle policemen, oil and gas field rig builders and handlers of explosives, railroad brakemen, structural iron workers, and window cleaners.

Other occupations known to be hazardous but for which no figures are available include diving, automobile racing, steeple jacking, and stunt flying.

34. How many days do workers lose because of sickness and accident?

It has been estimated that, on the average, a worker is disabled for five and one-half days annually by sickness or accidents.

Many workers escape accidents and disease altogether; others have more than their share. In one group of men studied for a year, there were about as many cases of disabling sickness or injury of one day or longer as there were workers, but all the disabilities occurred among about three-fifths of the men. More than one-quarter were sick or injured two or more times. In a survey of a number of companies, the average duration of absences because of illness or nonoccupational accidents lasting at least 8 days was 36 days.

35. What are the chief causes of lost time due to illness in industry?

A study of absences from illness or injury lasting one day or longer among a group of public utility workers shows that respiratory diseases, of which the most common were colds and influenza, caused more than half of the absences and about one-third of the days of disability; the experience was the same for both male and female workers. Next in importance as a cause of lost time were digestive diseases, principally diseases of the stomach (not counting cancer), and appendicitis; injuries were third. A combined group of rheumatic diseases, including rheumatism, diseases of organs of movements (except joints), neuralgia, neuritis, and sciatica made up the fourth-ranking class.

36. Do women lose more time than men because of sickness disability?

Lost time from sickness and accidents averages 5.6 days annually for female workers compared with 5.5 days for male workers. Women workers are absent on the average about twice as often as males, but lose less time per absence.

37. Do older workers lose more time than younger workers?

The U.S. National Health Survey, 1959–60, indicates that the average number of work-loss days per person per year increases with age for both male and female workers. The annual number of days lost per person for medical reasons increases sharply with age.

38. Do physically impaired workers lose more time because of illness than other workers?

Limited information available in one study of manufacturing plant workers indicates that the number of days lost because of illness was only slightly greater among the physically impaired as a whole than among unimpaired workers subject to the same job incentives and exposed to the same hazards. Persons with hernias or with arrested tuberculosis did not lose any more time from work because of illness than unimpaired workers. Those with vision and hearing defects lost less time. Workers with serious orthopedic or cardiac defects, peptic ulcers, diabetes, and epilepsy lost somewhat more time than the unimpaired workers. On the whole, however, the number of days lost was low—a fact which tends to lessen the importance of the differences between impaired and unimpaired workers in the days lost from work because of illness.[5]

39. Do the physically handicapped find a place in the labor force?

Organized efforts on the part of government, business, and industry, union and various health services have added several million handicapped persons to the labor force. An indication of what is being done to rehabilitate the handicapped and find them jobs is to be found in the services provided by the Office of Vocational Rehabilitation of the Federal Security Agency, which works with many state agencies for the handicapped. These services include individual counseling and guidance; medical, surgical, psychiatric, and hospital care; the provision of prosthetic devices and the training necessary for their use; supplying occupational tools; job placement and followup after placement. In 1961, over 250,000 handicapped men and women were completely rehabilitated through the program of the Office of Vocational Rehabilitation and placed by state agencies.

40. To what extent has the work week been shortened in the last 50 years?

The average scheduled work week of wage earners in manufacturing plants is estimated to have been around 50 hours in 1914, in contrast to the 40-hour week of today.

41. To what extent are workers protected against loss of income due to occupational injury by workmen's compensation laws?

Every state has a workmen's compensation law designed to provide for income, medical care, and other services to persons accidentally injured at work regardless of who was at fault in the accident. Provision is also made to pay compensation to dependents of workers killed in industrial accidents. Within recent years the trend has been to extend this protection to diseases attributable to

[5] See answer to Question 39 of Chapter 16, page 253.

the hazards of the occupation. The premiums on workmen's compensation insurance are paid by the employer.

Not all groups of workers, however, are included under the various state laws. It has been estimated that not more than 50 or 60 percent of the gainfully employed are actually protected by state workmen's compensation. The largest group usually excluded is in agriculture. Others also usually left out are domestic servants, casual workers, and employees of charitable institutions. In some states, employers may choose not to operate under the act if they prefer to risk an injured worker's suit for damages. Some states limit the coverage to certain "hazardous" employments and some exempt employers having fewer than a specified number of employees.

Federal compensation laws cover government employees, longshoremen and harbor workers, private employees in the District of Columbia, railroad employees in interstate commerce and seamen.

42. To what extent are workers assured an income in old age under the Social Security Act?

Monthly old-age insurance benefits are payable at age 62 to a retired insured worker and to the wife or dependent husband of the retired worker. Survivor benefits are paid at age 62 to a widow, dependent widower and dependent parent. Benefits are also paid to a wife or widow at any age if she is caring for a child who is entitled to child's benefits, and to the worker's unmarried child under age 18 (or over 18 if the child was permanently and totally disabled before 18).

Full monthly benefits are payable in the case of widows, widowers, and dependent parents age 62 or over, but benefits to retired workers, wives or dependent husbands are in actuarially reduced amounts if paid before age 65.

To qualify for benefit payments for himself and his dependents or survivors, a worker must have a specified amount of work in employment or self-employment covered by Social Security. The primary insurance benefit amount is based on the worker's average monthly earnings. A table in the law specifies a primary insurance amount for each average monthly earnings amount. For most workers the average monthly earnings are computed by adding up the worker's total covered earnings in a number of years specified in the law (generally from 1951 up to age 65 or 62 for women) and dividing by the number of months in those years. In computing this average, the five years of lowest earnings are omitted. The primary insurance amount is approximately 59 percent of the first $110 of average earnings and 21.4 percent of the next $290.

Benefits for dependents and survivors are figured as a percentage of the insured person's primary insurance amount. A wife, dependent husband or child each receives 50 percent of the primary insurance amount; a widow, widower, or a single parent receives 82.5 percent. If two dependent parents are entitled to benefits they each receive .75 percent. The ceiling on total benefits payable to a family is $254 or 80 percent of the average monthly wage, whichever is less. In no case, though, is the total family benefit less than one and one-half times the primary insurance amount.

The law provides that a person receiving benefits who has substantial amounts of earnings from work will have some or all of his and his dependents benefits withheld, depending on the amount of his earnings and how many months he works. However, benefits are payable to persons age 72 or over regardless of their earnings.

Nearly 113 million persons had earnings credits at the beginning of 1963, of whom 91 million had worked long enough to be insured. In December 1963 about 62 million people (including members of the armed forces and railroad workers) were employed in covered jobs. Excluded from coverage were about 4 million federal, state, and municipal employees who have not been brought under OASDI but who had their own public retirement programs. In addition, it is estimated that at the beginning of 1964, nearly 24 million persons were covered by private retirement plans.

43. To what extent are workers assured of an income when unemployed?

All 50 States and the District of Columbia have unemployment insurance. Federal employees are covered under the federal unemployment insurance law. Persons who qualify under the law and who are unemployed through no fault of their own are referred to suitable jobs or, if none are available, paid weekly benefits for a limited time. Aside from certain broad federal standards regarding financing and administration of the law, each of the states has the responsibility for its own unemployment insurance program. Federal functions relating to this law are carried out by the Bureau of Labor Standards of the U.S. Department of Labor. In general, most workers in private industry and commerce are covered. Excluded in most states are agricultural workers, state and municipal workers, domestic workers, workers in religious, charitable, and certain other nonprofit organizations, casual laborers, and railroad workers, who are covered by the Federal Railroad Unemployment Insurance Act. In most states only persons in establishments employing four or more persons during 20 weeks in a year are covered; in some states, firms having one or more employees are covered. The average weekly benefit in 1964 was about $36.

44. To what extent are disabled workers assured of an income under various governmental and voluntary health and accident plans?

More than half of the wage and salary labor force has some protection against loss of income from temporary sickness or disability through private employer plans and union-management plans. It is estimated that in 1962 the benefits provided by such private and public disability insurance and sick-leave plans replaced barely 20 percent of the aggregate earnings lost by employees in private industry because of nonoccupational short-term disability (during the first six months of the disability).

The Social Security Act protects against earnings loss when employees and the self-employed have an impairment that renders them unable to engage in any substantial gainful employment and is expected to continue indefinitely. Benefits are payable after six months of disability, provided the disabled worker meets the special work requirements to be insured for disability protection. At the start of 1964, 53 million workers were insured in the event of disability (compared to 91 million insured for old-age and survivor's benefits). Benefits under this program were going to 827,000 workers, about two-fifths of the long-term disabled with work experience. In all, about two-thirds of such severely disabled workers were receiving payments under some public income-maintenance program including workmen's compensation, programs for railroad and government workers, for veterans, or public assistance.

45. To what extent do states help to provide benefits for nonoccupational illness?

Four states, Rhode Island, California, New Jersey, and New York, have inaugurated compulsory plans of insurance to provide cash benefits to workers absent from work because of nonoccupational sickness and injury. Normally there is a waiting period of seven days before employees are entitled to these benefits. Maximum benefits in New York and New Jersey are $50 a week, in Rhode Island about $43, and in California $75. The California plan provides an additional $12 daily benefit for the first 20 days of hospital confinement, with no waiting period. Weekly benefits are payable for up to 25 weeks. Certain types of employment are excluded from participation in the program. In general, although the provisions in this regard are not entirely uniform, the principal employments not covered include agriculture, domestic service, work for certain non-profit organizations, and government.[6] The railroad industry has a separate social insurance program which provides workers with partial compensation for loss of wages caused by temporary nonoccupational illness.

46. Can persons in hazardous occupations get life insurance?

Life insurance companies have developed special insurance policies at somewhat higher than standard premiums for persons unable to meet the regular requirements because of impaired health or hazardous work. At the end of 1962, Americans had close to six million "extra rate" ordinary life policies for a total of over $22 billion.

Persons in especially safe work, such as white-collar jobs, can get special low-cost policies with some companies, provided they can meet the health and other requirements.

47. Are group life and group accident and health insurance available only to employed persons, and how many workers have it?

Group insurance, which is usually low in cost, is written only on a company or on a special group, not on an individual basis. The group must have at least a certain number of employees, and a maximum percentage of them must apply for coverage in order to get group insurance. Such group insurance often includes life insurance protection for dependents of group members. At the end of 1962, well over 48 million workers in this country were insured under group life policies. About 10.25 million were covered by group accident and health insurance, and more than 6.66 million by group accidental death and dismemberment policies. As already indicated, about 141 million workers and their dependents were insured for

[6] See answer to Question 46 of Chapter 6, page 91.

hospital expenses under voluntary plans by 1962. Of this number, 131 million were covered for surgical expenses; over 38 million for major medical expenses; and close to 45 million were insured against loss of income. These numbers are growing rapidly each year and represent the activities of the private insurance companies through their group accident and health policies and the similar operations of the Blue Cross and Blue Shield plans.

Chapter 19

Human

Impairments

1. How may impaired persons be classified?

The classification may be on the extent and nature of the deviation of physical or mental health from the normal state, or in terms of working capacity. Thus departures from a normal state of health may result in either temporary or permanent disability, and each of these forms may be either a total or partial disability. Impairments may range all the way from such minor conditions as nearsightedness, hay fever, or loss of a finger to severe crippling, blindness, or advanced chronic disease.

2. How many impaired persons are there in the United States?

By the broadest standard, most people would be considered impaired. Thus, Selective Service examinations of men of military age, when physical capacity should be at its peak, showed relatively few individuals entirely free from impairment. The National Health Survey of 1959–61 indicated that over 19 million persons in the noninstitutionalized population were limited to some extent in their activities due to chronic disease or impairment. Approximately four million of them were unable to carry on their major activity, that is, work, keep house, or go to school.

3. How does the incidence of chronic disease or impairment vary wth sex and age?

Chronic disease or impairment is, like sickness, reported some-what more frequently among women than among men. Among those unable to carry on their major activity, however, the proportion of males (3.1 percent) is twice that for females (1.5 percent).

The frequency of impairment and of chronic invalidism in-creases steadily with advancing age in both sexes, the rise being particularly rapid among older persons. Thus, while only 2.9 percent of those 45 to 64 years old were unable to carry on their major activity, 15.5 percent were in this category at ages 65 and over. At these advanced ages the percentage of males unable to carry on their major activity is more than twice that of females.

4. What are the principal impairments causing limitation of activity?

The National Health Survey, 1959–61, showed that the heart conditions ranked first in the list of chronic ailments and impair-ments with limitation of activity, followed immediately by arthritis and rheumatism. Next in order were mental and nervous diseases, high blood pressure, impairments of lower extremities, impairments of back or spine, conditions of genitourinary system, and visual impairments.

As estimated by this survey, there are 3.2 million persons with heart disease, over 3 million with rheumatism and arthritis, and nearly 3 million with orthopedic impairments causing limitation of activity.

The total number of persons with these leading impairments is, of course, much larger. According to recent estimates there are more than 5,000,000 people with heart disease and about 11 million persons suffering from some form of rheumatism and arthritis. About 830,000 people are undergoing treatment for cancer, and the number of known diabetics in the country has been placed at 1,600,000 with a like number of undisclosed cases.

5. How do the various diseases or impairments differ in importance among men and women, and according to age?

Among young men, orthopedic impairments rank highest in frequency, followed in order by mental and nervous conditions, asthma-hayfever, cardiovascular-renal conditions, arthritis and rheumatism, and peptic ulcers; among older men, ages 65 and over, the highest ranking causes are: heart conditions, arthritis and rheumatism, orthopedic conditions, and visual impairments.

Among women at ages under 45, the first ranking causes are: orthopedic conditions and conditions of the genitourinary system. The next highest ranking conditions are: mental and nervous conditions, arthritis and rheumatism, and heart conditions. Among women at ages 65 and over, the leading conditions are: arthritis, rheumatism, and heart conditions, followed by high blood pressure and orthopedic impairments.

6. What are the chief defects disclosed by periodic health examinations?

Data on periodic health examinations relate primarily to persons who are going about their daily tasks in apparently good health. Consequently, these data cannot be expected to show any large proportion of currently serious or disabling defects, but chiefly conditions or habits which are likely to be harmful in the long run. Among types of defects found in great frequency in these examinations are defects of vision (either uncorrected or insufficiently corrected), elevated blood pressure, hemorrhoids, and dental and mouth conditions, such as carious teeth, septic roots, gum infections, and pyorrhea. However, even among these apparently healthy people some serious conditions are occasionally found for the first time in periodic health examinations. While no single disease or condition of major import is found in large numbers, the aggregate with significant adverse findings is sizable.

7. How do the findings from periodic health examinations differ among men and women and according to age?

Most defects show an increased frequency with advancing age. This is particularly marked for hypertension and other cardiovascular impairments, urinary impairments, overweight, dental and mouth conditions, and hemorrhoids. On the other hand, the prevalence of upper respiratory disorders and defects of goiter is greater in young adults than in older persons.

The principal conditions which show a markedly higher prevalence among women than men are goiter, digestive complaints, varicose veins, hemorrhoids, and defective vision. Men have higher rates for cardiovascular impairments, dental and mouth conditions, and defective hearing.

8. How is the frequency of various impairments related to body build?

Most of the serious defects are found with greater frequency among overweights than among average or light weight persons. On the other hand, tuberculosis, anemia, and thyroid disease are the most important conditions which are more frequent among underweights. However, differences in the reported frequency of defects according to build are not always easy to assess, since the examiner may have difficulty in determining the presence of certain types of defects among overweights. An excellent example of this is arterial thickening. This is detected less frequently in overweights than in persons of lighter build because the method used, palpation of the arteries, is likely to give an inaccurate result in stout persons.

9. What do the records of life insurance companies show regarding the prevalence of impairments?

Life insurance companies record for the most part only those defects that are likely to cause some reduction from average longevity. Nevertheless, the facts are of special interest because applicants for life insurance are presumably healthy and able to go about their daily affairs. A recent survey of a number of insurance companies showed that only 3 out of 100 applicants had such serious defects or were in such hazardous occupations that they were unacceptable as risks. About another 9 of the 100 were such risks that they could be accepted only for extra rated insurance. In recent years the proportion of persons ineligible for standard insurance and the proportion rejected for any insurance has perceptibily declined.

10. Which of the impairments are the most frequent causes of rejection for life insurance?

Almost one-half of the applicants ineligible for any insurance were declined because of some cardiovascular-renal condition. Not quite one-third were rejected because of other medical impairments disclosed by examination of the applicant or by his medical history. A very small proportion were ineligible for insurance because of extreme overweight or underweight. Likewise, relatively few were rejected because of the hazards of their occupation.

Among those granted insurance at extra rates, about one-seventh were either overweight or underweight, and approximately one-fifth had some cardiovascular-renal condition. Other poor medical histories and physical findings together accounted for about one-fifth of those charged higher than standard premiums. Among all applications for ordinary life insurance, only about 1 in 10,000 is turned down for occupational hazards, and only about 1 percent involve extra premium for this reason.

11. What did the examination of draftees in World War II show as to the prevalence of impairments?

Most men examined for Selective Service showed some defect, but the findings were influenced by the extent of the examination, which varied, and by the amount of detail that appeared in the records. Of those examined before Pearl Harbor, 72 percent had defects; but in a wartime sample, 63 percent were recorded as having defects. In the peacetime sample, those with defects averaged 1.9 defects per registrant. Even of the men accepted for general military service, 43 percent showed one or more defects. The most frequent of these were flat feet, eye defects (chiefly refractive errors of vision), missing or carious teeth, pyorrhea, diseased or enlarged tonsils, varicocele, hernia, and minor skin disorders.

12. What proportion of the draftees in World War II were rejected for military service?

Of all the men examined for military service through Selective Service up to the end of the war, 30.2 percent were rejected. The proportion rejected varied widely within the country. New Jersey, Nevada, Kansas, and Iowa had rates somewhat less than 25 percent. Georgia, North Carolina, and South Carolina had rates above 40 percent. In general, the best record was found in sections of the East, Middle West, and Pacific Coast, and the poorest in the South and Southwest. These gross findings, however, must be interpreted with caution because they are influenced to a great extent by the varying proportion of rejections for failure to meet minimum educational standards. Unfortunately, there are no good data relating specifically to medical causes of rejection. Rejection rates were also subject to a number of other influences. Thus, they were lowest among young men and highest among older draftees, reaching a figure of nearly 50 percent for those over 38.

13. What were the most important causes of rejection for draftees in World War II?

Mental disease (chiefly psychoneurosis) and mental deficiency (chiefly inability to meet minimum intelligence or educational standards) were the leading causes of rejection. Of the physical defects, first place was held by musculoskeletal defects such as absence or deformity of any part of the body due to accident or disease; and next in importance were cardiovascular defects, including heart disease, high blood pressure, and related disorders. Other frequent causes of rejection were hernia, syphilis, neurologic defects, bad eyes, and ear defects.

The frequency as well as the causes of rejection for military service during World War II were greatly influenced by the requirements, both physical and mental, for effective service in modern warfare. They were also influenced by the pressure of manpower needs, the standards used, the varying quality of the examination, and the detail in which the conditions were recorded. Consequently, Selective Service statistics concerning impairments or rejections cannot be accepted at their face value as definitive measures of the prevalence of serious impairments or as proof of widespread deficiencies in national health; they are, rather, indicative of the existence of conditions that vary widely in their import and in their potentiality or need for correction.

14. What differences were found between draftees of the first and second World Wars?

A number of factors make it difficult to compare rejection rates for the two World Wars. These are differences in the age composition of the men called for service, examination standards, techniques of the examining physicians, and the improved medical facilities available in World War II, such as the use of chest x-rays. Moreover, in 1917–18 all men were given physical examinations before classification for deferment, but in World War II physical examinations were given only to those who had no reason for deferment.

In general, the principal causes of rejection were much the same in the two wars, particularly when allowance is made for the various factors involved. However, for many leading causes the proportion of men rejected was smaller in World War II. Cardiovascular and musculoskeletal defects, for example, each of which accounted for a little over 14 percent of all rejections in World War I, were responsible for only 8 and 7 percent respectively in World War II. There was also a decrease in rheumatic heart disease. On the other hand, hypertension was more frequently a cause of rejection in World War II. Two factors contributed to this situation—first, blood pressures were taken routinely in World War II but not in World War I, and second, a higher proportion of older men were examined in World War II. Tuberculosis showed a great decline, from 8 percent to 3 percent. This decrease is the more remarkable because for a greater part of the time chest x-rays were taken routinely in World War II, whereas this was exceptional in World War I. "Flat feet," another major cause of rejection in World War I, was not important in World War II. Rejections for mental disease, on the other hand, were many times higher in the second World War than in the first. One reason for the greater number of rejections for psychoneurotic disorders was that these conditions had been found to constitute a very important cause of disability in the armed forces, and consequently a concerted effort was made to screen out such cases in World War II.

15. What are the principal impairments of school children?

The National Health Survey 1959–61 disclosed that 18.0 percent of the children under age 17 had at least one chronic condition. The rate of prevalence of hay fever, asthma, and all other allergies was 74.3 per 1,000, and for sinusitis, bronchitis, and other respiratory diseases 34.2 per 1,000. These two groups accounted for almost half of all the chronic conditions reported for children under age 17. In addition, paralyses and orthopedic impairments accounted for 26.3 per 1,000 children; hearing impairments for 6.5 per 1,000; speech defects for 8.8; and heart disease for 4.2 per 1,000. It was noted in this connection that because of the small size of the sample used, the above figures on chronic conditions of limited prevalence among children, such as heart disease, cannot be considered entirely reliable.

The rate of prevalence of chronic conditions among children increases with age and is higher for boys than for girls. For all chronic conditions, 61.9 percent had received medical attention within the year preceding the date of the survey interview, and almost 90 percent of the children with chronic conditions were not limited in their normal activities.

16. What is the effect of overweight on mortality?

Recent life insurance studies have shown that those that are overweight for their height and age have a significantly higher mortality than those of average weight or less than average weight, the excess mortality rising rapidly with each increase in weight. Thus, men 10 percent overweight had an excess of 13 percent mortality; those 20 percent overweight 25 percent excess, and those 30 percent overweight 42 percent excess mortality. The penalty for added weight shows up even more clearly when compared with those who are in the desirable weight range—that is, the weight groups recording the lowest mortality. The excess mortality tended to be somewhat higher among older overweights than among those under 40 years old at the time of the issuance of the insurance.

Among women, much the same conditions were found. Those 10 percent overweight showed an excess mortality of 9 percent; those 20 percent overweight 21 percent excess, and those 30 percent overweight 30 percent excess mortality. The penalty for degrees of overweight appears to be lighter for women than for men.

The insurance investigation points out that if persons of any particular build kept their weight down to the average in the early twenties, it would be fairly close to the desirable weight at ages over 25. The usual additions to weight which occur as men and women grow older carry severe health penalties.

17. Which major conditions show increased mortality in overweight persons?

In both sexes, diabetes and degenerative diseases of the heart and arteries, nephritis, and gallstones and other biliary tract and liver disorders account for the higher mortality among overweights. Overweights are generally poorer risks for surgery than persons of lighter build. Even cancers and accidents show higher rates for overweight men and women than for average or underweight persons. Among obese persons the death rate for pneumonia also is above average. In addition, maternal mortality appears to be higher among stout women than among those who are average or thin.

18. What effect has medical progress had on the relative mortality of underweights?

As a result of the sharp reduction in the death rates from tuberculosis and pneumonia in recent decades, especially at the younger ages, these diseases account for a much smaller proportion of the total death rate than before. This reduction favors particularly the underweights who are more susceptible to these diseases than are heavier persons. Consequently, the downward trend in the total death rate has been fastest in underweights. This has improved their standing relative to those of heavier build. In fact, it is no longer true that underweight is a disadvantage in young adult life. Certainly, from the long-term point of view, underweight is conducive to long life once the age of maturity is reached.

19. What are the principal reasons for making urine tests?

Routine tests of the urine are most commonly made to determine the presence of undue amounts of albumin, sugar, pus, blood, and casts. At the same time the specific gravity of the urine may be determined. These urine tests can be made quickly and cheaply and, therefore, can be repeated as necessary. They serve a variety of uses, although in themselves they do not give sufficient information for a definitive diagnosis.

20. What is the significance of findings in urine tests?

Sugar in the urine, if significant in amount and persistent, is usually indicative of diabetes. In fact, many physicians teach diabetic patients how to test their urine for sugar to indicate how well their disease is kept under control. In some rare instances where sugar may be found in the urine regularly, it is due to a minor defect in kidney function. This condition, known as renal glycosuria, has little or no effect on health and longevity. Nowadays when sugar is present in successive urine specimens of a patient, a blood sugar test is made. A high blood sugar with glycosuria is usually a positive indication of the presence of diabetes. Albumin, casts, and blood, if found in the urine persistently in significant amounts, and with persistent low specific gravity, are indicative of either kidney or urinary tract disease or a disturbance in kidney function due to other conditions. Pus in the urine may be due to infection of the urinary tract or elsewhere.

Insurance studies of persons with small amounts of albumin show a significant increase in mortality, particularly among older persons with persistent albuminuria. The mortality is highest for overweight persons with this abnormality. Among those with casts only, mortality is slightly increased, but those with albumin and casts found together in the same specimen have a death rate two times the normal.

21. At what stage of tuberculosis are the chances of cure best?

For patients who receive appropriate chemotherapy, the chances of cure are very good no matter what the stage of their disease. Those with minimal disease can be rendered noninfectious within a few weeks and will recover from their disease in essentially all cases. Under proper management, over 90 percent of advanced cases will also recover. Minimal cases, of course, have less residual scarring of the lung.

Another advantage of tuberculosis being discovered at the minimal stage is that the patient has had less opportunity to spread the disease to others.

22. What effect does pleurisy have on longevity?

The significance of pleurisy varies greatly according to its cause, duration, and the age and weight of the patient. Many people use the term rather loosely to describe a chest pain of some severity which lasts for just a short time, but attacks of this kind are usually not due to pleurisy and may be of little significance. Sometimes pleurisy is a complication of an acute disease like pneumonia. In many cases it is also due to tuberculosis; this is particularly true of so-called wet pleurisy. Often, however, the cause of the disease is not determined. Life insurance investigations of persons with a history of pleurisy, the cause of which is not known, show them to have an appreciably higher mortality than average. Among those with dry pleurisy, the death rate was found to be somewhat under one and one-half times the average, and for those with wet pleurisy it was somewhat less. The record is poorer for young underweights and persons with attacks of long duration. Tuberculosis, pneumonia and influenza, and cancer were the principal diseases responsible for the excess mortality.

23. What effect does bronchitis have on longevity?

Mild degrees of bronchitis are of little significance, but chronic bronchitis is attended with considerable extra mortality. The mortality is particularly high among underweights, but it is also excessive among overweights. The extra mortality is due to high death rates from pneumonia and heart disease.

24. What are the prospects for persons with various types of allergy?

Allergies vary greatly in nature and severity. Hay fever, which is the most common, causes a great deal of temporary disability and discomfort but is without any effect on longevity so long as it does not develop into true asthma. In like manner, most of the other common allergies, such as eczema, have little or no effect on the duration of life, however troublesome they may be. Asthma, however, does effect longevity. Studies of insured persons with a history of the disease show a significant increase in the death rate. The mortality is especially high among those who had several recent severe attacks. Build is a factor in the outlook, the highest mortality being found among underweights and the next highest among those who were overweight. The record for cases complicated with chronic or severe bronchitis was particularly poor. Respiratory diseases, particularly pulmonary emphysema and pneumonia, account for the major part of the increased death rate among asthmatics, but there is also a significant excess in mortality from heart disease among them.

25. What is the effect of elevated blood pressure on longevity?

The recent insurance mortality study by the Society of Actuaries indicates that elevation of blood pressure carries with it a distinct probability of eventual development of hypertensive disease. With marked elevation of blood pressure, this probability is much increased and is revealed in excessive mortality. Thus, at age 35, men with average blood pressure have an expectation of 41.5 additional years. Those with a mild elevation (systolic 130, diastolic 90) show a life expectancy of only 37.5 years—a loss of 4 years. Those with higher blood pressure, namely, in the range of 140/95 show an expectancy of only 32.5 years or a loss of 9 years and those with marked elevation of blood pressure, 150/100, had an expectancy of only 25 years or a loss of 16.5 years. The magnitude of the reduction of life expectancy thus increases with the elevation of blood pressure. The loss in life expectancy is considerably less among women at all ages than among men. The excess mortality is accounted for by higher death rates from the diseases of the heart, blood vessels, and kidneys.

26. How does diabetes affect longevity?

Although the outlook for diabetics has improved greatly and steadily with successive advances in the treatment of the disease, the longevity of diabetics is still below the average for nondiabetics. The experience of patients of the George F. Baker Clinic, who are probably better than average diabetics, shows a reduction of about one-fourth to one-third in their length of life compared with the general population. For example, the expectation of life of the diabetic child of 10 is estimated at 44 years, as against 61.5 years in the general population. At age 40 the expectation for the diabetic is 23.7 years as against 33.3 for the general population. The chief reasons for the poorer longevity of diabetics are the high death rates from heart disease and nephritis. Specific hazards to diabetics directly related to their disease are diabetic coma, and diabetic gangrene. However, modern methods for the control of the disease have reduced these hazards to relatively small proportions.[1]

27. What is the effect of thyroid disease on longevity?

The most common form of thyroid disease is simple enlargement, which is rather prevalent in certain geographic areas. The areas principally affected in this country are around the Great Lakes and in certain inland mountain areas. It has been found that this type of goiter is due to iodine deficiency. The use of iodized salt has brought a reduction in the frequency of the condition, and it is now of much less importance than formerly. Thyroid enlargement is also particularly common in young women, but this is in great part a normal physiologic process and not an abnormality.

For the most part, simple thyroid enlargement of slight degree has no effect on longevity. Other types of thyroid disease and simple enlargements of greater extent are potentially more harmful, but fortunately surgical correction is easily made in these conditions. More serious are hyperthyroidism or so-called toxic goiter or thyroid tumors, some of which are cancerous. Uncorrected, these conditions can eventually be fatal, but toxic goiter and benign tumors of the thyroid can be cured by operation. Mortality studies of persons operated on for these conditions show that the mortality among them

[1] See Chapter 10, pages 149 and 150.

is little higher than average. Much can also be accomplished for cancer of the thyroid. As a result of atomic research, radioactive substances have been developed which appear to be helpful against this condition.[2]

28. What is the effect of anemia on longevity?

Simple anemia is in many respects much less a problem today because of the rapid increase in knowledge of nutrition. Persons with simple anemia have shown no marked increase in mortality due directly to the condition, but they appear to have a reduced efficiency and activity, and more illness because of their susceptibility to certain diseases. Of far greater seriousness is pernicious anemia in which the disturbance is due to a lack of substances necessary to the production of red blood cells. Such a substance was discovered in liver by Dr. G. R. Minot and Dr. W. P. Murphy, for which they were awarded the Nobel Prize in Medicine in 1934. Prior to that time the average duration of life after diagnosis of pernicious anemia was only two and one-half years. Today many persons with pernicious anemia who adhere to a prescribed medical regimen are able to carry on their customary pursuits and usually live long enough to succumb to another cause. However, longevity in the presence of this disease is reduced appreciably.

29. What is the mortality of persons with kidney stones?

Renal colic is a relatively frequent condition, but despite the great pain and distress it causes, it is rarely fatal. However, in some of the more severe and chronic cases, the condition requires relief through surgery, and among them the death rate is somewhat higher than average. Insured persons with a history of this condition but without operation have an approximately average mortality. The chief risk in this condition is the damage to the kidney; consequently, mortality from chronic nephritis is substantially increased among persons who have had renal colic. Fortunately, the nature of this condition is better understood today, and its frequency is declining.

30. What is the mortality among persons who have had a kidney removed?

Persons who had a kidney removed and are otherwise in good condition show some increase in mortality over average, particularly in the early years after operation. Subsequently the excess mortality

[2] See answer to Question 38 of Chapter 21, page 347.

decreases. The degree of excess mortality is, however, not very large; even for cases with a recent history, the death rate is about one and one-half times the average. Chronic kidney disease is the chief contributing factor to the excess mortality in these cases. This reflects the inability of the remaining kidney to carry the burden, particularly if it is overtaxed or if there is a recurrence of the condition for which one kidney was removed. The reasons for removal of the kidney vary, most important being tuberculosis of the kidney or damage to the kidney resulting from stones in the kidney or in the urinary passages.

31. What are the prospects for persons with gallbladder diseases?

Early and proper care of diseases of the gallbladder bring relief, and in such cases there is no impairment of longevity. Gallstones and inflammation of the gallbladder, which often occur in combination, are relatively common conditions. In fact, so frequently are they found at autopsy that it is obvious that the number of persons who show symptoms and receive treatment is only a fraction of the total affected. The condition is reported about six times as frequently in women as in men. Overweights are particularly prone to gallbladder disease. Many patients get well with medical treatment alone, but delay in operation for those where it is indicated may result in serious complications and premature death. For those treated medically the proportion surviving is below that of standard insured risks. The relative mortality is about normal where the time elapsed since the attack is three years or more. Where there is a history of multiple attacks the relative mortality is moderately high, one and one-third times that of standard risks. For those undergoing surgical treatment, the prognosis is better for cases where the gallbladder has been removed than for those in whom it simply had been drained. For cases operated within 10 years prior to acceptance for insurance, the relative mortality following removal of the gallbladder was one and one-fifth times the standard and for those with drainage one and one-third times. The mortality from diseases of the digestive system is high among these persons.

32. What is the mortality among persons with ulcer of the stomach or duodenum?

The outlook for persons with ulcer varies greatly according to the location of the ulcer and according to various individual characteristics of the patients. The frequency of ulcers in the duodenum, the portion of the intestine next to the stomach, is far greater than those in the stomach itself. Men are far more susceptible to the disease than women. These conditions are essentially chronic in nature and are characterized by more or less frequent acute recurrences which, however, may be prevented. The special hazards in these conditions are hemorrhage and perforation of the ulcer with resulting peritonitis. Most cases can be handled successfully with medical treatment alone. While the treatment calls for strict diet, modern medical management is greatly concerned with personal and emotional factors which apparently play an important part in the development and course of the disease. In many cases it is necessary to operate.

Persons with a history of either duodenal or gastric ulcer within five years prior to acceptance for insurance showed a lower proportion surviving than standard risks. The record was appreciably better for cases responding to medical treatment than for those which came to operation. Recurrences accounted for a major part of the excess mortality in all groups. Mortality from digestive tract cancer was also elevated.

For cases with a history within five years prior to acceptance for insurance (the medically treated group, excluding those with a history of hemorrhage), the relative mortality over 15 years was as follows—for duodenal or gastric ulcer, with medical treatment— one and one-fifth times the standard and with surgery about twice the standard.

Mortality from cancer of the digestive tract is very high among persons with a history of stomach ulcer. In some of these cases it is likely that the original diagnosis was at fault.[3]

33. What is the mortality among persons who have had venereal disease?

Gonorrhea apparently is without any significant effect on the duration of life, although it causes temporary disability and is a factor in the sterility of women. Syphilis, on the other hand, if untreated, frequently brings serious complications that greatly shorten life and may cause serious disability. This is due to the late complications of the disease such as syphilis of the heart and circulatory system. The peak of the death rate from such complications occurs

[3] See answer to Question 47 of Chapter 21, page 351.

between 40 and 50 years of age. The central nervous system is also the site of serious late complications. These often resulted in gross mental deterioration and accounted for a sizable proportion of the total number of persons in hospitals for mental disease in previous decades.

Proper treatment of early syphilis generally prevents these complications, and the mortality among such persons is not much higher than average. The use of penicillin has greatly improved the outlook in syphilis, with regard to both the prevention and treatment of late complications of the disease.

34. How many cripples are there in this country?

The number of persons with lost or crippled limbs is estimated at approximately 3,000,000. Males account for about 60 percent of the total. Only about 30 percent of the total number of cripples are unable to carry on their major activity because of their deformity, although many are disabled for other reasons. The prevalence rate of crippling, whether disabling or nondisabling, increases steadily with age, but the percentage with incapacitating impairments is highest in childhood and old age. The occurrence of new cases rises with age among males. Among females there is a decrease from childhood up to the middle thirties and thereafter a rapid rise with age.

35. What are the major causes of crippling?

Among males, approximately 70 percent of the crippling is due to accidents or other violence, but among females only about 40 percent is due to these causes. Among cases incapacitated by crippling, however, diseases are the major factor, accounting for about 55 percent in the males and 70 percent in the females. Occupational accidents overshadow all other accidental causes among males, but among females home accidents lead. Automobile accidents are the cause of about 6 percent of crippling among men and 5 percent among women. Of the diseases, apoplexy is the leading cause, both among men and women, particularly among those incapacitated by crippling, where it accounts for more than one-third of the total cases among men and more than two-fifths of incapacity among women. Poliomyelitis accounts for 5 percent of the male cripples and 10 percent among females. Congenital causes and rheumatism are other leading causes of crippling.

Among males, slightly less than half the crippling involves loss of members or limbs, but among females, only about one-sixth are of this type. Among those not disabled, the proportion with lost members is somewhat higher in both sexes. Among those incapacitated, however, crippling or paralysis predominates, accounting for about 90 percent of the cases among males, and 96 percent among females. The absence of one or more fingers accounts for about two-thirds of the cases with lost members. Only about one-fifth have lost a foot, leg, hand, or arm, and the number with two or more major members missing is very small indeed.

36. What effect does crippling have on longevity?

The longevity of cripples varies greatly according to the type, severity, and cause of the condition. Thus, the loss of toes, fingers, hands, or feet can be expected to have little if any effect on longevity. Even persons who have suffered major amputations as a result of accidents are not seriously affected in this respect. In fact, life insurance studies of men thus impaired have shown a relatively small increase in mortality over the average. In like manner, crippling resulting from poliomyelitis generally brings little or no impairment of longevity. The mortality experience of persons with spinal curvature is also generally favorable. However, the outlook is not as good for severe cases, particularly those due to tuberculosis, because of recurrence of that disease. Crippling due to stroke has a relatively poor prognosis because of the underlying and usually major impairment of the heart and arteries. This is true also for those who have suffered amputation for diabetic gangrene because these diabetics generally have serious impairment of the heart and blood vessels. In the experience of one clinic, the average duration of life after operation in these cases is about three years.

37. How many blind persons are there in the United States?

The number of blind persons in the country has been variously estimated, depending on the definition used and the method of data collecting. The National Health Survey 1957–58 estimated the number of blind at 960,000, which is a much higher figure than obtained in other national estimates. About 60 percent were females, and almost 90 percent were at least 45 years old, and more than two-thirds 65 and over.

38. What are the chief causes and types of blindness?

In a high proportion of cases the cause of blindness is unknown or not determined. Infectious diseases are implicated in a significant proportion of the cases, the most important of these diseases being syphilis and trachoma. Fortunately, blindness due to these conditions is rapidly decreasing. Sizable numbers of the blind are born so or become blind in infancy as a result of congenital causes or infection. Cases of the latter, particularly from gonorrhea, are much rarer than before because of the great improvement in measures to prevent blindness in the new born and the reduction in the incidence of congenital syphilis.

Accidents account for approximately one-twelfth of the cases of blindness. This cause is most important at the working ages, although the majority of these accidents are nonoccupational in origin. Glaucoma and cataracts are also important causes of blindness in adults.

39. What is the mortality among the blind?

The mortality of blind persons is greatly affected by the type and cause of the condition as well as age. Those whose blindness is not due to disease and who live under suitable conditions have a relatively favorable record. The most recent insurance experience with carefully selected cases of this type has been very satisfactory, showing a mortality about average. However, as a group, the blind suffer a high mortality. An earlier investigation showed that mortality was 20 times the average among children under 10, and 35 times average at ages 10 to 14. After that age, the ratio decreased rapidly; after 70 it was less than twice the average. The high mortality at the younger ages was due to the frequency of malignant tumors of the brain as a cause of blindness; in these cases, the deaths are usually due to the tumor.

Mortality among the blind is particularly high from such diseases as syphilis, cerebral hemorrhage, diabetes, arteriosclerosis, and kidney disease. In large part, the excess mortality from these causes is due to the existence of these conditions at the onset of blindness, and often they are actually the cause of it. Other diseases in which the death rates of the blind are distinctly above average are heart disease and pneumonia. Mortality from accidents, while above the average, does not show as great an excess as other causes. This is due to a markedly reduced exposure to accidents as a result of the sheltered and restricted environment in which blind persons live.

40. How does the incidence of defective teeth rank among the physical impairments?

Among children, defective teeth rank ahead of all other impairments. Almost everyone has had an experience with a decayed, missing, or filled tooth before early adolescence. At age 18, the average white person has 30 serviceable teeth. It is estimated that for the average white adult one tooth is extracted or indicated for extraction every two and one-half years of adult life. Based on health interviews in the recent U.S. National Health Survey, there were about 22 million persons in the United States who have lost all of their permanent teeth—about 1 in every 8 in the population. Of this total, over 200,000 were at ages under 25. Females generally have a higher prevalence of defective teeth than males. The increasing use of fluoridated water supplies by our cities suggests the hope that the high prevalence of caries in children's teeth will be materially reduced.

41. How comprehensive is the program of official and voluntary agencies in the rehabilitation of handicapped persons?

Specific but generally small-scale projects in behalf of various groups of the handicapped have been in operation for a long time. A great stimulus to measures for rehabilitating handicapped persons was provided by the need for workers in World War II and by the desire to rehabilitate the war veterans who became disabled by disease or injury while in the service. Consequently, this problem was given greater attention than ever before. At present, the most comprehensive effort is the joint federal-state program administered by the Office of Vocational Rehabilitation in the Department of Health, Education, and Welfare. This program, according to which the federal government gives financial support to the states for their work, now operates in all states, the District of Columbia, Puerto Rico, and outlying regions. The program combines all the necessary services to prepare the disabled person for a job which utilizes his best skills and his full capacities, and to secure his placement in such a job. These services include not only counseling and guidance but also medical and surgical care needed for rehabilitation, artificial appliances, job training, and, if necessary, the occupational tools and equipment. In fiscal year 1963 alone, nearly 370,000 persons were served by the various state vocational rehabilitation agencies, and an all-time high of over 110,000 disabled persons were rehabilitated. In the twenty years from 1944 to 1963 inclusive, a total of over 1,500,000 disabled persons completed their rehabilitation under this program.

In addition to those rehabilitated under the federal-state program, there are sizable but undetermined numbers who are served by private agencies and the Veterans Administration. However, the available facilities are far short of the needs, for it is estimated that there are between 1,500,000 and 2,000,000 men and women of working age so severely disabled that they cannot support themselves or their families. Moreover, each year about 250,000 men and women become disabled by chronic illness, congenital defects, and accidents, who would benefit from rehabilitation services.

Chapter 20

Mental

Health

1. What is mental health?

Mental health has been defined as "the ability to face problems and make choices, to find satisfaction and happiness in the accomplishment of daily tasks, to work efficiently and to live effectively with others." It is much more than the mere absence of disease and defect; it is a positive state of mental integration, efficiency, and happiness that enables one to adapt to the environment, to have a feeling of confidence and security, to understand oneself and be capable of love and enjoying life. This is a large order; it is a goal rather than a norm. Just as there are relatively few who do not have some slight physical defects—perhaps poor teeth, or imperfect eyesight, or a weak joint which is favored a little—so there are few individuals who do not also have some form of emotional disturbance.

The universality of emotional or mental disorders means that they are probably the most widespread of all health problems. It is only recently that their importance has been recognized, and they are still far from completely understood.

2. What are mental deficiency and mental disease?

Mental deficiency, a subnormal state of development of some or all mental functions, results in most cases from some constitutional defect of the brain or nervous system. It may be inherited, congenital, or acquired through injury or disease; it is essentially incurable and unremediable, except as treatment and training form habits by which the mental defective, under favorable circumstances, may compensate to some extent for his limitations.

Idiots, the lowest grade of mental defectives, are unable to do anything for themselves and cannot be taught even the simplest rules of hygiene and cleanliness. The next grade of mental defective, the imbecile, can be taught simple routine tasks, particularly of a manual nature. Morons have a mental capacity reaching to the borderline of low normal intelligence. They are fundamentally incapable of the achievements of the normal mind since they are defective in reasoning and judgment and live by habit. With some guidance they are, however, often able to manage their affairs and get along fairly well if situations are not too complicated. Because of their lack of self-control and judgment, many become social problems. These deficiencies, together with their susceptibility to suggestion, may make them dangerous tools of more intelligent criminals.

Mental disease is a category of illness which prevents effective use of a person's mental and emotional equipment. It is often independent of intellectual capacity. Even a genius may have so narrow or distorted a view of reality that he cannot get along. Then he is mentally sick. Mental disease may be caused by "physical" or by psychologic disorders. It is a product of the interaction of an individual's constitutional make-up with his total environment and experience. The emotions and intellectual processes are so closely bound up that it becomes increasingly difficult to separate the two. Mental disease is disease of the whole person.

3. What are the more common forms of mental disease?

There are two general types of mental disease distinguished by the degree of the individual's awareness of the world around him.

Persons suffering from neuroses are usually in fairly good touch with their environment, although they may have a somewhat warped view of it, whereas those suffering from psychoses tend to live in worlds of their own.

The neuroses are more frequent than the psychoses. It is even probable that no person is entirely free from neurosis, a category that includes the phobias, obsessions, complexes, hysterias, and anxieties. Despite the universality of neuroses, they are seldom severe enough to require placing a person in an institution. Less than one-eighth of the first admissions to mental hospitals in this country are so-called "psychoneurotics."

The psychoses, on the other hand, although not always more serious than the neuroses, more often require institutional rather than other types of care. The most common of all psychoses is schizophrenia or dementia precox, a disease usually marked by retreat from reality and sometimes by obvious scattered personality. About one-fourth of all first admissions to mental hospitals are schizophrenics. The psychoses of old age, technically called senile psychosis and psychosis with cerebral arteriosclerosis, are together responsible for almost as many first admissions as schizophrenia. Alcoholic psychosis and alcoholism account for less than one-seventh of the first admissions; manic-depressive psychosis for about one-thirtieth, and involutional psychosis—a depression of late middle age—about the same.

Paresis, the mental degeneration caused by syphilis, was once a relatively frequent form of insanity, but is now the diagnosis in less than 1 percent of the new cases entering mental hospitals. The convulsive disorders, including epilepsy, account for only about 1 percent. There are a number of other mental diseases, but they are relatively rare. A few, like paranoia, have been publicized out of proportion to their frequency.

4. How prevalent is mental disease?

About one out of every eight men examined for the draft in World War II was rejected because of personality or mental difficulties. One percent of the total population is incapacitated on any given day by mental illness or mental deficiency or by complaints arising from mental disorders. More than half of the hospital beds in the country are occupied by mental patients. In 1963, well over one million persons received treatment in our mental hospitals and in the psychiatric wards of general hospitals.

Careful checks in the Eastern Health District of Baltimore and in Williamson County in Tennessee brought to light a mental disorder case rate between 60 and 70 per 1,000 persons. When an even more detailed survey was made in three selected areas, the rate was almost doubled.

In the more recent Midtown Manhattan study of life stress and mental health, the authors found that 70.8 percent of the respondents evidenced mixed anxiety, and that 51.7 percent reported some psychosomatic symptom. The writers were careful to point out, however, that the majority of persons with these symptoms are not significantly impaired by them. On the other hand, 17.1 percent of the respondents belonged to such important psychiatric symptom groups as epilepsy, schizophrenia, cycloid affective psychoses, and brain disease.

All this adds up to the conclusion that a substantial fraction of the population (some estimates are as high as 10 percent) either are now suffering from some form of serious mental difficulty or will be at some time in their lives.

5. Is mental illness increasing in this country?

There is no evidence that mental illness is more prevalent in any given age group today than 50 or 100 years ago, but it is true that a greater proportion of the total population is now hospitalized for mental disease. Since the turn of the century the rate of hospitalization for mental illness has more than doubled. This is the result of a growing awareness of the problems of mental health, of increasing urbanization of the nation, of the gradual aging of the population, and, most important of all, of the marked increase in mental health facilities. The rate of first admissions to mental hospitals rises rapidly with age, and an increasing proportion of the population is in the old-age group. For generations some writers and doctors have been claiming that mental disease was on the increase, even on an age-for-age basis. The statistics do not seem to bear this out. Before the Civil War and in what is considered the relatively stable Victorian Age, many people were saying the pace of "modern" life was causing proportionately more and more crackups. Actually, the only field in which there is any sign of a true rise in mental disease is in the psychoses associated with alcoholism. At the same time, there has been a marked decline in paresis.

6. How does this country compare with others in regard to mental health?

The United States has one of the highest rates of hospitalization for mental disease in the world, but this is not a cause for alarm. It means that this country at least realizes that the mentally disordered need help. How the United States compares with other nations in incidence or prevalence of mental disease no one can tell, as international figures on a comparable basis are not available. Outside of North America, Western Europe, and the British Commonwealth, relatively little is done about mental disease.

7. Are there relatively more mental patients in some sections of the country than others?

New England and the Middle Atlantic states have the highest rates of hospitalization for mental disease and deficiency, and the South Central states the lowest. New York, with 555 resident mental patients per 100,000 population in 1960, had proportionately more than five times as many as Utah, the lowest state. These rates of hospitalization have a tendency to increase or decrease with the degree of urbanization of the states. Even within a state the relative number of mental patients from cities is usually much higher than from rural areas. The excess of mental patients from cities is explained partly by the fact that doctors and clinics are concentrated there. The crowded conditions of living in urban sections also make home-care there, for the mentally sick, difficult if not impractical. According to some authorities, the stresses and strains of city life may also play a role in increasing the frequency of mental disease.

8. Is mental illness especially prevalent among certain racial, religious, and nativity groups?

There apparently are some differences, but there is no proof that they reflect differences in susceptibility. It is not a question of inherent weakness but rather of the kinds of lives various groups live, whether by choice or by force of circumstances. Minority groups in communities often exhibit somewhat higher rates of hospitalization for mental illness than the majority groups. A racial or religious group may have a high frequency of mental disease in one place and not in another. In many sections of the country the rates for Negroes are much higher than for whites, although in some Southern surveys mental disease was found more frequently among the whites.

The foreign-born have often shown more mental illness than the general average. Native children of the foreign-born do better on that score than their parents, but not so well as second or third generation natives. So many conflicting factors are involved in the causation of mental illness that no reliable conclusion can be drawn in regard to the true prevalence in various population groups.

9. Is mental disease more common in old age?

Mental disease is much more common among the old than among those at other periods of life, but it is not true that all mental diseases increase in incidence with age. Senile psychosis and psychosis from cerebral arteriosclerosis are by nature primarily diseases of later life. On the other hand, schizophrenia, the most common form of functional psychosis (as distinguished from psychosis having organic cause), has its peak of onset in early adult life. Manic-depressive psychosis may come on at almost any age, but particularly between 20 and 60. The highest rate of first admissions to mental hospitals is among the old. Relatively few young children are hospitalized for mental illness. This does not mean that children are immune to mental disease, but rather that the diseases are usually not diagnosed until later. Furthermore, only a fraction of the state mental hospitals have facilities for the treatment of mentally ill children. It is hoped that as local day-care treatment centers are constructed under the 1963 Federal Mental Care Act, many thousands of sick children will receive the professional services they sorely need.

10. Are there significant differences in the recorded incidence of mental disease by sex and marital status?

At every age, men have higher rates of first admission to mental hospitals than women. Some of the difference in rates by sex may arise from a greater reluctance to commit women than men to mental hospitals.

Marriage is so fundamental a part of normal living that it would be strange if the degree of marital success were not connected with emotional balance and with mental health. Marital status is a current indication of a person's mental health as well as a factor in future changes. As might be expected, the married have the best mental health record, and the divorced have the worst. In between come the widowed and the single; the widowed on the whole do somewhat better in regard to mental health than the single.

11. Is mental illness more common among the poor than the well-to-do?

Mental disease, like so many physical diseases, is brought about by the interaction of individuals and their environment. The environment includes all the surroundings, not only physical but also psychologic. It includes the comfortable situations which money can arrange and the frustrating ones which poverty brings. In addition to creating circumstances particularly suitable for breeding mental illness, poverty may also be a symptom of emotional or mental disorder already present.

By far the largest proportion of state hospital patients come from poor homes, where outside financial aid is required, or from families just barely able to support themselves. However, since state hospitals are free, a bias in the direction of those unable to afford private care has crept into studies of state hospital patients. Other investigations indicate the same social and economic trend in mental disease hospitalized. The poorer communities have more mental disease. Within cities, the prevalence of mental illness receiving hospitalization decreases from the crowded center toward the residential suburbs.

12. Does mental illness run in families?

Current opinion is that mental disease is not directly inherited, but that some predisposing factor can be passed on. Parents with mental disorder are more likely than others to have mentally ill children, probably because the home in which the children are raised is conducive to its development. Even mild mental disorders resulting in family disruption may have bad effects on the mental health of children. The incidence of mental illness among the children of the mentally ill is many times higher than in the general population. It has also been suggested on the basis of studies of mental disease in twins that there may be an inheritable predisposing factor in some kinds of mental illness.

13. Do "physical" health problems contribute to mental illness?

Mental disease can be caused by "physical" illness, particularly if the brain is directly affected. The psychoses of old age and of cerebral arteriosclerosis and paresis are examples. Serious nutritional deficiencies and metabolic disturbances may also affect mental health. A starvation diet is likely to make persons who were previously quite friendly abnormally suspicious and antagonistic. It is a commonplace that patients with chronic physical difficulties are likely to be chronically irritable as well. Almost any serious illness is sure to affect the mental outlook of the patient. Illness in which the chances of cure are small or in which the hospitalization is likely to be prolonged have an especially serious impact.

14. Does mental disease contribute to other health problems?

The sharp division between mental and "physical" health problems has almost disappeared. Estimates of the importance of mental health in the so-called "physical" disorders vary, but Dr. William C. Menninger, when he was psychiatric consultant to the armed forces during the war, suggested that between 35 and 70 percent of the persons consulting physicians do so because of mental disorders known or unknown. Almost half of all the patients going to gastroenterologists (specialists in stomach and intestinal troubles) have no organic stomach or intestinal disorders, but display symptoms which are essentially the result of emotional difficulties.

15. How many patients are currently treated in mental institutions in the United States in the course of a year?

There were more than one million patients (including the mentally retarded) treated in the country's approximately 600 mental hospitals and institutions at the close of 1962. The population of mental institutions has been declining in recent years.

16. How many psychiatrists and other technical personnel are there in the field of mental hygiene?

There are about 15,000 psychiatrists in the country. For the 7,500 working in mental hospitals and clinics, the case load averages about 111 patients per doctor. There are about 18,500 nurses working in mental hospitals and clinics and there are about 5,200 clinical psychologists and about 7,500 social workers. These trained men and women work in approximately 600 mental hospitals and institutions and about 1,800 psychiatric clinics. In addition, there are 128 public and 209 private institutions for the mentally retarded. This is the limited field force to deal with the huge mental health problems of the country.

17. How great is the unfilled need for trained psychiatric personnel?

The level of care for mental patients, while greatly improved in recent years, is still incredibly low in many areas of the country. The heavy case load of patients per psychiatrist in mental hospitals means that the patients in the majority of hospitals cannot possibly be effectively treated. As a result, years of life are wasted. There is a need for at least twice as many psychiatrists as there are now in the country, to make a total of 30,000. Although more than half of all hospitalized patients are mental cases, less than one-fortieth of all registered nurses were in psychiatric service. The shortage of clinical psychologists is equally serious. It was estimated recently that there was a need for at least 10,000 more clinical psychologists. Psychiatric social workers are also in great demand and short supply. In 1963, there were 7,500 in mental health establishments, whereas 15,000 are needed to satisfy the standard recommended by the American Psychiatric Association.

18. How many more mental hospitals and clinics are needed?

A large expansion of the mental hospital system is needed. There are at present about 450,000 acceptable beds, not counting those for mental defectives or epileptics, and another 300,000 are necessary. The present overcrowding in mental institutions is almost universal; mental hospitals average about one-sixth more patients than their rated capacity and in some states they have 50 percent more patients than they were built to care for.

The shortage of clinics and community mental health centers which can do a great deal of preventive work and help to relieve the load on hospitals is even more acute. In some states there are no psychiatric clinics. About 1,800 full- or part-time community clinics exist in the country and most of them have long waiting lists. The movement for community mental health centers prepared to give both inpatient and outpatient treatment is now underway and supported by the recent federal legislation. These centers together with the development of psychiatric services in general hospitals will, it is hoped, take the burden of care from the state mental hospitals in the future.

Psychiatric services for schools, colleges, universities, and for courts and prisons are pitifully few. The problem is twofold: many of these institutions are not yet aware of the valuable use they could make of psychiatric personnel in preventing mental illness; second, many which are conscious of this need cannot find trained persons to do the work.

19. How does care for the mentally ill vary from region to region?

In expenditures per mental patient, the Mountain states, the Middle Atlantic states, and the North Central states lead. The Southern states spend the least on their mental patients. In the number of staff members per patient, the West North Central, the Mountain, and New England states lead, and the Southern and the East South Central state trail.

20. How much does mental illness cost the country annually?

The cost of maintaining more than half a million patients in public mental hospitals, including federal institutions, was more than 1¾ billion dollars in 1962. That, however, is only the beginning. In 1962, the cost of care of neuropsychiatric patients in the veterans hospitals was about 275 million dollars. No figures are available for the cost of private care, the loss in income because of mental illness, the cost of accidents or of crime resulting from mental disorder. Without question, the annual bill to the country for mental illness runs into many billions.

21. Do the patients in public mental institutions receive adequate care?

The average daily expenditure for mental patients in public hospitals, except those of the federal government, was about $5.53 per individual in 1961. The expenditure of hundreds of millions of dollars each year on hospitalized mental patients buys them only the minimum in facilities and food, and purchases relatively little in the way of psychiatric treatment. Hospitalization for mental illness too often means merely custodial care in many sections of the country.

22. Is mental disease curable?

A great many types are. As yet, there is scant hope for cure for senile or cerebral arteriosclerotic psychosis. Likewise, by the time a patient develops paresis, his syphilis has gone so far that the chances of cure are not good. Most of the functional psychoses, however, can be cured, but the proportion which are actually cured is still relatively small. In part this is the result of a deficiency in funds for treatment and personnel. Also, some cures require prolonged and intensive care, which is not available for large groups of patients. The neuroses are on the whole much more curable. It is encouraging, however, that in some institutions where facilities are more adequate, a high proportion of the patients suffering from schizophrenia, manic-depression psychosis, and involutional psychosis achieve recovery or are greatly improved at the time of their discharge.

23. What are the methods of treatment and for what kinds of mental disease are they used?

Aside from the medical and surgical treatments for mental illness having primarily "physical" origin, there are a number of essentially psychologic or psychiatric treatments for mental illness. Psychotherapy ranges from suggestive and supportive treatment, in the form of reassuring and explanatory talks, through hypnosis and psychoanalysis. Psychoanalysis is the most intensive and longest type of treatment, often requiring two or more years. An increasingly important form of therapy includes the use of drugs to relax the patient and to help block the development of symptoms. In some more advanced states, about 40 percent of the patients receive some form of this drug therapy with favorable results. Group psychotherapy, in which a number of patients meet with the psychiatrist at one time, is also widely practiced.

A highly publicized psychiatric treatment a few decades ago consisted in the use of shock—electrically or drug induced—in manic-depressive and involutional psychoses and in schizophrenia. While this treatment in conjunction with psychotherapy often proved successful, the trend in recent years has been away from these approaches in the care of such patients and directed more toward the use of certain of the tranquilizing drugs.

Another dramatic form of treatment, known as a prefrontal lobotomy, in which certain lobes are disconnected from the rest of the brain, was employed at first hopefully in the treatment of severe cases of mental disease but has been largely discontinued in recent years.

24. How much could be saved in cost of care by more widespread use of therapy already available?

If all patients in mental hospitals could receive the intensive and skilled care now available to the more fortunate ones, much could be accomplished in restoring thousands of the sick to their families and to their communities while they are still in the active and productive period of their lives. This would, moreover, ultimately decrease the annual bill for hospitalization by many millions of dollars.

At the same time, a newer concept in the care of mental patients is developing out of recent experience. The trend is more and more away from the large custodial institutions and in the direction of smaller, well-staffed establishments, near the patients' homes, where there are facilities for intensive care leading to their early discharge. Such facilities may include day-care, in which the patient goes home at night; or night-care, where the person does his work during the day and returns at night; open-door hospitals, where patients are free from close restriction; convalescent homes; and even foster homes. The emphasis is increasingly on skilled intensive therapy, under close supervision, so that the individual may return to normal life in the community in the shortest period.

In addition, much more must be accomplished through preventive effort at the local level, through more adequate community facilities, such as the all-purpose mental health centers now made possible country-wide by the recent federal legislation.

25. What is the average duration of hospital stay of mental patients?

Marked changes have occurred in recent years as the result of the newer treatment of mental patients. Where only a decade or two ago, those who were hospitalized remained for an average period of three to four years, today up to 75 percent of admissions to state mental hospitals are discharged within a matter of months. In some favorable institutions, up to 85 percent are discharged within a year. Even schizophrenia patients who, in the past, spent the longest time in the hospitals, under present conditions get out within a few months in the great majority of cases. Only those who do not recover under the initial intensive treatment stay on for long periods. Alcoholics, manic-depressives, and those with involutional psychosis have an average hospitalization time somewhat longer than that of the schizophrenics, but they, too, are showing improvement in their rates of recovery. Patients with paresis and senile dementia are likely to be hospitalized for around two years and those with psychosis with cerebral arteriosclerosis for about two and one-half years. The hospital stay of persons with these conditions usually ends in death rather than discharge. There is great variability in the duration of hospitalization for various mental disorders in the institutions of the various states. Much depends on the adequacy of facilities and particularly of trained personnel.

26. Are most discharged mental hospital patients readmitted later?

Over one-quarter of all persons admitted to New York State mental hospitals in a year are former patients; about six-tenths of the manic-depressives and about 40 percent of the schizophrenics admitted in a year are former patients. Even in cases where the patient is able to remain outside the hospital, he may not be fully cured. In some areas, where there are limited facilities for mental care, there is a conscious effort made to discharge patients after a short stay in order to give someone else an opportunity to use the hospital space.

Preparation of the home and the community to which the patient is to return is very important in helping the mentally ill to complete his recovery or at least retain what improvement he has made in the hospital. Too often the interpersonal problems in the home which have contributed to the mental illness in the first place may still be present when the patient returns. In one study of two groups of discharged patients, among those whose return home had been prepared by intensive social work, 83 percent were able to remain outside of the hospital for more than six months; of the others, for whom no special preparation had been made, only 40 percent stayed out of the hospital for more than six months.

27. How do death rates among mental patients compare with those of the general population?

Although mental disease is seldom a direct cause of death, the mentally ill have much higher death rates than the general population. In 1958, the death rate for patients in New York State mental hospitals was more than seven times as high as for the state as a whole. Part of this difference is due to the higher average age of the patients, but even when the mortality is compared on an age period basis, there is a markedly higher rate for the hospitalized population.

In the organic mental diseases, such as paresis and psychosis with cerebral arteriosclerosis, the excess of deaths among mental patients is especially great; but even in the functional psychoses, such as manic-depressive psychosis and schizophrenia, the death rates, on an age-for-age basis, are generally much higher among mental hospital patients than among the general population.

28. Is alcoholism a mental disease and can it be cured?

Many cases of alcoholism are due to mental illness. Alcoholism and alcoholic psychosis are responsible for about 7 percent of the first admissions to mental hospitals, more for males than for females.

Many state hospitals are reporting a large number of discharges of their alcoholic patients as recovered or much improved. Many of these patients, however, are soon readmitted to the hospitals for further treatment. It should be noted that the major part of the problem of alcoholism with its resulting emotional disorders is not met by treatment in mental hospitals. It is much more widespread in its impact on society.

29. How prevalent is alcoholism, and is it increasing?

It is estimated that there are more than 4,500,000, chronic excessive drinkers in the country. Alcoholism is more prevalent today than a half century ago, and is involving an increasing number of women. From the turn of the century until the enactment of Prohibition, there was a steady decline in the rate of hospitalization for alcoholic mental disease. Right after Prohibition came into effect the decline was accelerated, but it was soon followed by a steady rise in the rate. The peak was reached in 1941. During World War II the rate fell again, only to start up once more after its close.

In more recent years health authorities in many states have realized that alcoholism is a serious medical problem and have set up facilities for medical care and rehabilitation of alcoholics and for research into the problem.

30. Are most criminals insane and can criminality be cured?

Legally, criminals are not insane until ruled so either by a court trial or by court-appointed psychiatrists. The word "insane" refers to a state defined by law; it is not a medical term. Only a small proportion of criminals are either legally insane or actually psychotic, probably from 3 to 8 percent. Mental deficiency and other serious abnormalities, including psychopathic personality, account for probably no more than one-quarter of the criminals, but most of the others can be considered as maladjusted and mentally disordered to some degree.

The conflicts and disorders which result in criminal behavior are so often deep-seated and ingrained that cure is ordinarily exceedingly difficult. In most parts of the country no attempt is made to give criminals psychiatric treatment.

31. How widespread is criminality and delinquency?

Crimes reported in the country in 1961 numbered close to two million. The prison population of the country is over 220,000 (excluding local jails), and the number of children in all institutions for delinquents, public and private, is one-fifth as great. The number of prisoners in the country was increasing before the war but from 1940 until 1945 the trend was reversed; since then the prison population has again been rising.

32. Is epilepsy a mental disease and can it be cured?

Epilepsy is an organic disorder of the nervous system often accompanied by convulsions and by mental and emotional disturbance. Drug therapy is used for epilepsy and psychoanalysis and other psychotherapies for the accompanying emotional problems. An ordering of the patient's life is usually necessary to avoid fits from coming on. Although many epileptics have their disorder brought under control, and some seem to grow out of their difficulty gradually, there is no cure for the disorder. It is possible, however, to live with epilepsy. There are a large number of epileptics in the country whose disease is so well controlled, in many cases by drug therapy, that they can lead almost normal lives; most have never been inside a mental hospital.

Statistically, epileptics are frequently grouped with mental defectives. This is a carry-over from the days when epilepsy was considered a form of deficiency. Although some epileptics are also mentally deficient, there is no necessary connection between the two conditions. In many states epileptics are still treated in the same institution as mental defectives rather than in hospitals for mental disease. As a result, little benefit is received from their treatment.

33. How many epileptics are there in the United States?

Estimates based on draft records of the two World Wars and special surveys indicate that 500,000 to 800,000 persons have epilepsy in this country. Only a fraction of the epileptics are hospitalized or kept in institutions of any sort.

34. What are the grades of mental deficiency?

Mental deficiency is classified according to the level of intelligence which the individual can attain. The lowest form, idiots, reach a mental age of 3 years or less; the mental age of imbeciles, can be as high as 7 years, and of morons as high as 12. These classifications are not hard and fast because intelligence is difficult to measure precisely, and many defectives are borderline cases. In addition, solving emotional problems may on occasion result in an apparent increase in intelligence.

The least severe deficiencies are the most common. In institutions for defectives there are about two and a half times as many morons as idiots, and nearly twice as many imbeciles as idiots.

35. What is the prevalence of mental deficiency?

Institutionalized mental defectives in the country now number over 160,000, but a great many are never placed in institutions. Estimates of the total number are 1,500,000 or more.

36. Is mental deficiency inherited?

Much mental deficiency is congenital. Familial mental defects are the most common forms, amounting to almost half of the classified hospitalized cases of defectives. Mongolism, which accounts for about one-tenth of the hospitalized cases of deficiency, can occur in families with no previous record of mental deficiency. Most nonfamilial and nonmongoloid types of deficiency are the result of disease or injury.

37. At what age are most mental defectives admitted to institutions?

The median age at admission for mental defectives is just under 14 years. Although more than three-quarters of the defectives in special schools or institutions were first admitted before they had reached the age of 20, some came in at ages past 60. The median age at admission for idiots is about 9 years, while for imbeciles it is nearly 14 and for morons almost 15. On the whole, female defectives are about a year and a half older at admission than males. Since deficiency is present at birth in almost all cases, regardless of sex, the difference in age at admission is probably accounted for by the lesser difficulty in caring for girl defectives at home and possibly also by a greater unwillingness to send girls than boys off to institutions.

38. What is the length of stay in institutions of mental defectives?

Defectives, on the whole, spend more time in institutions than the seriously mentally ill, although a smaller proportion of them are being cared for in institutions. The lower rate of hospitalization for the defectives may be a result of their lesser involvement in bizzare situations calling public attention to their state. Their length of institutional stay reflects the relative incurability of mental deficiency. More than half of the resident mental defectives in New York State hospitals in 1958 had been there over 10 years.

39. How does the mortality of mental defectives compare with that of the general population?

Mental defectives as a group have a mortality many times that of the general population. The highest death rates are found among the lowest type of feeble-minded—the idiots. In a study in Massachusetts their death rates were nearly five times as high as the rates for the general population; at the younger ages the rates were more than ten times as high. Among imbeciles, the crude death rate was more than twice as high as in the general population. Both imbeciles and idiots had higher death rates in every age group than nondefectives. Among morons, mortality was much lower than among the other feeble-minded, but it was higher, on an age-for-age basis, than for the general population.

40. Can mental defectives be trained to lead nearly normal lives?

A large number of persons who have been in institutions for the mentally deficient are later able to work and to get along fairly well. They are the borderline cases. Of those aged 15 or more who were discharged from public institutions in New York State during 1958, 44 percent were judged capable of supporting themselves entirely and an additional 39 percent of helping to support themselves.

41. How general is the practice of sterilizing mental defectives?

In 1963, 30 states scattered throughout the country had laws permitting the sterilization of defectives and, in some instances, also of psychotics. By the end of 1963, a total of 63,678 individuals had been sterilized since the first of these laws was passed in 1907. In 1963 alone there were 467 such operations in the states having sterilization laws and of those, a little more than half were performed in North Carolina.

42. How many mentally handicapped children are there in the public school system?

There were 222,000 children enrolled in special public schools for the deficient and the socially maladjusted in 1958. In addition, 490,000 children were attending classes for speech defectives in 1958. While not all speech defects are the results of mental deficiency or emotional disorder, a great many of them are.

43. What provisions are made for psychiatric help to school children?

In some parts of the country, there is still no provision for psychiatric help to school children. Approximately 75 percent of all psychiatric clinics, including a number which also treated adults, worked with school-age children or 1 for every 1,300 children (5 to 18 years of age). A few states have systems of traveling clinics. In New York, for example, teams composed of a psychiatrist, a psychologist, two psychiatric social workers, and a clerk go from place to place testing school children and making recommendations.

44. What can be done to prevent mental disease?

A great deal can be done in every community toward giving the problems of mental health adequate attention. Teachers, lawyers, social workers, personnel workers, public health workers, doctors, nurses, and others have the primary responsibility for preventive work because their close contact with many individuals brings them opportunities to detect emotional stress. If they understand the needs of mental hygiene, situations which might result in mental disease can be avoided, and incipient cases of disorder can be dealt with before they become serious. There is obviously also a need for clinics to which the early cases of mental illness can be referred.

Educational institutions offer great possibilities for preventive work. Mass testing of students in schools and colleges, as some experiments in this direction have proved, would uncover a great many cases of mental illness which had not yet become acute. Psychiatric orientation of teachers would lessen the adjustment difficulties which arise among school children. Proper sex education would go a long way to avoid misunderstandings and conflicts which may later result in mental illness.

All of these suggestions require a great expansion in training and clinical facilities. This can be accomplished only by a coordinated program of voluntary and governmental agencies on all levels, local, state, and national.

45. What is the federal government doing about mental health?

Under the Mental Health Act passed in 1946, a mental health program was set up within the Public Health Service. The act created the National Institute of Mental Health at Bethesda, Maryland, to handle research both at its own 500-bed hospital and in field projects. It also provided funds for grants to states for expansion and operation of clinics, and to professional schools for expansion of psychiatric and mental hygiene training and for stipends to students.

From this modest beginning, a major mental health operation has developed which has given leadership and direction to the entire country in this important field. The National Institute of Mental Health is now a $200,000,000 a year agency with a research grant program of about $75,000,000 a year and a training grant budget of about 50,000,000. As a result, a vast field of research on a large variety of subjects related to mental health is supported by federal funds. Included in this effort is the Title V or Mental Health Projects Program, which is a most important innovation and accounts for many of the new developments in community mental health services.

In addition, many demonstrations and clinics on mental health are held by the public health service in conjunction with local medical and psychiatric organizations in various parts of the country. Techniques for prevention and group therapy and for accelerated individual therapy are receiving special attention because of the great need to use more effectively the limited personnel and facilities there are.

The Institute of Mental Health also issues pamphlets and other educational material for wide distribution to the general public. Finally, the Public Health Service, under the Hospital Construction Act, aids in the construction of mental hospitals.

46. What is the new National Mental Health Program?

A major development occurred in 1963, when Congress approved basic legislation which will affect the course of mental health care in every state of the Union. This program should advance operations on four fronts.

1) It provided grants-in-aid to the states for planning a comprehensive approach to the problems of mental health. For the first time in the history of the country, each state will be able to formulate a well-coordinated program in its area. A total of $8 million was appropriated for this purpose.

2) An appropriation of $150 million was made available for a three-year period beginning in July, 1964, for grants-in-aid to construct comprehensive community mental health centers. This should make possible the construction of approximately 145 centers where patients can receive preventive and diagnostic services, outpatient and inpatient treatment, as well as rehabilitation services, all of this near their homes. The centers are planned also to provide assistance to the mentally retarded. When all states have their community mental health centers fully organized, the total effect should be to materially change the direction of mental health care from the large custodial hospitals to community-oriented and dynamically administered smaller institutions.

3) A total of $6 million was appropriated to initiate a broadly conceived hospital improvement program. The state hospitals will thus be encouraged, through grants, to develop changes within their organization to help move many patients from custodial care to community-centered care.

4) An inservice training program provides $3.3 million for the fiscal year 1964, to increase the effectiveness of the staffs in mental hospitals.

As Dr. Robert Felix, the recent Director of the National Institute of Mental Health, has pointed out, this new legislation and its provision of sizable resources by the Congress creates a new era for the more effective prevention and control of mental disease and retardation.

47. What are the states doing about mental health?

All states maintain hospitals for the mentally diseased. They also have educational programs on mental health for either the general public or professional personnel, or both, and they all have training programs and provide professional services outside of state hospitals.

The new Federal Mental Health Act of 1963 will unquestionably increase state participation in mental health work, increase the amounts provided for mental disease prevention and mental health care to match federal funds as provided for in the recent legislation. But even before the passage of the recent federal legislation, most states had been carrying on strong programs for community health services, including the development of psychiatric services in general hospitals, mental health clinics, etc. In perhaps 20 states there are now state-wide community health services which establish a coordinated system of local mental health work under the supervision of a state commission and supported by state funds.

48. What is the World Federation for Mental Health?

The World Federation for Mental Health is a voluntary, nongovernmental organization started in 1948 by representatives from 22 nations. Recognized by UNESCO and the World Health Organization, it has already made a number of recommendations on programs to promote mental health. Membership in the federation is open to all nongovernmental organizations interested in the field of mental health. The world body is not only a medium for the exchange of ideas on mental hygiene problems and for the correlation of work, but is also a consultative agency for nations and international groups.

49. What are the voluntary organizations in the field of mental health in the United States?

There are a large number of professional groups, of which the American Psychiatric Association is probably the best known. The National Committee for Mental Hygiene, founded in 1909, was for many years a recognized leader in the field. Recently it merged with The National Mental Health Foundation and the Psychiatric Foundation to form The National Association for Mental Health. This organization, combining as it does the leadership in voluntary effort and professional skill, will increasingly serve to promote adequate care and treatment for the mentally ill and to improve the training programs for the psychiatric and allied professions.

Chapter 21

Other Diseases
of Public Interest

NOTE: Many questions of general interest relating to population and human biology have not yet been touched upon in this volume because they did not readily fit into any of the preceding chapters. A number of diseases which now hardly merit a separate section, formerly played an important role in our public health record; quite a number of these are still pressing problems in other parts of the world. Still other conditions illustrate the remarkable progress of medicine and surgery, as well as the advance of the public health program. Some questions of this type have been brought together at this point. The choice has necessarily been arbitrary, but it is hoped that those included help to round out the scope of this volume.

1. How does mortality from typhoid fever in the United States now compare with that in 1900?

The death rate from typhoid fever in the United States has virtually dropped out of the mortality record of the country since the turn of the century—from 31 per 100,000 in 1900 to 0.0 per 100,000 in 1961. In 1900, typhoid fever was an important cause of death and accounted for about 1 in every 50 deaths in our country; at present only a few sporadic deaths are due to this cause. The elimination of typhoid fever has resulted largely from the purification of water, milk, and other food supplies, as well as from the development of efficient sewage disposal systems very widely over the country.

2. Where is typhoid fever still a public health problem?

Typhoid fever is still a problem of considerable magnitude in many areas outside of the English-speaking countries, the Scandinavian countries, and The Netherlands—that is, outside the countries where sanitary facilities and the general way of life are on a relatively high level. Examples of areas of relatively high mortality from typhoid fever are Mexico, with a rate of 8.7 per 100,000 in 1959; Ecuador, with 21.5 in 1958; and Burma, with 21.0 in 1961. Measures for the control of typhoid fever are under way in a number of areas, with the cooperation of the World Health Organization.

3. What are the common "pestilential" diseases that frequently become epidemic?

These diseases are cholera, smallpox, plague, yellow fever, and typhus. Measures for the control of their spread across borders have been sought by international conventions and treaties. The current tendency is to depend less upon quarantine measures and to emphasize the importance of preventive measures at the source of the disease. These preventive measures require the development of public health and medical services in the countries where these diseases are still widespread.

4. Has cholera ever been an important factor in mortality in the United States?

There were several serious outbreaks of cholera in the United States during the nineteenth century. These usually had their origin at seaports to which they were brought from overseas, and from which the disease spread inland. Several outbreaks were traced to immigrant ships. The last such occurrence was in New York City in 1892.

5. In what areas of the world is cholera still prevalent?

Very few and isolated cases of cholera have been reported in recent years from any part of the world. Yet only a few decades ago this disease was a great and imminent menace in the world. China and India were reservoirs from which it did spread through the usual channels of communication to other parts of the world. Religious pilgrimages were a common mode of spread. Although cholera is now relatively rare in the rest of the world, there is always the danger that the disease may spread from these two endemic centers. A sizable epidemic with more than 10,000 deaths occurred in Egypt in 1947. It was brought under control through the intervention of the skilled workers of the World Health Organization.

6. What is being done to combat cholera?

By attacking cholera at its sources—in China and India—it should be possible to eradicate the disease. The usual measures taken against cholera are protection of the food and water supplies and adequate sewage disposal. Where there is exposure to the disease, use is made of anticholera vaccines. Treatment of cholera by means of sulfa drugs is reportedly effective. A system of radio broadcasts has been established by the World Health Organization to inform the world of any epidemics of cholera which develop. This gives other countries an opportunity to institute preventive measures.

7. What is brucellosis (undulant fever) and where is it found?

Brucellosis, or undulant fever, is an infectious condition transmitted to man from cattle, goats, and sheep. Infection is usually acquired through raw milk or milk products. Brucellosis is rather common in livestock throughout the world, and causes great economic loss. It is often difficult to diagnose the illness in man and many cases are either undetected or are attributed to other diseases. Brucellosis is a special hazard to farmers, livestock workers, and slaughter-house employees. Infection rarely results in death. The disease has been reported in man in practically all areas of the world.

8. What steps are being taken to reduce the incidence of brucellosis (undulant fever)?

Under the auspices of the World Health Organization, techniques for the diagnosis of brucellosis are being standardized and, with knowledge and experience now available, it should be possible to control and even to eradicate the disease in large areas of the world. A number of centers for this purpose have been set up jointly by the World Health Organization and the Food and Agriculture Organization.

9. How does mortality from syphilis vary according to age, sex, race, and marital status in the United States?

The death rate from syphilis is relatively high in the first year of life, when the disease is almost invariably congenital in origin. In the childhood ages the rates are virtually zero and, although they rise steadily from early adulthood, the rate in infancy is not reached again until midlife. The highest death rate is found in the seventies, after which it falls off somewhat. The death rate from syphilis among males is almost three times that of females; among nonwhites, the rate is nearly five times that for white persons.

Mortality from syphilis among single men is more than twice that for married men. Widowers have three and one-half times the syphilis death rate of married men, while for the divorced it is four times as high. Single women and married women have practically the same mortality from syphilis, but for the widowed and divorced the rate is over three times that for the married.

10. What has been the recent trend in mortality from syphilis in the United States?

The death rate from syphilis has been greatly reduced in the last four decades, from 18 per 100,000 population in 1920–24 to only 1.6 per 100,000 in 1961. Many elements have contributed to this improvement, particularly in more recent years. An important preventive measure has been the legislation making blood tests mandatory before marriage and for pregnant women; most states now have these requirements. Control measures instituted by civilian and military health authorities during World War II have contributed much toward the improved situation. The physical examinations for Selective Service uncovered a large number of cases of syphilis; these were recommended for treatment. Mass screening surveys of the civilian population bring to light many unknown cases of the disease. Health education campaigns have not only a preventive effect, but also bring new cases for early treatment. Treatment with penicillin and the spread of rapid treatment centers have undoubtedly brought benefits in reduced mortality and promise even greater reductions in the future.[1]

11. What are some of the major complications arising out of syphilis?

After initial symptoms, the disease may not manifest itself again for many years, when it may produce inflamed enlargements of the

[1] See answer to Question 33 of Chapter 19, page 308.

heart, brain, kidneys, and other organs. The disease may lead to locomotor ataxia, a condition affecting principally the spinal cord, or to a general paralysis with mental disorders. The pregnancy of a woman infected with syphilis may result in a fetal death. Newborn babies may also acquire the disease, with all of its manifestations, from an infected mother.

12. To what extent is syphilis a world-wide problem?

It is estimated that there are more than 2,000,000 deaths from syphilis in the world annually. No area of the world is free of the problem. The disease is particularly prevalent in countries which have a low standard of living. Special measures have been undertaken by the World Health Organization against syphilis. Attempts have been made to eradicate the disease in Haiti and in parts of Asia and the Americas, and in the Eastern Mediterranean. All phases of public health activity against syphilis are being strengthened in many areas, with particular attention to health education. Nevertheless, after marked improvement in the incidence of the disease due to the wide use of the antibiotics, syphilis is again being reported in increasing numbers, reflecting both the carelessness associated with the presumed quick and easy cure and the resistance the organism has acquired to the drugs.

13. What are yaws and bejel?

Yaws and bejel are diseases very much like syphilis in characteristics, but are not transmitted in the same way. These diseases are nonvenereal and most frequently found among children. Yaws and bejel are widely prevalent in the countries around the East Mediterranean, and are also common in the South Pacific, the southern areas of Asia, the central belt across Africa, Central America, and the northern tier of South America. An estimated 50 million cases are believed to exist today. The World Health Organization has conducted a number of successful campaigns against yaws closely tied in with its activities against syphilis, since the treatment for both diseases relies heavily upon the use of penicillin.

14. How prevalent is gonorrhea in the United States?

It has been estimated that about 1,800,000 people in the United States have gonorrhea. However, the disease takes a very small death toll, only 38 deaths being reported in 1960. The incidence of gonorrhea among nonwhites is about 20 times that of the white population. The disease is about two and one-half times as frequent among males as among females. It is reported more frequently in the lower income groups than among those better situated.

Gonorrhea often results in sterility and not infrequently causes blindness in the new born of mothers with the disease.

15. Is there an adequate treatment for gonorrhea?

Gonorrhea has been treated effectively with the antibiotics and the sulfonamides. Although the modern treatment is safe, simple, rapid, and inexpensive, it is not an unmixed blessing. As knowledge of the new treatments has become more widespread, fear of the disease has lessened, with the result that reinfection is commonplace and the disease appears on a rising trend.

16. What was the "Black Death"?

The "Black Death" was an epidemic of plague during the fourteenth century that swept through all the world as it was then known—Asia, Africa, and Europe. It is said that about one-quarter of the population of the world died from this extremely virulent communicable disease. Whole communities were wiped out and its devastations greatly altered the economy of nations. No one then knew how to cure or prevent it, and terror and panic were widespread as people saw their families stricken and die from the mysterious illness.

17. Where is plague still common and how is its spread prevented?

Human plague is endemic in India and other parts of Asia. It is also found in some areas of South America and in North and South Africa. Except for a rare case, the United States is free from the disease. One death was reported in 1959.

Plague may be controlled by modern sanitary means. The disease is generally spread by rats and their fleas, and their eradication is therefore essential to its control. Among the steps taken in this direction are the rat-proofing of buildings and limiting the food supply of the rodents, chiefly through proper disposal of garbage. In places where ships arrive from plague-infested ports the preventive measures are quarantine and fumigation of the holds and cargoes.

18. How prevalent is leprosy today?

Leprosy was quite common throughout the world up to the Middle Ages. Since then, it has practically disappeared from Europe, except from countries on the Baltic and Mediterranean Seas. The disease is still fairly common in the Far East and all part of the tropics. Some estimates place the number of cases in the world above two million. In the United States, only about 60 new cases have been found annually in recent years.

19. Has leprosy ever been a serious threat in the United States?

Although leprosy has been brought into the United States many times, it has never been a major health problem here. Cases have been reported at one time or other from every state. A few cases were discovered among veterans of World War II, and among former inmates of Japanese concentration camps. The conditions favorable to the spread of the disease are now limited to a few states bordering the Gulf of Mexico. It is no longer a menace here.

20. What is tularemia and at what time of the year is it most common?

Tularemia, commonly known as rabbit fever, is a disease contracted from infected rodents, particularly rabbits. The infection in man is most often acquired by handling infected animals. Except for complicated cases, there is usually recovery from the disease. The number of cases of tularemia rises sharply with the beginning of the hunting season late in fall and reaches a peak in December. At that time the number of cases reported is about six times as high as in the period from February to October, the low level of the year. About 360 cases were reported in 1961 and the case fatality rate is about 5 percent.

21. Is tetanus important as a cause of death?

Tetanus is an infectious disease generally contracted through an injury or wound exposed to contamination. In 1961, a total of 379 cases were reported in the United States, but many more must have occurred in view of the fact that about 230 deaths from this disease are registered each year. During World War II, tetanus among the armed forces was practically eliminated by routine immunization with tetanus toxoid. The treatment of the disease has been aided by the recently developed chemotherapy.

22. What is the history of smallpox in the United States?

Although Edward Jenner, an English physician, developed effective vaccination against smallpox in 1796, many years passed before it was used to full advantage. Meanwhile epidemics of the disease occurred repeatedly throughout the nineteenth century. In 1872, the smallpox death rate was 270 per 100,000 in Boston and 365 in Philadelphia. New Orleans, long a breeding spot for the disease, had a rate of 565 in 1883. Control over smallpox was finally achieved when vaccination was made compulsory in most of the country. However, incidents occurring from time to time show the value of vaccination and revaccination to guard against flare-ups of the disease brought into the country. In 1920, about 109,000 cases of smallpox were reported in the United States; in 1948, only 56 cases and five deaths were reported (see Chart 18). No deaths have occurred in the last 15 years, but there were sporadic cases of smallpox which caused tremendous stirs in the local health departments affected, in the state organizations, the U.S. Public Health Service, and even the World Health Organization. Thus, in the summer of 1962, the young son of a missionary returning from Brazil was found to be suffering from smallpox when the family reached New York. All media of communication were used to locate persons who had been in contact with the family and an investigation was launched to find out why the inadequate vaccination certificate had not been detected.

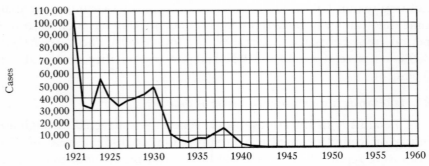

Chart 18. Cases of smallpox reported in the United States, 1921–1960.

23. In what areas of the world is smallpox still relatively common?

Much remains to be done before smallpox is eradicated from the world. The disease is still relatively prevalent in India, China, and other parts of Asia; it is also an important health problem in large sections of Africa and Latin America.

24. What is dengue and where is it prevalent?

Dengue is a virus disease that is transmitted to man by a mosquito (*Aëdes aegypti*). The disease, rarely fatal, is widely prevalent in tropical and subtropical countries. Huge epidemics of the disease appear to have occurred during the Second World War period in some of the belligerent countries. It has been fairly common in a few of our Southern states and has occasionally been found as far north as Philadelphia. Only a few cases of dengue are now reported in the United States.

25. What has been the history of yellow fever in the United States?

There were severe outbreaks of yellow fever in New York and Philadelphia in 1668, the first time the disease was reported in North America. Up to 1821, there were 20 epidemics reported in Philadelphia, 15 in New York, 8 in Boston, and 7 in Baltimore. About one-eighth of the entire population of Philadelphia was carried off by the yellow fever epidemic of 1793, and one-tenth by another epidemic five years later. In some Southern towns, outbreaks of the disease occurred almost continuously. As late as 1878, an epidemic of yellow fever in New Orleans killed off almost 2 percent of the population. In 1905, that city had the last epidemic of the disease experienced in this country. No cases of yellow fever have been reported in the United States for many years.

26. What is the outlook for eliminating yellow fever from the world?

Since the cause of yellow fever, its means of spreading, and the methods of prevention are known, it should be possible to eradicate the disease. Although the yellow fever mosquito (*Aëdes aegypti*), which carries the disease to man, is widely prevalent in most of the tropical and subtropical countries of the world, including our Southern states, control measures have been successful in most of these areas. At present, yellow fever is confined to certain parts of West Africa and South America. In many places the disease has been prevented from spreading by the simple expedient of drying up small amounts of stagnant water near homes. Stringent quarantine measures and vaccination of persons going to infested places are very important. Air transportation increases the chances of spreading yellow fever, for the traveling time from an infested area to one free of the disease is considerably less than the incubation period. Care is, therefore, taken to destroy mosquitoes on planes after their arrival from such areas. To date, the disease has not appeared in the Far East where its occurrence would be nothing short of a public health catastrophe.

27. Where is trachoma still prevalent?

Trachoma is a contagious disease affecting the eyelids and may result in total blindness unless there is early and adequate treatment. The disease is found in all parts of the world but it is especially prevalent in China, India, Egypt, and the Middle East. In some countries nearly the entire population is affected, according to the World Health Organization.[2] In the United States, the disease is rare, except among the Indian population of the Southwestern states. The incidence of the disease in this country has been decreasing for many years. The newer methods of treatment with the sulfa drugs are effective.

28. What progress has been made against sleeping sickness?

Sleeping sickness, a particularly virulent disease, is spread by a biting fly (tsetse) from infected wild animals, which are the source of infection, to domestic animals and man. The disease is a serious public health problem in many parts of Africa. Clearing away the brush is effective as a measure of control in some areas, but the most practical approach is to scatter insecticides, such as DDT, on a wholesale scale. A large number of substances have been used to destroy the parasite in animals and some new promising drugs have been developed recently to achieve the same result in man. Despite these gains, the toll from sleeping sickness is still high.

29. Where is malaria still an important disease?

In terms of the amount of sickness, disability, and economic drain it causes, malaria ranks very high among the debilitating diseases. Throughout the world, there are annually hundreds of millions of cases of the disease and millions of deaths from it, accord-

[2] It is estimated that over one-seventh of the total world population is affected by trachoma and that 10 million of these will ultimately become blind.

ing to the World Health Organization. The only areas comparatively free of the disease are the United States, Canada, the northwestern countries of Europe, the south of Australia, and New Zealand.

30. What is being done to wipe out malaria?

Malaria is controlled by draining swamps, marshes, and other breeding places of mosquitoes, and by spraying with DDT. These methods are being applied on a large scale by the World Health Organization, the Institute of Inter-American Affairs, and by the Economic Cooperation Administration, the latter working mainly through personnel from the United States Public Health Service. In Greece, for example, where malaria was very widely prevalent, the number of cases was reduced by concentrated efforts from at least 2,000,000 in 1942 to about 50,000 in 1949. Improvement has continued and, at the same time, the incidence of other diseases likewise has been reduced. The nation benefited by increased productive capacity. In other parts of the world, vast areas have been freed from malaria by intensive and modern sanitary measures. The World Health Organization is planning malaria eradication programs in many infested areas of the world. Malaria is still one of the most acute health problems today.

31. What is typhus fever and how widespread is it?

Typhus fever is an acute, infectious disease spread to man by lice, ticks, and fleas. The epidemic form is transmitted by the body louse, hence its spread is greatly facilitated by crowded conditions, and by poverty, squalor, and war. The disease is widespread in Asia, Eastern Europe, Egypt, and some other parts of Africa. It is relatively infrequent in the United States, Canada, and Western Europe.

32. How can typhus fever be controlled?

Under ordinary conditions of life, epidemic typhus fever is easily controlled by personal cleanliness. Where war has disrupted the customary sanitation practices, as in Italy during World War II, an effective control measure is to spray DDT on individuals, their clothes, and about their surroundings. Our servicemen have been made safe against the disease by routine vaccination. Recently developed antibiotics, such as chloromycetin and terramycin, have proved effective for the treatment of the disease.

33. What is schistosomiasis and where is it prevalent?

Schistosomiasis (also called bilharziasis) is a parasitic disease widespread throughout the world. The parasite is a water-borne blood fluke which spreads to various parts of the body but particularly to the liver, bladder, and rectum. The infection may become chronic and last from 20 to 30 years. The disease is very common in tropical Africa, Asia, and Latin America. According to the World Health Organization, there are about 150 million victims of the disease; in some countries as much as 90 percent of the rural population may be affected by it. Control of the disease is sought by destroying the eggs of the parasite, by treating infected people, and by destroying the snails which carry the parasite from water to man.

34. What is filariasis and how many are affected by it?

Filariasis is a disease caused by parasitic worms which live one stage of their life cycle in mosquitoes and invade the human lymphatic system following the bite of the mosquito. The parasite may live in the human body for some time without causing inconvenience until the lymph channels are blocked. One of the common forms of the disease is elephantiasis, in which the lower arms and legs and the external genital organs swell to enormous size.

According to the World Health Organization, filariasis probably affects more than 250 millions of people in the tropical areas of the world. It was formerly found in the southern part of our country but is now rare.

There is no satisfactory medication that destroys all the filariae in the blood and treatment is only palliative. The best way to control the disease is by eradication of mosquitoes and by the use of screens.

35. What is trichinosis and how is it being controlled in the United States?

Trichinosis is a disease caused by the trichina worm, a parasite of the pig. Entrance into the human body occurs when undercooked, infected pork is eaten. Light infections may cause no symptoms, but if the pork is heavily contaminated, severe illness and death may result. In this country the disease is quite common, although it is usually so light as to be unrecognized. It has been estimated from autopsy and other records that millions are infected in this country, but only about 300 cases were officially reported in 1961.

Thorough cooking is sufficient to kill the parasite in infected meat. Proper refrigeration and salting also kill it. Meat inspection does not seem to be of much value. Protecting pigs from rodents, and prohibitions against feeding them on offal from slaughter houses help to prevent infection.

36. How common is hookworm disease?

Hookworm, or ancylostomiasis, is commonly found in all warm countries, especially where sanitation is not highly developed and the inhabitants are accustomed to go without shoes. The disease has brought much ill health and misery in tropical countries. Distribution is world-wide, affecting upwards of 400 million persons. Early in this century, surveys in our Southern states showed that from 12 to 60 percent of the population were infected. In the period from 1945 to 1949, there were 15 to 16 thousand cases reported annually in this country. It was especially prevalent in Georgia, Florida, and Mississippi, where almost 90 percent of the cases were reported.

The campaigns for building sanitary waterproof privies and other measures have helped to control the disease in the South. The Rockefeller Foundation deserves great credit for the intensive sanitary and therapeutic measures carried on in the South and in Puerto Rico.

37. What are the most important diseases transmitted from animals to man?

More than 75 diseases can be contracted by man from animals. The most important of these are bovine tuberculosis, brucellosis, tularemia, rabies, trichinosis, and tapeworm infections. Also included in this group are glanders, anthrax, foot-and-mouth disease, psittacosis, and food poisoning of some kinds. Bovine tuberculosis has been practically eradicated here but it is still a problem in some other countries.

38. How much of a problem is goiter in the United States?

In some parts of the country, especially in those states surrounding the Great Lakes—the so-called "goiter belt"—the disease is still an important health problem. According to surveys in some of these states, about one-half of the school children show signs of simple goiter. The continued use of iodized salt is helping to reduce this incidence.

Goiter is not an important cause of death. In 1960, there were only 532 deaths from toxic or exophthalmic goiter. The disease takes a much greater toll among women than men. Mortality from exophthalmic goiter is decreasing. In recent years marked advances have been made in the medical treatment of thyroid conditions, and where surgical intervention is required, the risk has been appreciably reduced. Not only has there been an improvement in diagnostic technique and surgical skill but there has also been wider use of chemotherapy and the antibiotics to combat the infections, particularly pneumonia which may follow surgery.[3]

39. What variations occur in the mortality from toxic goiter by age, color, and sex?

The mortality from toxic goiter, especially among women, increases with age. This disease is one of the relatively few in which women have higher mortality rates than men. There is little difference in mortality between white and colored persons.

40. What is beriberi and how is it being brought under control?

Beriberi is a vitamin deficiency disease caused by lack of sufficient thiamine, or vitamin B_1 which is found in yeast, certain meats and vegetables, milk, and the germ of rice and cereals. The disease is prevalent where most of the people live chiefly on a diet of polished rice from which the vitamins and minerals have been removed. The principal areas affected are Malaya, China, the Philippines, Japan, and, to a lesser degree, India.

Substituting whole rice for the polished or refined kind, or enriching rice by the addition of rice bran or vitamin B_1 is effective in preventing beriberi. Large doses of the vitamin in concentrated form are valuable in the treatment of the disease.

41. Where was pellagra once prevalent in the United States?

Pellagra was very common some years ago in the southern part of this country, particularly in small cotton mill villages, and in mining and sawmill camps in rural areas. In these places, poverty and tradition narrowed the diet to corn meal, fat salt pork, and carbohydrates with few green vegetables, especially in the winter and spring months. The disease was also found in orphanages, poorhouses, prisons, and hospitals for mental patients where the diet was lacking in fresh lean meat and fresh fruit and vegetables.

[3] See answer to Question 27 of Chapter 19, page 305.

42. What discovery made it possible to control pellagra?

From studies started in 1914, Dr. Joseph Goldberger and his co-workers of the United States Public Health Service proved that pellagra was a result of an inadequate diet. An adequate diet requires sufficient amounts of certain vitamins, a proper food balance in general, as well as an ample quantity of food. Goldberger and his associates cured a number of cases by large daily doses of yeast added to the diet. Since then, yeast, which is a rich and economical source of vitamin B, has played an important role in the control of pellagra. The population in former pellagra areas now plant gardens for fresh vegetables and many keep a cow for a good supply of milk.

43. What medical development led to the rapid decline in mortality from pernicious anemia?

Simple anemia is in many respects much less a problem today because of the rapid increase in knowledge of nutrition. Persons with simple anemia have shown no marked increase in mortality due to the condition, but they appear to have a reduced efficiency and activity, and more illness because of their susceptibility to certain diseases. Of far greater seriousness is pernicious anemia in which the disturbance is due to a lack of substances necessary to the production of red blood cells. Such a substance was discovered in liver by Doctors Minot and Murphy, for which they were awarded the Nobel Prize in Medicine in 1934. Prior to that time the average duration of life after diagnosis of pernicious anemia was only two and one-half years. Today many persons with pernicious anemia who adhere to a prescribed medical regimen are able to carry on their customary pursuits and usually live long enough to succumb to another cause. However, longevity in the presence of this disease is reduced appreciably.

44. What is multiple sclerosis and where is it found most frequently?

Multiple sclerosis is a chronic disease of the nervous system. The most common symptoms and signs are blurred vision, numbness of the extremities, tremors of parts of the body, weakness, difficulties in speech and in balacing and walking. The disease may develop suddenly or it may be gradual and progressive. Remission of the disease often occurs and the victim improves, but relapses usually recur. Since the cause of the disease is unknown, there is as yet no effective remedy for preventing or stopping its progress.

Multiple sclerosis is found most often in cold damp climates. In the United States, it is most common in the North Atlantic Coast states and the Great Lakes region. In Europe, the highest prevalence is in France, Germany, Scotland, and the Baltic countries. The disease, which seems to be increasing in frequency in the United States and Europe, is now receiving more adequate professional attention.

45. What is the significance of the Rh factor?

Rh is a blood factor present in 85 percent of the white population and in a higher proportion among the nonwhite. If a woman lacking this blood factor marries a man whose blood contains it, about half of the children of the couple will inherit the father's positive blood type. In these instances, during pregnancy the mother's system produces antibodies against the baby's positive blood, and these antibodies very often injure the unborn child. There is usually no danger to the first child, but in subsequent pregnancies these antibodies are likely to be numerous enough to destroy the baby's blood cells. Sometimes the baby is born dead; usually, however, it is born alive but suffering with a jaundiced condition known as erythroblastosis fetalis. In about one-fifth of the infants suffering from this condition, a typical form of cerebral palsy develops. It is estimated that only 13 percent of all marriages involve women with Rh negative and men with Rh positive blood.

46. What is cerebral palsy and how many in the United States have this condition?

Cerebral palsy is a nerve and muscle condition caused by damage or faulty development of areas of the brain. Most cases occur before or during birth. The condition prevents normal use of one or more of the muscles involved in speech, sight, walking, standing, and movements of the hands and arms. Only about one-third of the cerebral palsied children are mentally retarded, and many of these can profit from specialized training. The remaining two-thirds range from slight mental retardation to superior intelligence; with long-continued, systematic, special training, most of those with the disease can become self-maintaining.

It is estimated that there are about half a million cerebral palsy victims in the country today, and that about 7 per 100,000 population are born each year. Many of these infants are so severely handicapped that they are especially susceptible to infections; almost one-seventh die within the first five years of life.

47. What factors have contributed to the recent reduction in mortality from ulcers of the stomach?

The death rate from ulcers of the stomach has been declining for more than two decades. Diagnostic procedures have advanced rapidly with increased use of the gastroscope and x-ray techniques. At the same time medical management of the disease has improved. Treatment is now planned on a long-range basis instead of being directed singly to the relief of acute episodes. The small proportion of cases undergoing surgery are benefiting from new procedures and other advances that have reduced the frequency of fatal postoperative complications.

48. What has been the trend in mortality from appendicitis in recent decades?

The death rate from appendicitis in the United States fell from a high 15.2 per 100,000 population in 1930 to only 1.0 in 1960. This reduction reflects a variety of factors, particularly improved diagnostic procedures which have helped bring patients to operation before complications set in, and improvements in the care and treatment of cases. In the past two decades, additional impetus was given to the downward trend by application of chemotherapy in cases complicated with peritonitis. In a number of hospitals the case fatality rates have been reduced to less than 1 percent. The rapid growth of prepayment hospital insurance plans has enabled patients to seek medical care more promptly.

Credit must also be given to the campaign to educate the people against the dangers in taking laxatives to relieve abdominal pain, a practice which greatly increases the chances of perforation and peritonitis when appendicitis is present. It is significant that where education stressing the value of early hospitalization and avoidance of laxatives has been actively carried on, the percentage of cases complicated with perforation and peritonitis has shown an especially marked decrease.

49. How does mortality from cirrhosis of the liver vary with age, sex, and marital status?

Under age 35, the death rate from cirrhosis of the liver is negligible, but thereafter it rises rapidly with advance in age. Thus, in

1960 the rate in the United States increased from 11.8 per 100,000 at ages 35 to 44 years to 37.4 at ages 65 to 74. From ages 40 to 80, the death rates from cirrhosis of the liver for white males are more than double those for white females.

The mortality from cirrhosis of the liver among married men is considerably lower than that of single or widowed or divorced men. The rates among married women, on the other hand, are higher than those of the unmarried, but somewhat lower than for widows. Divorcees have much the highest mortality at practically every age group.

50. Has rabies been eradicated in the United States?

Rabies has not been eradicated from our country. However, because prompt treatment is usually available, the loss of life from this infection is relatively small. In 1960, there were 2 deaths reported from this disease. In the same year, over 3,500 cases of rabies were reported in animals in the United States.

Rabies is a rapidly fatal infection which is generally contracted by a bite of some animal, usually a dog. Rabies can be controlled, and in large measure eradicated, by muzzling dogs. Annual vaccination of dogs against rabies has also been used. Rabies was eradicated in England after a muzzling order was enforced, and a quarantine put on dogs coming into the country. The disease can be a menace in countries where there are large numbers of stray, uncared for dogs, and where there are wolves, jackals, foxes, and hyenas.

Chapter 22

Our Body Build

1. What is the average weight and length of babies at birth?

At birth, boys weigh 7⅖ pounds on an average, and girls 7⅖ pounds. An infant weighing less than 5½ pounds at birth is generally considered premature. The average length at birth is 20½ inches for boys and 20 inches for girls.

2. At what rate do babies increase in weight in their prenatal period?

The rate of growth is rapid during prenatal life. At the fourth fetal month it is about 3½ ounces per month; just before birth, it is nearly 2 pounds per month.

3. What is the average height and weight of children at successive ages?

The average baby, at the end of the first year of life, weighs about three times what it did at birth. The rate of gain is much less thereafter. At the end of the second year, the average boy baby weighs close to 26 pounds, about 1 pound more than the average girl. Except at ages 11 to 13, the average weight for boys is greater than that for girls of the same age.

At the end of the first year of life, the average baby is 8 to 10 inches taller than at birth. The average height at birth is doubled by the time the child is about 4½ years old, and tripled by 13 or 14 years of age. Boys are taller than girls except at 11 to 13 years.

The average height and weight of boys and girls from ages 4 to 17 years are shown in Table 1.

TABLE 1
AVERAGE HEIGHT AND WEIGHT* OF BOYS AND GIRLS
AGE 4 TO 17 YEARS

Age	Height (inches)		Weight (pounds)	
	Boys	Girls	Boys	Girls
4	40.9	40.9	38.2	37.3
5	43.9	43.6	43.2	42.0
6	46.1	45.8	47.6	46.4
7	48.2	47.9	52.5	51.2
8	50.4	50.0	58.2	56.9
9	52.4	52.0	64.4	63.0
10	54.3	54.2	70.7	70.3
11	56.2	56.5	77.6	79.0
12	58.2	59.0	85.6	89.7
13	60.5	60.6	95.6	100.3
14	63.0	62.3	107.9	108.5
15	65.6	63.2	121.7	115.0
16	67.3	63.5	131.9	117.6
17	68.2	63.6	138.3	119.0

* without shoes
Source: "Basic Body Measurements of School Age Children" U.S. Dept. H.E.W., Office of Education, W. Edgar Martin, June, 1953.

4. What changes in body build (other than height and weight) occur among children in the course of development?

There are great differences in the body proportions of adults and children. The head of a child is relatively larger than that of an adult and the legs are relatively shorter. As the infant matures to an adult, the size of the head doubles, its arms become four times as long, the legs five times as long, and the trunk three times. An idea of the changes in some body measurements for boys and girls as they pass from ages 4 to 17 may be obtained from Table 2. For all but a few of the measurements shown, the body dimensions of boys exceed those of girls.

TABLE 2
SELECTED BODY MEASUREMENTS OF BOYS AND GIRLS
AT AGES 4 AND 17 YEARS (IN INCHES)

	Boys		Girls	
Body Measurement	*4*	*17*	*4*	*17*
Chest girth	20.8	33.8	20.3	30.1
Waist girth	20.3	28.3	19.8	25.4
Upper Arm girth	6.4	10.1	6.3	9.5
Neck Bone girth	10.9	16.1	10.7	14.4
Thigh girth	12.5	20.5	12.8	21.1
Hip girth	19.4	35.3	19.5	32.4

Source: "Basic Body Measurements of School Age Children," U.S. Dept. H.E.W., Office of Education, W. Edgar Martin, June, 1953.

5. At what age do boys and girls reach puberty?

Among boys, the average age at puberty is about 15 years, and among girls about 13. However, in individual cases it is not uncommon for puberty to appear as early as age 10 or as late as 17. In girls, the onset of fertility generally lags four or more years behind the onset of the menses.[1] The age at puberty is influenced by a number of factors, such as social conditions, nutritional status, and health status. Contrary to popular impression, girls in tropical and subtropical countries do not mature earlier than those living in temperate climates. In subtropical and tropical countries development is relatively slow. Long periods of extreme cold retard development much as does tropical heat.

There has been a trend, at least within the last half century, for puberty to occur at a somewhat earlier age, on the average. This is particularly evident in the United States, Canada, and Western Europe. In large degree, this change represents better nutrition and greater freedom from debilitating diseases during childhood.

6. Has there been any change in the average height of young people during the past few decades?

Comparable figures, as far as available, show that present-day adolescents weigh more, and are somewhat taller than those of a few decades ago. For example, the young men entering service in World

[1] See answers to Questions 1 and 2 of Chapter 2, pages 16 and 17.

War II were, on an average, about ⅔ inch taller and about 10 pounds heavier than those accepted in World War I. Increases in height and weight have been observed in many comparisons of college students with those of the preceding generation. A comparison of heights of mothers and daughters who attended college showed that on the average, the daughters were 1⅛ inches taller.

7. What factors influence the rate of growth of children?

External factors, more than anything else, influence the rate of growth of children. The food they eat, the water they drink, the climate they live in, their standards of living, and their opportunity for play and exercise contribute toward their development. Inheritance is obviously an important factor also in the growth of children. The occurrence of certain diseases may also have noticeable effects on their rate of growth.

8. Does the growth of children vary with the seasons?

The growth of children tends to be slowest during winter, somewhat more rapid during spring, and most rapid during summer.

9. Are height and weight an index of good nutrition of children?

The usual tables showing the height and weight of children corresponding to their ages do not provide a satisfactory index to select the undernourished. Only by a careful physical examination can a physician tell whether or not a child is undernourished. In one test survey, only one-quarter of the children considered undernourished by a physician would have been judged so according to the standard height and weight tables.

10. What is the average height of adults in the United States?

According to insurance records, the average height of adults, taken with shoes on, is 5 feet 8½ inches for men and 5 feet 4¼ inches for women. Ten percent of the men were over 6 feet tall; only a fraction of 1 percent were under 5 feet. Just 1.5 percent of the women were under 5 feet tall, but only 0.1 percent were over 6 feet.

11. Are there regional differences in average height within the United States?

The average height of white men taken for service in World War II ranged from 5 feet 8⅖ inches in the Western States to 5 feet 7⅖ inches in the Northwestern states (all measurements were taken without shoes). The four states with the tallest men—Texas, Oklahoma, Mississippi, and Tennessee—are in the South Central Region of the country. The seven states with the shortest men—Rhode Island, Connecticut, Pennsylvania, New York, Massachusetts, New Jersey, and New Hampshire—are in the Northeast Region of the country.

12. Are there differences in the average height of ethnic groups within the United States?

The Scottish, with an average height of 5 feet 8 inches, were the tallest among the men demobilized after World War I. Shorter than they, in order, were the English, Germans, Irish, Poles, French, Jews, and Italians, the last with an average of 5 feet 5 inches.

13. How does the height of adults vary throughout the world?

People tend to be short where the environment is harsh or the food supply poor. Tropical jungles and arctic areas are the homes of most of the races of excessively short stature: for example, the Negrillos of Central Africa, some Indian tribes of Central South America, and the Eskimos, Lapps, and Siberians in the extreme North. There is a great range in height among the peoples of the temperate zones. In the Northern Hemisphere, the citizens of the United States and Canada, the Scandinavians, Scots, and some groups of English are the tallest among the nationality groups of European origin. Some of the native tribes of East Africa outstrip all of them with an average height for men of six feet or more. In South America, the Patagonians—where the men also average better than six feet—are the tallest.

14. What is the significance of dwarfism and giantism in terms of longevity?

For the most part, very short and very tall persons merely represent the extremes of normal height distribution, and their longevity does not differ materially from the average. True dwarfism and giantism, however, reflect pathologic conditions and are often accompanied by bodily disproportions or physical manifestations in addition to abnormal height. In most cases giantism is the result of pituitary dysfunction. Dwarfism is usually the result of thyroid deficiency, but some cases are due to pituitary or other disorders.

Longevity of giants and dwarfs depends partly upon the cause of the abnormality. Pituitary giants do not live long. The longevity of dwarfs whose condition is of thyroid origin is also impaired, but not to as great a degree.

15. What is the average weight of adults in the United States?

The average weight of adults (not the "desirable" weight, which is discussed in Question 16) varies both with height and age. Table 3

TABLE 3
AVERAGE WEIGHT FOR MEN AND WOMEN
ACCORDING TO HEIGHT AND AGE

Height (in shoes)	*Weight in Pounds (in indoor clothing)*					
	Ages 20–24	*Ages 25–29*	*Ages 30–39*	*Ages 40–49*	*Ages 50–59*	*Ages 60–69*
	Men					
5′ 2″	128	134	137	140	142	139
3″	132	138	141	144	145	142
4″	136	141	145	148	149	146
5″	139	144	149	152	153	150
6″	142	148	153	156	157	154
7″	145	151	157	161	162	159
8″	149	155	161	165	166	163
9″	153	159	165	169	170	168
10″	157	163	170	174	175	173
11″	161	167	174	178	180	178
6′ 0″	166	172	179	183	185	183
1″	170	177	183	187	189	188
2″	174	182	188	192	194	193
3″	178	186	193	197	199	198
4″	181	190	199	203	205	204
	Women					
4′ 10″	102	107	115	122	125	127
11″	105	110	117	124	127	129
5′ 0″	108	113	120	127	130	131
1″	112	116	123	130	133	134
2″	115	119	126	133	136	137
3″	118	122	129	136	140	141
4″	121	125	132	140	144	145
5″	125	129	135	143	148	149
6″	129	133	139	147	152	153
7″	132	136	142	151	156	157
8″	136	140	146	155	160	161
9″	140	144	150	159	164	165
10″	144	148	154	164	169	*
11″	149	153	159	169	174	*
6′ 0″	154	158	164	174	180	*

* Average weights not determined because of insufficient data.
Source: Build and Blood Pressure Study, 1959, Society of Actuaries.

shows the average weights of men and women according to their height and age, as reported in the recent study of the Society of Actuaries (1959).

16. What is meant by "desirable" weight?

"Desirable" weight is that most conducive to health and longevity. Most people continue to grow heavier throughout the greater part of their lives, but insurance studies have shown that it is healthier for adults to remain at a fairly constant weight, usually that suitable at about age 30.[2] Although "desirable" weight is independent of age after maturity, it is dependent upon both height and body frame. Table 4 shows "desirable" weights for men and women according to height for each of three types of body frame—small, medium, and large. The table is based on the experience of hundreds

TABLE 4
DESIRABLE WEIGHTS FOR MEN AND WOMEN
AGES 25 AND OVER

Height (in shoes)	*Weight in Pounds (in indoor clothing)*					
	Men			Women		
	Small Frame	Medium Frame	Large Frame	Small Frame	Medium Frame	Large Frame
4' 10"	—	—	—	92–98	96–107	104–119
11"	—	—	—	94–101	98–110	106–122
5' 0"	—	—	—	96–104	101–113	109–125
1"				99–107	104–116	112–128
2"	112–120	118–129	126–141	102–110	107–119	115–131
3"	115–123	121–133	129–144	105–113	110–122	118–134
4"	118–126	124–136	132–148	108–116	113–126	121–138
5"	121–129	127–139	135–152	111–119	116–130	125–142
6"	124–133	130–143	138–156	114–123	120–135	129–146
7"	128–137	134–147	142–161	118–127	124–139	133–150
8"	132–141	138–152	147–166	122–131	128–143	137–154
9"	136–145	142–156	151–170	126–135	132–147	141–158
10"	140–150	146–160	155–174	130–140	136–151	145–163
11"	144–154	150–165	159–179	134–144	140–155	149–168
6' 0"	148–158	154–170	164–184	138–148	144–159	153–173
1"	152–162	158–175	168–189	—	—	—
2"	156–167	162–180	173–194	—	—	—
3"	160–171	167–185	178–199	—	—	—
4"	164–175	172–190	182–204	—	—	—

Source: Prepared by the Metropolitan Life Insurance Company from data of the Build and Blood Pressure Study, 1959, Society of Actuaries.

[2] See answer to Question 16 of Chapter 19, page 301.

of thousands of insured persons, as prepared by the Metropolitan Life Insurance Company from data of the Build and Blood Pressure Study, 1959, Society of Actuaries.

17. Are the adult women in the United States thinner today than a generation ago?

An insurance study showed that over a recent period the average weight of women at each height declined. The reduction was generally from 3 to 5 pounds at the younger ages.

18. What are the averages for the principal body measurements of men?

Average body measurements of men are available from studies of servicemen in World Wars I and II most of whom were between ages 20 and 30. Table 5 is based upon the records for such men at demobilization. It appears that the average height of the men in the second world war was ¾ of an inch taller; the chest girth 1⅖ inches larger and the waist girth about the same.

TABLE 5
SELECTED BODY MEASUREMENTS OF WHITE SERVICEMEN,
WORLD WARS I AND II (IN INCHES)

	World War I	*World War II*
Height, standing	67.7	68.4
Height, sitting (from bench to top of head)	35.6	35.8
Chest circumference at rest	35.0	36.4
Waist girth	30.7	30.6

19. What are the averages for the principal body measurements of women?

Body measurements of more than 10,000 white women were compiled by the Department of Agriculture for the guidance of clothing manufacturers. From the averages in Table 6 it can be seen that the proportions vary somewhat with age. The girth measurements are uniformly larger for the older women (up to about age 52, after which they recede) and the height measurements are slightly smaller. Since there is a generation between the two groups of women listed here, some of the differences may be accounted for by changes in height and weight which have gradually been taking place in the country.

TABLE 6
SELECTED BODY MEASUREMENTS FOR WHITE WOMEN, 1939–40

	Ages 25–29	*Ages 50–54*
Height, standing	63.4 in.	62.6 in.
Hip height	31.7	31.2
Knee height	17.3	17.0
Arm length (from shoulder and around elbow to back of wrist with arm flexed)	23.0	23.0
Bust girth	34.2	38.2
Waist girth	27.3	32.9
Hip girth	37.8	40.7
Angle girth	9.2	9.5
Upper arm girth	10.9	12.4
Weight	124.7 lb.	149.6 lb.

20. How may the various types of body build be classified?

The three body build classifications used today by many anthropometrists are: endomorphic, or chubby persons, with a predominance of soft, round contours and with relatively massive viscera; mesomorphic, or athletic, with more normal proportions and a predominance of muscle, bone, and connective tissue; and ectomorphic, or long, thin, and relatively fragile, with the greatest skin area and brain weight in relation to body weight. Seldom, however, does any individual fit perfectly into one of these categories. Instead, although a person may be largely of a certain type, he usually presents some of the characteristics of the others.

21. Is body build influenced more by heredity or environment?

Heredity sets the direction in which the body will develop but external factors, such as the amount and quality of food, exercise, etc., greatly influence the outcome. Consequently, neither heredity nor environment can be said to be the more important.

22. Is body build a factor in disease?

This appears to be true in certain diseases, but the cause for the high incidence of those ailments in persons of a certain build are not yet understood. It is known that fat persons are especially susceptible to diabetes, cardiovascular-renal diseases, and arthritis. They also seem to have a somewhat higher prevalence of gallbladder trouble than other types. Tall, thin persons, on the other hand, are more likely to develop stomach ulcers.

23. Is personality influenced by body build?

Only very rough generalizations can be made about the personality characteristics likely to be found among persons of different body builds. The exceptions will certainly be many, and the relationship is far from invariable. Both personality formation and body build may be controlled by a third common factor, or it may be that one of the two has a strong influence on the development of the other.

Studies have shown that endomorphs, or chubby persons, are likely to be relaxed and to have a love of comfort. They often take great pleasure in eating, exhibit a hunger for affection and approval, have a need for company when they are troubled, and they are frequently sound sleepers.

Mesomorphs are more likely to be assertive and energetic, to have a directness of manner and an unrestrained voice. Their appearance may be overmature; they often show a need of exercise and when troubled feel a necessity for action.

Ectomorphs tend to be restrained, and inhibited in talking and in social relations, will have fast reactions, and a youthful intentness. Frequently they are light and restless sleepers and when troubled feel a need for solitude.

In addition to these general conclusions, there may also be a direct causal relationship between extreme body builds and personality. A very short person, for example, could hardly remain unaffected by his stature, which would undoubtedly influence and perhaps restrict his social activities.

24. Is mental development influenced by body build?

There is no evidence that body build influences mental development. Tall persons are not in general brighter than shorter chubby persons nor are athletic types generally unintelligent. Variations in intelligence appear to be independent of the type of body build, but some studies have shown that children with superior intelligence are also likely to be better developed physically than others, regardless of type.

25. When does growth cease?

Human beings ordinarily reach their full stature before the age of 25. After about 40, humans usually begin to shrink about 0.4 of an inch a decade as the cartilage in the joints and in the spinal column contracts.

26. How does the average weight of the human brain vary from birth to maturity?

At birth, a baby's brain is bigger in relation to its body than the brain of any other animal. The brain of a normal newborn infant weighs about 1 pound, or approximately one-seventh of the baby's total weight. For the first five years the human brain grows rapidly, then more slowly, and at about the age of 20 it stops increasing in weight. Late in life it may even become somewhat lighter. The brain of an adult man weighs on an average about 3 pounds $1\frac{1}{2}$ ounces (about $\frac{1}{40}$ of his total weight) and that of an adult woman about 2 pounds 12 ounces.

27. Is there any relation between brain size and mental ability?

In general, there is not. At the extremes of brain size, however, one is more likely to find disease or deformity which is associated with mental deficiency.

28. What is the size of the adult heart?

At birth the heart of a normal baby weighs less than an ounce. In adults the heart is usually about $\frac{1}{250}$ of body weight. The range is from about 7 to 14 ounces, averaging about $10\frac{1}{2}$ ounces for men and nearly 9 ounces for women.

29. What is the average pulse rate for men and women?

The average pulse rate of adult men at rest is about 72 beats a minute and of adult women is about 80. Pulse rates as low as 35 and as high as 100 may be still within the normal range.[3] During an ordinary day there are great fluctuations in the pulse. The rate usually is lowest during sleep and goes up toward the middle of the day. Activity, digestion, and emotional changes cause temporary speeding of the heart beat.

The pulse also varies with age. The average rate at birth is about 130 beats a minute and at the end of the first year around 100 or 110. By 12 years of age the rate has usually fallen to around 85, and after puberty it decreases to the adult rate.

30. How many times does the heart beat in a lifetime?

If a person has a pulse rate of around 72 beats per minute and lives for a full three-score and ten years, his heart beats more than two and one-half billion times.

[3] See answer to Question 20 of Chapter 12, page 178.

31. How much blood does the human heart pump each day?

In a normal healthy adult the heart pumps at a rate of approximately 3,000 gallons a day. At each beat the average adult heart discharges about four ounces of blood.

32. How many quarts of blood are there in the body?

The amount of blood in the body varies from about 3½ to 5½ quarts or from 5 to 7 percent of body weight. It is possible to lose about one-third of this and still survive.

33. What is the average blood pressure for men and women?[4]

The average systolic blood pressure is about 115 to 120 mm for men in their twenties and rises gradually with age to about 132 to 135 mm at age 60. The average diastolic is about 75 mm at age 20 and increases to about 80 at age 60. The blood pressure of an individual, however, may differ to some extent from the average for his age and still be regarded as normal in the sense that he is able to follow his daily tasks without an appreciable degree of extra mortality. For the systolic blood pressure this variation may be as much as 15 to 20 mm above or below the average, and for the diastolic 10 to 12 mm above or below the average. The proportion of men and women with significantly higher blood pressure rises with advance in age. The frequency of such elevated blood pressure is higher for men than for women up to age 40, but after that age is higher for women.

34. Are there racial differences in blood pressure?

The average blood pressure of American Negroes is higher than of whites. In contrast, the blood pressure of African Negroes has been found to be approximately the same as that of white men in this country at ages up to 40, but after that age the averages for the Negroes were lower; moreover, these averages tend to decline with advancing age. The blood pressures of Asiatics generally are appreciably below those of Europeans.

The reasons for these differences are not definitely known. In part they may represent differences in climate, nutritional status and diet, because these factors influence the blood pressure level. The low blood pressures recorded among the Chinese have been ascribed by some to the low level of protein in the diet or to some factor in

[4] See answer to Question 21 of Chapter 12, page 179.

rice, their chief food. However, their nutritional status is generally greatly inferior to that of Western peoples. Also they tend to be of slight build. This itself partly explains their low blood pressure, (since even among Western peoples a definite association is found between body build and blood pressure), with underweights showing significantly lower levels of blood pressure than heavier people.

35. What are the principal factors influencing blood, pressure?

Emotional stress usually causes a temporary rise in blood pressure, often of considerable degree and, if frequent and long-continued, may eventually result in a permanent rise. Heredity also plays a significant role in high or low blood pressure. The decrease in the elasticity of the arteries with advancing age is considered by some authorities to be a prime cause of the gradual rise in blood pressure. Certain types of kidney disease and endocrine gland disorders also may elevate the blood pressure well above the average for age.[5]

36. What is the average rate of respiration?

In the new born, the respiration rate lying down is ordinarily about 40 breaths per minute or even higher, about 30 in infants, 25 in five-year-olds, and 13 in adults. Occasionally, cases are reported with extremely slow rates: healthy men with rates as low as 6 and healthy women with rates as low as 3. In general, however, women breathe faster than men by about 2 to 4 breaths per minute. Disease —particularly fevers—exercise, and glandular activity increase the rate, and sleep slows it down. The additional energy expenditure necessary to sit up raises the respiration rate about 5 breaths per minute over what it is while lying down. The rate standing is about 4 breaths per minute above that sitting.

37. What is the average temperature of the body?

The temperature is ordinarily taken by mouth or rectum. The average mouth temperature is about 98.6° F, and rectal temperature 1 degree higher. Children are likely to have a normal temperature about 1 degree higher than most adults, and the very old may also have a slightly higher temperature. The temperature of children is easily disturbed and a high fever at young ages is not nearly so significant as in middle life. The time of day, activity, season, climate, clothing, and food affect temperature slightly. Body temperature

[5] See answers to Questions 22 and 24 of Chapter 12, pages 179 and 180.

is normally lowest between three and five in the morning and rises during the day to a high in late afternoon or evening. In some persons the normal temperature may be 1 degree or more above or below the average.

Temperatures that are too low or too high can be a serious threat to life. Persons can live only a short time with a temperature below 95° F, although it is possible to recover from a brief drop to as low a point as 75° F. Fever of about 111° F is usually fatal.

38. What is the normal rate of basal metabolism for men and for women?

Basal metabolism is the minimum rate at which the body produces energy when it is at rest. The surface area of the body, the glandular balance, and the state of health or disease affect the basal metabolism. It is measured in terms of heat (energy) units per hour. A healthy adult man has a rate between 38 and 40 calories per hour and a woman between 36 and 38. Variations of as much as 10 percent from the average are not unusual.

The basal metabolic rate in very young children is higher than in adults, but the mature rate is normally reached around the ages of three to six years.

39. Does physiologic age differ from chronologic age?

Physiologic age generally parallels chronologic age, but in some cases differs greatly. At age 70 or 75, for instance, some men are vigorous and productive, while on the other hand some at 50 may be almost physically or mentally senile. Even in the individual, different organs of the body may not age at the same rate. A man whose chronologic age is 50 may have a liver physiologically comparable to the average man of 65 or 70; the same person, however, may have a heart as young, strong, and efficient as in most men of age 30. It is common arbitrarily to label a person mature at age 21 or old at 65, but such characterization may be far from warranted in a physiologic sense.

Chapter 23

The Public

Health and Its

Administration

1. What is meant by "public health"?

The term "public health" has been defined by Professor C.-E. A. Winslow, one of the great leaders of the public health movement in this country, as: ". . . the science and art of preventing disease, prolonging life, and promoting physical and mental health and efficiency through organized community efforts. . . ." More recently the American Medical Association issued the following definition of "public health":

"Public Health is the art and science of *maintaining*, protecting, and improving the health of the people through organized community efforts. It includes those arrangements whereby the community provides medical services for *special groups* of persons and is concerned with prevention or control of *disease*, with persons

367

requiring hospitalization to protect the community and with the medically indigent."

2. What do public health agencies do?

The United States Public Health Service has listed more than three dozen specific types of public health activity. Roughly, public health work can be divided into two main categories: the environmental and the human. The first involves control of the surroundings to make them healthful and free from contamination or danger. The second involves services to the people themselves, to build up their strength and immunity and to prevent the spread of disease if it should break out. The chief public health activities to be found in this country are shown as follows.

MAIN PUBLIC HEALTH SERVICES

ENVIRONMENTAL	HUMAN
Sanitation of sewage and other wastes	Communicable disease control and reporting
Protection of water supplies	
Insect and rodent control	Laboratory testing for various diseases
Inspection of food, drugs, and cosmetics	Provision of vaccines and serums
	Research into causes of disease and methods of spread
Licensing of certain businesses and professions	
	Case finding surveys (i.e., mass x-rays for tuberculosis, blood tests for venereal disease, etc.)
Control of narcotics	
Regulation of health standards for housing and industry	
	Provision of public health nursing
Control of smoke, fumes, odors, and exposure to ionizing radiation	Provision of hospital and medical care for needy and for those with certain ailments (tuberculosis, venereal disease, cancer)
Examination of incoming aliens, and of plants, animals, and other shipments	
	Operation of hospitals for tuberculosis and mental patients
	Operation of special clinics for: maternal and child health dental health mental hygiene
	School health examinations and other school health services
	Collection of vital statistics
	Health education
	Planning of community resources to promote personal health

3. How did modern public health work begin?

Modern public health work dates from the social crusades of the first half of the nineteenth century in England. With the industrial revolution came harsh working conditions and crowded and unsanitary housing. Agitation for reform resulted, in 1848, in the first Public Health Act in England and in the creation of the General Board of Health. This board was in existence for only about 10 years, but it was the beginning of a century of extraordinary developments in sanitation, hygiene, preventive medicine, and other branches of public health.

4. Did the ancients know about public health?

The ancient Hebrews had sanitary codes which may well have been passed down from the rule of Hammurabi, King of Babylon about 2000 B.C. The Minoans, whose civilization on the island of Crete flourished about 1500 B.C., had sewers and baths. The later Greek and Roman civilizations also had some excellent sanitary provisions. The Romans built elaborate aqueducts to get pure drinking water to their city; their public baths were famous; and their main sewer, the Cloaca Maxima, is still in use. Both Demosthenes and Plutarch served as health officers. Unfortunately, after the fall of the Roman Empire, interest in sanitation and public health practically died out, and the whole field had to be developed again in modern times.

5. When was the first state board of health established in the United States?

The first permanent state board of health was established in Massachusetts in 1869. It was the delayed result of Lemuel Shattuck's study of health and sanitation in Boston, which was published in 1850. Shattuck, who is generally thought of as the founder of the American public health movement, had discovered the most appalling conditions, not much different from those which had started the social crusades somewhat earlier in England.

The Massachusetts law setting up a State Board of Health was used as a model by most of the other states. California established a board in 1870, and Congress set one up in the District of Columbia in 1871. The last state to follow suit was New Mexico, in 1919.

6. How has public health work expanded during the last 100 years?

In the beginning, the public health movement in this country, as in England, was largely concerned with cleaning up physical filth. This was a natural development of Lemuel Shattuck's historic exposure of the conditions in some sections of Boston. At that time the filth and miasma theory of disease—that it was caused by decaying matter in sewage, waste, and rubbish, and spread through the air by drifting particles—was gaining popularity. Although the theory was not correct, sanitation did result in great improvement in mortality. Many of the diseases which had killed large numbers of people— typhoid fever, cholera, and infant diarrhea and enteritis, for example —were directly connected with lack of cleanliness.

In the last two decades of the nineteenth century, the field of public health was revolutionized by the researches of Louis Pasteur and Robert Koch and their associates. The germ theory of disease, which they had done so much to establish, opened a new approach to preventive medicine. By 1900, most of the populous states and the larger cities in this country had regular health departments or boards of health and were campaigning against the communicable diseases, particularly smallpox, typhoid fever, tuberculosis, anthrax, cholera, and diphtheria, and the other principal childhood infections. Isolation, quarantine, and often vaccination and inoculation were used. The success, in general, was startling. However, this was not the case for tuberculosis, which infected a large proportion of the population. There was no effective means of vaccinating against this disease.

The achievements of Edward L. Trudeau in treating tuberculosis patients at his Saranac Lake Sanatorium lent weight to a theory about the importance of vital resistance, namely, that it could be built up by rest, personal hygiene, proper diet, and a well-ordered life. The wide application of this theory to public health work reduced the deaths from tuberculosis to a marked degree. Later still, the discoveries of immunology and biochemistry and their wide application in therapy have made it possible for the medical profession to reduce the incidence of and the mortality from pneumonia, tuberculosis, and many other infections.

By a combination of sanitation, preventive and curative medicine, personal hygiene, and health education, public health work has now cut down the dangers of infancy, childhood, and early adult life. The challenge of tuberculosis is now concentrated at the older ages. Today, the other chronic diseases, including mental illness, are consuming a large share of the efforts of physicians and health officials. As the knowledge of health and medicine has grown, the field of public health has expanded to include many new activities along with the older ones.

7. What is the World Health Organization?

The World Health Organization, which in 1964 had a total of 121 member nations, is open to all countries regardless of whether or not they are in the United Nations. It is not just a consultative body but engages actively in the promotion of health on an international scale. At present, its main efforts are aimed at the control of malaria, tuberculosis, and venereal disease, and at the prevention of future pandemics of influenza and other epidemic infections. With teams of experts and special equipment and drugs, it has been attacking disease in many parts of the world. It was also the organization responsible for the radical revision of the International List of Causes of Death and one of its commissions drew up an international pharmacopoeia. It has committees now working in the fields of mental, maternal, and child health. With headquarters in Geneva, regional offices in New Delhi, Alexandria, Hong Kong (temporary office), and Washington, and an epidemiologic intelligence station in Singapore, the World Health Organization can truly be considered a world-wide public health agency. In 1964, its budget was $36,788,000.

8. How does the United States rank among the nations of the world in public health work?

International comparisons of public health are possible only in the most general terms. Only a few countries of the world are known to provide health services anywhere near the level of modern standards. They are the English-speaking nations, the Scandinavian countries, The Netherlands, Finland, and a few of the other European nations. Not too much is known today about public health work in Russia and the Eastern European countries, but the marked reductions in mortality reported by these countries to the Statistical Office of the United Nations in recent years can only reflect the ever-improving public health facilities and their better administration. Elsewhere health protection is generally a privilege of the few; it is more a private than a public concern.

Even among the few nations with modern public health movements, satisfactory comparisons cannot be made because the approach to this work varies from country to country; one may do outstandingly well in a certain field and lag behind in another. If mortality and expectation of life reflect the level of public health work, the United States ranks near the top of the list. Certainly it is among the best in sanitation, communicable disease control, standards of technical training of personnel and of medical and hospital services.

9. How much is spent for governmental public health work in this country?

In 1962, a total of $2,351,000,000 was spent by the states for community health protection, including hospital care. If one adds public health expenditures by federal and local government agencies, the figure is raised to more than $5.1 billion.

10. Is there much geographic variation in public health expenditures?

Some states spend more than three times as much per capita as others on public health work and state hospitals and institutions. The expenditures are not necessarily greatest where mortality is lowest and longevity is highest. Some of the states spending large sums may do so because the need is great; it may take a long time to reduce mortality and increase longevity.

The average expenditure per capita in all states was $23.37 in 1962. The highest per capita expenditures were made by the District of Columbia ($58.23), Alaska ($40.69), New York ($38.89), and Nevada ($37.89). At the other end of the scale we find South Dakota ($9.08), Arizona ($12.34), North Dakota ($12.79), and West Virginia ($14.57). These figures include expenditures for health and hospitals by state and local governments combined.

11. What has been the trend in public health expenditures in recent years?

There has been a phenomenal increase of interest in public health in the last several decades and consequently a rapid rise in the funds spent for public health activities. In 1915, the Public Health Service received an appropriation of about $3,000,000. The budget for the same agency for the fiscal year ending in 1951 was about $290,000,000, and for 1965, the budget rose to $1,673,000,000. State government expenditures for health activities, aid to local health agencies, and health facilities have risen almost as remarkably. In 1915 they totaled $61,000,000; in 1948, $712,000,000, and in 1962, over $2.3 billion. Local expenditures have undoubtedly also gone up sharply. The expansion of health services is still proceeding and expenditures in the future are likely to continue to grow.

12. What is the United States Public Health Service?

From an agency established in 1798 to provide hospitalization for seamen, the United States Public Health Service has grown to be the largest single organization in this country and in the world in the field of public health. Its public health work began toward the end of the nineteenth century when the federal government took over the responsibility for foreign and interstate quarantine in order to combat cholera, yellow fever, smallpox, and plague, which were continually being reintroduced into this country by travelers and ships. In 1902, the service established its laboratory to study infectious diseases.

Today the Public Health Service acts as a coordinating and research agency for the nation's public health bodies. It operates the National Institutes of Health, conducts pilot studies in public health procedures, makes financial grants to states for health service and hospital construction, loans technical personnel and equipment, works on health education, and collects, analyzes, and publishes statistics on health and vital information. It also operates hospitals for seamen, American Indians, Alaskan natives, and other hospitals for drug addicts, lepers, and some additional groups.

13. What are the National Institutes of Health?

The National Institutes of Health are the research divisions of the United States Public Health Service. There are fourteen (14) separate, cooperating units:

National Cancer Institute
National Heart Institute
National Institute of Dental Research
National Institute of Allergy and Infectious Diseases
National Institute of Mental Health
National Institute of Arthritis, Rheumatism and Metabolic Diseases
National Institute of Neurological Diseases and Blindness

National Institute of General Medical Sciences
National Institute of Child Health and Human Development
Division of Biological Standards
Division of Research Facilities and Resources
Division of Research Grants
Division of Research Services
Clinical Center

Each fosters and conducts basic and applied research in their respective fields. The program of the National Institute of Allergy and Infectious Diseases, for example, is focused on the viruses, bacteria and other microorganisms which produce disease in man. The Division of Biological Standards administers the Biologics Control Law, setting standards for vaccines, serums, and toxoids used in curative and preventive medicine. The institutes operate laboratories and stations in various sections of the country. In addition, they administer the federal grants for research and teaching fellowships to public and private nonprofit research institutions.

The Clinical Center serves all National Institute of Health laboratories as the resource in which they carry out clinical or patient-oriented research. The patients admitted for study must be referred by a physician. The hospitals, clinics, family physicians, and specialists may not only refer their patients but, through consultation, follow-up treatment, and observation, also participate in the research. Patients often remain in the center for long periods at no cost to themselves, the main consideration being that their case presents a medical research problem of special interest to one or another of the institutes.

Altogether, the several institutes, the clinical center, and the several divisions constitute a biomedical research complex unlike that of any other nation. It is the largest such research facility in the world and has advanced the health of the American people and citizens of other countries immeasurably.

14. How is the responsibility for public health work divided among the federal, state, and local governments?

In most cases, the local government (municipal, township, or county) carries out the greater part of our public health work. It deals directly with the public and normally does most of the necessary inspecting, supervising, collecting of reports, and the direct work with the sick.

The responsibility for public health work, however, legally rests in the state governments. In most cases, states aid the local agencies, both with funds and with actual services. In addition, the state officials are usually the ones to distribute federal grants to local authorities. In most states, the standards for health and sanitation are written into state law or state health department regulations; where local agencies fail to meet them, the state may take action. Also, the state health departments act in emergencies, supplying funds, personnel, and facilities.

Although the federal government's direct responsibility for public health is confined by law to interstate and international matters, it does have general responsibility for protecting and improving the health of the people of the nation. This responsibility is carried out, in part, by a program of grants to: prevent the introduction and spread of diseases; aid in the development of health facilities and services throughout the nation; further the application of knowledge for the prevention and control of disease; and promote the maintenance of a healthful environment.

Through its financial grants to states for the improvement and maintenance of health services, funds for which are allocated among the several states on a "formula" basis taking into account population, financial need, and the extent of the problem, the federal government has, over a long period of years, encouraged and assisted state health agencies to expand and improve their activities and services in many areas, including communicable disease control, maternal and child health, environmental health protection, and, in more recent years, chronic illness. These formula grants to states in 1963 totaled $116,200,000 (1964—$115,350,000).[1]

15. What is the role of voluntary agencies in public health work?

The voluntary agencies play an important role in public health work in the United States because they can and do act in fields not yet entered by government agencies and in many ways effectively supplement the work of the official agencies. Practically the whole public health movement in this country can in large measure be traced to pioneer voluntary work of this kind. Besides the professional and technical societies, which set standards and study needs, there are

[1] Includes both Children's Bureau and Public Health Service formula grants.

many associations devoted to specific diseases (tuberculosis, cancer, heart disease, diabetes, the venereal diseases, poliomyelitis, mental retardation, cerebral palsy, and multiple sclerosis are the better-known ones) and a great many endowed foundations like the Rockefeller Foundation, the Ford Foundation, the Commonwealth Fund, the Kellogg Fund, and a large number of smaller agencies, which devote all or a good part of their annual expenditures to work in the field of health.

The primary nongovernmental agencies in public health, aside from those concerned with one special ailment, are the American Medical Association, the American Public Health Association, the American Red Cross, the National Health Council, the National Organization for Public Health Nursing, and a number of smaller agencies.

16. What are health councils?

Health councils are local organizations which bring together health officials and representatives of a community's voluntary organizations interested in public health. Councils have usually no operating functions but correlate the activities of member organizations and official agencies and help to interpret the work to the public. They are also active in health education to awaken the public to the need for full-time technically trained health personnel and for various specialized health services. In large centers the health council often has a full-time director and may be supported by the Community Chest. There are today hundreds of local health councils in the country, under the leadership of the coordinating National Health Council in New York.

17. How many official local health units are there in the United States?

On January 1, 1962, there were 1,591 local health units in the United States of which 914 served single counties, 324 served cities, 233 served local health districts, and 120 served state health districts. In addition, there were 1,213 primary public health centers and 1,020 auxiliary public health facilities such as laboratories or clinics. It was estimated that, as of that date, an additional 797 public health centers and 895 auxiliary facilities were needed to meet the requirements of the communities.

18. What standards are there for staffing health personnel as a ratio to population?

Minimum standards for the staffing of local health units were recommended some time ago by a committee of the American Public Health Association. They were 1 public health physician as administrator for every 50,000 persons or for every local health unit, 1 public health nurse for every 5,000 persons, 1 sanitation personnel for every 25,000 persons, and 1 clerk for every 15,000 persons. Many local health administrations in the country met these standards. More recently, however, these standards have been found inapplicable by individual communities to meet present conditions. It has been observed that some localities have been unable to increase the number of personnel beyond that contained in state and national ratios even when the local need could be adequately demonstrated, while a large number of other places were never able to obtain budget and personnel to reach the quoted figures. The result has been not to press for these standards but to recognize that the needs and resources of American communities vary greatly and that standards must vary accordingly. In general, the recent trend in personnel utilization by large city health departments has been toward increasing clerical staff and decreasing professional staff, resulting in a nearly equal transfer of gains and losses, so that total employment remains stabilized.

Those not living within the areas covered by full-time local health departments usually have a part-time local health agency or are served in some fashion by county or state authorities. A recent survey showed that a small fraction of the population was without any local health protection. Outside of cities, public health work is usually handled by county organizations or by health district administrations covering more than one county.

19. What is the minimum number of full-time health departments needed to care for the American population?

It has been estimated by a committee of the American Public Health Association that no more full-time health departments are needed than are at present in operation, but that the distribution should be changed. In rural sections, instead of having the jurisdiction of most health agencies correspond to political boundaries (townships, counties, and so forth), it has been suggested that there be one health unit for a group of adjoining counties, towns, or townships organized into a single and effective health district. The combined health district idea has been spreading rapidly in recent years.

20. How many states have complete coverage by full-time health departments?

In 1942, only the District of Columbia and four states—Alabama, Maryland, New Mexico, and South Carolina—had a complete system of local full-time health agencies. New York had a district setup providing fairly complete coverage. One state, Vermont, had no full-time local health departments. In the other states, the proportion of population covered by full-time health service ranged from 6 percent to more than 90 percent. Currently, most states have achieved fairly good coverage with their health services.

21. How has the improvement in sanitation and water supplies helped to combat typhoid and other diseases?

In 1900 it was estimated that more than 35,000 persons died in the United States from typhoid fever. Dysentery, and diarrhea and enteritis took additional large tolls. Stream pollution was already a serious problem and the contamination of water supplies was common. Today, despite the increase in pollution from sewage and industrial wastes, the contamination of water supplies has been cut to a safe level in most areas by the use of chlorination, filtration, and other engineering developments. Sewage and waste disposal is handled by plants and equipment costing many millions. The results are impressive. In 1960 there were only 21 deaths from typhoid and paratyphoid in the entire country; the death rate was less than one-thousandth of what it had been 60 years before.

22. Is a city legally responsible for water-borne disease contracted from its water?

Since 1910 the courts have made cities pay damages for typhoid contracted because of negligence in the operation of water systems. The first instance was a case of typhoid in Minnesota, but there have been several in other states. In California, a city water chlorination plant was shut down for 12 hours, resulting in 19 cases of typhoid and dysentery. By 1928 the responsibility of a city for its water supply was so well established that when 248 persons came down with typhoid in Olean, New York, the city voluntarily paid damages to avoid suit.

23. What businesses and professions connected with health require special licenses?

In addition to persons engaged in the healing arts (chiefly physicians, dentists, nurses, osteopaths, optometrists, pharmacists, and dental hygienists) many others are required in some or all states to obtain licenses. Among them are embalmers, funeral directors, midwives, plumbers, operators of swimming pools and of water supply and sewage treatment plants, barbers, beauticians, and food handlers. Restaurants, hotels, hospitals, nursing homes and similar health establishments are also usually licensed.

24. How is the public protected from harmful foods, drugs, and cosmetics?

The federal, state, and local governments take part in food, drug, and cosmetic control. The responsibility of the federal government is restricted to goods in interstate commerce. Inspection for contamination, adulteration, or improper labeling is handled by the Food and Drug Administration. The Federal Trade Commission is authorized to see that advertising claims for foods, drugs, and cosmetics in interstate commerce are correct.

Control of goods in intrastate trade is a state and local affair, usually administered by the health or agriculture departments. All states have laws or regulations covering food, drugs, and cosmetics, but there is a great deal of variation in the requirements and enforcement. The food which generally receives the most attention is milk. Most states inspect dairies and rigidly regulate the handling and marketing of milk. Dairy and meat products, bakery goods, and confections are also usually inspected, but the detection of defects in these is much more difficult. For example, meat containing the organisms which cause trichinosis shows no visible signs of contamination and might easily be passed by inspectors. The only guarantee against the disease is proper cooking.

In many states food handlers are examined and licensed. Here again the usefulness of the regulations is often questioned, since few individuals receive the kind of thorough medical examination necessary to determine if they are carriers of some of the less obvious diseases.

25. How are the sales of narcotics controlled?

Narcotics control is handled chiefly by the federal government. Since this control is legally founded on the power to tax, enforcement of the laws and regulations is undertaken by the Treasury Department. Only registered and licensed persons in a few fields (primarily in medicine and in the drug industry) may deal in narcotics. Drug companies and druggists are inspected at intervals, and individuals, ships, trucks, aircraft, coming into the country are also watched. To supplement federal regulations, many states have their own rules.

26. What communicable diseases must be reported to public authorities, and who is responsible for the reporting?

The list of diseases varies from state to state, but more than 100 are supposed to be reported in one state or another. The table below includes those for which the federal Public Health Service collects figures weekly. In general, they are communicable diseases which are or were once considered to be a threat to public health. Ordinarily the attending doctor is required to report the case, but if no doctor is called in, a nurse, the household head, or some other person must make the report in some states.

NOTIFIABLE DISEASES ON WHICH THE FEDERAL PUBLIC
HEALTH SERVICE COLLECTS WEEKLY FIGURES

Anthrax	Meningococcal infections
Aseptic meningitis	Poliomyelitis, total
Botulism	paralytic
Brucellosis	nonparalytic
Diphtheria	unspecified
Encephalitis, primary	Psittacosis-Ornithosis
Encephalitis, postinfectious	Rabies in man
Hepatitis, infectious and serum, total (by age, under 20; 20 and over; age unknown)	Streptococcal sore throat including Scarlet Fever
Leptospirosis	Tetanus
Malaria	Tularemia
Measles	Typhoid Fever

Typhus fever, flea-borne, murine, endemic
Typhus fever, tick-borne, Rocky Mountain spotted
Rabies in animals

In addition provision is made for special reporting of epidemics or unusual occurrence of communicable diseases. Cases of plague, cholera, smallpox, yellow fever, and other rare but quarantinable diseases must be reported immediately by telephone or telegram. Other diseases not on the weekly report list but under surveillance programs are required to be reported at certain intervals. Reports on the venereal diseases from states and larger cities are sent at regular monthly or quarterly periods. Finally, an annual summary of notifiable diseases is received from all states.

This system of morbidity reports together with the series of National Health Surveys have supplied the Public Health Service with a wealth of information on the prevalence of disease on which to base its extensive programs of research and of active cooperation with the states for their control.

27. What action is taken by public health authorities when a case of a communicable disease is reported?

If the disease is serious, the local health department, while reporting the case to the state and perhaps to the federal government, will investigate. A doctor is often sent to verify the diagnosis and sometimes a public health nurse to help in caring for the patient. The family and other persons who have been in contact with the patient may be quarantined, and the sick person is frequently isolated.

If the disease is one which is likely to spread, an epidemiologist is assigned to trace the origin of the infection. Depending on the ailment, it may turn out to be a human carrier, contaminated water or food, or an insect or animal host. In cases of diseases like typhoid, smallpox, yellow fever, dysentery, cholera, and plague, it is vitally important to locate the source before an epidemic can get started. If the danger seems acute, the local health department may even recommend immunization of the local population and sometimes supply the vaccine.

28. Is quarantining of exposed persons necessary in many infectious diseases?

Formerly quarantine was often used as a preventive measure. However, with greater medical knowledge of the way in which diseases are spread, public health authorities have reduced the number of diseases requiring quarantine. Isolation of the patient is still important and is common practice in most localities for about 30 relatively well-known types of infection. Although the regulations are not uniform throughout the country, many public health agencies insist on using quarantine procedures in the following diseases:

Cholera
Diphtheria
Infant diarrhea (quarantine of nursery)
Paratyphoid fever

Whooping cough (quarantine from nonimmune children)
Plague
Psittacosis (quarantine of birds, not people)
Rabies (quarantine of biting or bitten animals)
Typhus (quarantine of people, if they have lice)
Scarlet fever
Typhoid fever

29. How do epidemiologists work to protect public health?

There are many examples of what epidemiologists do in tracing the source of dangerous infections and in discovering those exposed to disease. Perhaps the most famous recent cases have been the smallpox scares in this country since the war.

In New York City, a man died of a serious rash in a city hospital. A few weeks later, his case was diagnosed as having been smallpox, and then three more cases were found. The source of the infection was traced to Mexico City, and as many as possible of those in this country who had contact with the first or later cases were found in order that they might be vaccinated. At the same time, other localities became involved because the first victim had traveled through many of them. Mass vaccinations were finally instituted and the outbreak stopped after 12 cases and 2 deaths occurred. More recently, the young son of a missionary, returning from Brazil, was found to be suffering from smallpox when the family reached New York. All media of communication were used to locate persons who had been in contact with the family and an investigation was launched to find out why the inadequate vaccination certificate had not been detected.

Although there have been cases of smallpox, typhoid, and even cholera and plague in this country in the last half century, the outbreaks have always been confined to a relatively small area.

30. Do all states have public health laboratories?

In all states there is a public health laboratory. The work undertaken by the laboratories varies, but there are some standard services which are normally provided. First of all, there are the tests for various diseases, such as blood tests, sputum tests, and so forth. Health laboratories also usually test drinking water, milk, food, drugs, and samples taken in connection with industrial surveys. In some states, the laboratories manufacture the biological products (serums, vaccines, and toxoids) for the prevention of certain communicable diseases and distribute them free. In a considerable number of states, the public health laboratory is an institution of distinction where important research has been conducted in addition to carrying out the essential routines which give scientific validity to the various activities of the health department of the state.

31. Do most health departments have tuberculosis, venereal disease, and cancer services?

All states have extensive programs for tuberculosis and venereal disease control and for cancer services. Many state and local health departments operate tuberculosis, venereal disease, and cancer clinics for diagnosis and treatment. In addition, the local affiliates of the national voluntary health associations often supplement the clinical facilities of the official agencies. This is particularly true in the fields of tuberculosis and cancer.

32. To what extent are maternal and child health services provided through public health agencies?

Under the Social Security Act, the federal government provides funds to assist the states and other jurisdictions through state and local public health agencies in extending and improving services to promote the health of mothers and children. In 1961, the federal government spent $18.3 million, and state and local governments spent $61.9 million on these services. In 1960, some 263,000 mothers received maternity medical clinic services and 551,000 obtained maternity nursing services. About 1.5 million infants and other children received well child conference services and 3.4 million received child health nursing service. In addition, $20.0 million in federal funds, and $51.1 million in state and local funds were spent on services for crippled children.

All but a few states help local authorities to assure either hospital delivery of babies or delivery by a doctor at home. Either clinic or home nursing care for infants and preschool children is a standard service in all states and the District of Columbia.

School children also are given medical examinations and there are regular arrangements made by the state authorities to follow up cases involving major health defects.

33. What are the functions of public health nursing, and how many public health nurses do we have in the United States?

Public health nurses form one of the most important groups in health work. They are active in health education, in maternal and child health services, in home-care for the sick, in communicable disease control, and, in fact, in almost all of the important preventive, rehabilitative, and curative functions of agencies providing health services. In rural areas, the public health nurse is often the only public health person in the area.

In 1962, there were 34,700 public health nurses in the country. It is estimated that almost two-thirds of them were working in urban centers and the remainder in rural areas.

34. Do many public health departments operate mental hygiene clinics?

There were 1,762 mental hygiene clinics in the United States in 1963, but relatively few of them were operated by health departments. The majority were under the control of other government bodies—in many cases the state mental hygiene or hospital services— or of private agencies.

35. Do many health departments provide dental service?

Dental care lags behind many other health services in this country. In a survey of health work shortly before World War II, the Public Health Service found that only half of the state health organizations actually rendered some dental service. Most of the others had educational campaigns for dental care, but they did not aid in the operation of clinics. Of those which did have some dental care activities, a great many attempted only demonstration work, without provision for help to large numbers of people. Most of the dental clinics and examination services run by states were for children rather than adults.

36. To what extent do health departments provide for general medical care?

Medical care for special patients is provided by a great many health agencies. The federal government, for example, cares for drug addicts, certain mental patients, for servicemen, seamen, and for veterans. Practically all levels of government provide medical care for prisoners under their supervision or for other institutionalized persons. Many state and local health agencies have budgets for medical care for patients suffering from certain specific conditions such as venereal disease, tuberculosis, mental illness, or cancer. General medical care is supplied by relatively few state or local health departments, and such care is limited to indigents for the most part. Maryland has had for some time a state-wide system of medical care for families on relief provided by the physicians and nurses of the local health units. The Florida and Kentucky state health departments participate to a limited degree in providing medical care to indigents. At one time, the state of Washington health department had such a program but later referred it to the State Welfare Department. Several cities have joint departments of health and hospitals, including Detroit, Denver, and Philadelphia; and San Mateo County, California, has a joint department of health, hospitals, and rehabilitation. This phase of public health service has not progressed in this country.

37. What is the role of health departments in the collection of vital statistics?

Birth and death certificates are usually collected by local health authorities and passed on, in original or transcript form, to the state health departments or boards. From there, copies of the certificates go to the National Office of Vital Statistics of the federal Public Health Service, where pertinent facts are abstracted and tabulated for statistical purposes. The annual collection of vital statistics on a uniform basis for the whole nation is quite recent. This annual collection began in 1900, when the Death Registration Area, containing 10 states and a number of cities including the District of Columbia, where the records were deemed sufficiently accurate, was formed by the federal government for this purpose. Additional states were taken into the Death Registration Area when their records were considered sufficiently accurate. A corresponding system of birth registration was started in 1915. The last state to join the two systems was Texas in 1933.

Marriage and divorce figures are also handled by health authorities of the state in many cases, although the original information comes in most instances from county or city clerks and from law courts. About three-quarters of the states require reporting of marriages to central state authorities and about three-fifths require reporting of divorces, but these laws and regulations are not always enforced.

38. In how many states is smallpox vaccination compulsory?

As of September, 1963, legislation authorizing some type of compulsory vaccination for smallpox existed in 18 States, the District of Columbia, and Puerto Rico. The affected groups varied from the general population to a requirement for admittance to school, school teachers, and school employees. Generally, the physically unfit and persons with religious beliefs against vaccination were exempted. In states where smallpox vaccination is not compulsory, it would appear that the state board of health, in case of necessity to suppress an epidemic, would have authority to require vaccination of the general population. If a state statute on the subject is not broad enough to require such vaccination, it would appear that the police power of the state, to protect its citizens against hazards, would supply the necessary authority.

39. In how many states are premarital and prenatal examinations required?

Premarital blood tests of the parties and prenatal blood tests of the mother to detect syphilis that, if untreated, might be transmitted to the child are required in all but five or six states and the District of Columbia.

40. How many public hospitals are there in the United States?

In 1962, there were 2,415 hospitals controlled or operated by government at all levels in the country, and they had 67 percent of the total bed capacity of all the nation's hospitals. Nongovernmental hospitals totaled 4,613, of which 79 percent were under the auspices of churches or other nonprofit groups. The private hospitals, although more numerous, are on the whole smaller than the government institutions. Most of the nonprofit hospitals and many of those owned individually or by partnerships or corporations have wards or beds which are free or for which only a nominal charge is made.

41. What legislative provisions have been made to assist in the construction of needed hospitals and other health facilities in this country?

In 1946, Congress enacted the Hospital Survey and Construction Act—popularly known as the Hill-Burton Program—to provide grants or loans to states to assist in constructing and equipping needed public and voluntary nonprofit hospitals and public health centers. In 1954, the program was broadened also to provide grants for nursing homes, diagnostic and treatment centers, and rehabilitation facilities.

Since 1947, Congress has made annual appropriations from $65 million to $220 million for the construction of health facilities under the Hill-Burton Program. The federal share varies from state to state, ranging from one-third to two-thirds of the cost of construction and equipment of each project.

By May 31, 1964, 7,300 projects had been approved since the beginning of the program. These projects, providing 310,558 beds in hospitals and nursing homes and also providing 2,066 other types of health facilities, involved a total cost of $6.7 billion. The federal contribution amounted to $2.1 billion with the remaining $4.6 billion paid by states, local communities, and voluntary nonprofit groups.

Legislative proposals now before the Congress would extend the Hill-Burton Program for an additional five years through June 30, 1969. In addition, they would authorize a new program of grants for the modernization of hospitals and other health facilities giving special consideration to facilities located in the more densely populated areas. Special project planning grants also would be provided for area-wide planning of hospitals and other health facilities.

Late in 1963, Congress enacted the Mental Retardation Facilities and Community Mental Health Centers Construction Act and the Health Professions Educational Assistance Act. The former Act authorizes (1) special project grants for constructing university-affiliated mental retardation facilities; (2) a formula grant program for the construction of other mental retardation facilities; and (3) a formula grant program for the construction of community mental health centers. The Health Professions Educational Assistance Act authorized a program of grants for the construction of teaching facilities for the training of physicians, osteopaths, dentists, nurses (collegiate schools only), professional public health personnel, pharmacists, optometrists, and podiatrists. The construction of new schools and the expansion, renovation, and replacement of existing schools is authorized.

42. How does the government keep disease from being imported into this country?

The federal government has quarantine jurisdiction over incoming vehicles (ships, airplanes, etc.). Some of the diseases which are watched for are cholera, yellow fever, typhus fever, smallpox, leprosy, plague, and anthrax. Ships and airplanes and their crews and passengers are the main concern. In addition to medical officers overseas and to international reporting of many of these diseases, incoming craft are inspected at the port of entry and quarantined if necessary. Plants and animals are also inspected in order to exclude plant blights and animal infections.

All immigrants are also now required to undergo medical examinations in the countries where they get their visas. Public Health Service medical officers are detailed overseas to make the examinations. Excludable groups are: the feeble-minded and the insane, epileptics, the tuberculous and those afflicted with "a loathsome or dangerous contagious disease." In addition, doctors are not to certify for admission persons who have any mental or physical defect which might interfere with their ability to earn a living.

43. What kinds of specialized personnel are needed by an up-to-date health department?

The key person in public health work is, of course, the health officer. The training usually required for that job includes not only a medical degree but also postgraduate work in the special field of public health. Sanitation personnel, public health nurses, and a clerical staff are also necessary. In the public health departments of some states and of large cities and populous counties, there may also be a need for other specialized workers; for example, water works engineers, many kinds of medical specialists, psychologists, dentists, laboratory technicians, health educators, nutritionists, and medical social workers.

44. How many schools of public health are there in the country and how many persons can they train?

There are currently 14 schools of public health in the United States and Canada which are accredited by the American Public Health Association. They are located in the University of California at Berkeley, Columbia, Harvard, Johns Hopkins, Michigan, Minnesota, Montreal, North Carolina, Pittsburgh, Toronto, Tulane, Yale, University of Puerto Rico, and the University of California at Los Angeles. In the academic year 1963, approximately 1,600 students were enrolled in these schools, and 819 received degrees or diplomas at the end of the school year.

In addition, a number of other colleges and universities offer programs to prepare specific categories of public health professions.

These courses include curricula in public health nursing, environmental health, community nutrition, and other specialties required in modern public health practice.

45. What are some of the more recent developments in public health work?

The two most important recent developments are in the fields of chronic disease control and general medical care. With the success of the older health activities, there has come a drop in mortality at the younger ages and a shift in the importance of causes of death. The diseases which take the largest tolls today are no longer the acute infections but the chronic conditions. Two of the most important of these—heart disease and cancer—are not communicable and cannot be controlled by immunization or epidemiological work. Their onset is difficult to diagnose and their damage has too often been done before they are noticed. In recognition of the growing importance of chronic disease, the Massachusetts Department of Health and the State Medical Society, with the cooperation of some voluntary agencies, have worked out a modern health protection program. A clinic has been opened where persons who are apparently healthy can have tests made without charge to detect diseases before serious or irreversible changes have taken place.

Gradually, the public health authorities are taking more responsibility in the area of medical care available to their communities. It is recognized that the medical care of individuals and families is as fundamental to the public health as are sanitation and immunization. Furthermore, extensive resources, both private and public, now exist in the country to provide modern and adequate medical care. There are, however, obvious defects in the organization, distribution, utilization, and financing of these resources. It is here that dynamic public health leadership can be helpful. Health officers have already acquired considerable experience on a community-wide basis in this direction. This experience has included planning and licensing of hospitals and nursing homes, the operation of some medical services and facilities and the administration of outpatient services and many other similar activities.

The health officer, as the representative of the government, is interested in the medical services in the community and has for many years had experience in working closely with medical societies in studies of quality of medical care in such areas as maternal and child health, tuberculosis, and home nursing programs. He can utilize similar channels in studies of quality, accessibility, continuity and cost of care in the enlarging areas of governmental medical responsibility. It is the consensus of public health leadership that the time has come for a new effort to augment the benefits of medical care in the service of the nation's health. It is believed that with this leadership a more effective organization of medical service at the local level can be evolved through a better coordination of effort and a more effective utilization of the resources available, to the great benefit of all concerned.

46. Is there enough technical public health personnel in the country and is health administration adequate?

Despite the great improvement in recent decades in both the numbers and the qualification of public health personnel of all varieties of skills, there is still a marked lack to keep pace with the increased demands for efficient health services. This is due to the explosive growth of the populations, their increasing shift toward urban areas, and the consequent changes in the social and economic structure of the populations. There is not only the serious problem of insufficient numbers of well-trained personnel but also the need for a new look at the type of administrative setup required to meet community health needs adequately. Fortunately, the whole picture of community health service is under careful review by a national commission jointly sponsored by the American Public Health Association and the National Health Council. Its report is eagerly awaited and will guide new developments in the coming decades.

Chapter 24

How Long
We Live

1. What is meant by the "life span" and by the "average length of life"?

The life span is the greatest number of years that a human being can live. What this biological limit to life may be is not known precisely, but we do know that relatively few persons survive more than 100 years. It is unlikely that man has experienced any increase in his life span over the centuries.

The average length of life is the average number of years lived per person in a group of people traced from birth to the death of the last survivor. Although the life span is probably unchanged, the average length of life has increased greatly in modern times as a larger proportion of people have survived to the higher ages.

2. Are there many authentic cases of persons who have lived to be 100?

Cases of extreme old age are usually reported where illiteracy is frequent and where record-keeping is notoriously poor—in other words, where the facts cannot be verified. Since official registration of births is a relatively modern development, authenticated cases of old age are hard to find. An English actuary who searched British insurance and annuity files found only 30 acceptable cases of centenarians among 800,000 lives. In Canada there is an authenticated instance of a man who lived 113 years and 124 days. Another frequently cited case is that of the Dane, Christen Jacobsen Drakenberg, who supposedly was born in 1626 and lived for 146 years. But much uncertainty surrounds this man's life and length of years.

3. What is the average length of life in the United States?

In 1960, the average length of life in this country was approximately 70 years, an increase of about 30 years since the middle of the nineteenth century. From 1850 to 1900, the average length of life in the United States rose by about nine years. Since the turn of the century the advance has been accelerated, and the gain has totaled 21 years.

4. What was the average length of life in the United States when the country was founded?

According to a table prepared from death records in Massachusetts and New Hampshire for a period ending in 1789, the average length of life was then 35.5 years. The recent figures for white females in the United States are more than double this.

5. How does the average length of life in the United States compare with that in other countries?

In only a few countries—Australia, New Zealand, Norway, Sweden, Denmark, and The Netherlands—is the average length of life greater than in the United States. The best recent records are found in The Netherlands, Norway, and Sweden, where the expectation of life at birth is about two years greater than for the United States. However, there are many of our states that have a record even better than some of the countries that exceed the national average.

Figures for the average length of life or expectation of life at birth in many countries may be compared in the following table.

India still has one of the poorest records of longevity of any

major nation for which data are available. There, the expectation of
life at birth in 1957–58 was only about 46 years. On the other hand,
Japan has reported an average length of life for 1960 of about 68
years.

EXPECTATION OF LIFE AT BIRTH IN SEVERAL COUNTRIES

Country; Period	Expectation of Life at Birth, Years		Country; Period	Expectation of Life at Birth, Years	
	Males	Females		Males	Females
Australia			Northern Ireland		
1953–55	67.14	72.75	1959–61	67.37	72.11
Austria			Italy		
1960	65.00	70.98	1954–57	65.75	70.02
Belgium			Japan		
1946–49	62.04	67.26	1960	65.37	70.26
Bulgaria			Mexico		
1956–57	64.17	67.65	latest	45–55	
Canada			Netherlands		
1955–57	67.61	72.92	1956–60	71.4	74.8
Chile			New Zealand		
1952	49.84	53.89	1955–57	68.20	73.00
Czechoslovakia			Norway		
1960	67.81	73.18	1951–55	71.11	74.70
Denmark			Poland		
1956–60	70.38	73.76	1960–61	64.8	70.5
England and Wales			Portugal		
1961	68.0	73.8	1957–58	59.8	65.0
Finland			Russia		
1951–55	63.4	69.8	1958–59	64.42	71.68
France			Scotland		
1961	67.6	74.5	1961	66.13	71.78
Germany			Spain		
Federal Republic			1950	58.76	63.50
1959–60	66.69	71.94	Sweden		
West Berlin			1960	71.24	74.92
1949–51	63.70	68.39	Switzerland		
Hungary			1948–53	66.36	70.85
1958	65.14	69.36	U.S.A.		
Iceland			1961	67.0	73.6
1941–50	66.1	70.3	Venezuela		
India			latest	40–50	
1957–58	45.23	46.57			
Ireland					
1950–52	64.53	67.08			

A rather close relation has been found between expectation of
life and the plane of living among the countries of the world. Life
is short and death rates are generally high in those areas where the
average daily per capita caloric consumption is low.

6. What is the average length of life for the world as a whole?

The only estimate made relates to the pre-World War II situation, when the average length of life was placed at about 35 years. It is now unquestionably higher in view of the marked improvement in health conditions in the last two decades.

7. Are there signs that longevity increased in ancient times?

The average length of life of prehistoric man has been estimated at about 18 years. Judging from the many skulls found with marks of blows, violence was the usual cause of death. Very few fossils or bones show survivorship beyond age 40 in prehistoric times. Estimates

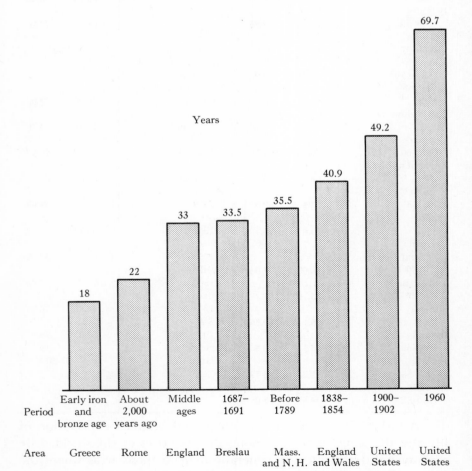

Chart 19. **Average length of life from ancient to modern times.**

of the average age at death made from Greek skulls for the period 3500 B.C. to 1300 A.D. suggest only a small rise in longevity over those centuries.

The bones from the period when civilization was rising in Greece show evidence of better teeth, increased body size, and fewer arthritic conditions. At the same time, archeological findings point to improvements in nutrition and in the general conditions of life. During those years there was also a growth of medical skill in Greece. Burial inscriptions for the time of the Roman Empire indicate that the average length of life may then have been between 20 and 30 years. (See Chart 19.)

8. What gains in longevity were made up to the beginning of the modern public health era?

During the Middle Ages, the average length of life in England may have been near 33 years. Another estimate, based on the records of the ruling classes of Europe during the Renaissance, is 30 years. From death records in Breslau for 1687–91, the English astronomer, Edmund Halley, arrived at an average length of life of 33.5 years. In Massachusetts and New Hampshire in the late eighteenth century the average was about 35.5 years, according to a report published by Wigglesworth in 1793. There was, therefore, only a slow and rather insignificant rise in longevity in the many centuries from the time of the Roman Empire to the American Revolution. However, in the subsequent period up to 1850, the average length of life in English-speaking countries went up by five years. In the century after that, the rate of improvement was greatly increased.

9. What social and scientific influences have brought about the progress in longevity within the last century?

Basically, the rapid gains in longevity during the last century— from an average length of life of 40 years for the United States in 1850 to 70 years in 1960—were made possible by the great industrial and agricultural progress in the Western world. An integral part of this progress has been the great advance in sanitary practices and the wide expansion of medical knowledge. The first modern efforts at public health reform, which started with the English social reforms of little more than a century ago, were devoted to the pressing problems of local sanitation and housing. Out of this movement developed the modern codes of law designed to protect the quality of food, the supply of water, and the work and home environment.

With the discovery of the infectious nature of many diseases, it became possible for community leaders to take effective steps for their virtual eradication. These efforts have had their greatest success against smallpox, cholera, yellow fever, typhoid fever, diarrhea and enteritis, diphtheria, scarlet fever, whooping cough, measles, and tuberculosis.

Modern developments in medicine have been along many lines. The skill of the surgeon has been greatly increased. Vaccinations and inoculations to prevent infections are common practice. The use of insulin—a hormone—has greatly altered the outlook for diabetics; more recent discoveries regarding hormones give great promise for relief from some of the most common ailments, like the rheumatic conditions. The role in disease played by nutritional deficiencies has become a study by itself; the outstanding development here is the discovery of the vitamins. The x-ray has become an important tool in diagnosis and treatment. Physiotherapy, in its various phases, has taken a prominent place in treatment and rehabilitation. In addition to the beneficial effects presently offered by radiotherapy, new fields of research have been opened by the use of radioactive tracers in physiologic processes. Recent advances in chemotherapy and the antibiotics have already produced spectacular reductions in mortality, notably from pneumonia, appendicitis, syphilis, and the puerperal infections; tuberculosis has also responded very favorably to such treatment.

The recent rapid rise in the general conditions of life has contributed much to our better health status. Shortened hours of labor now provide greater opportunity for leisure; food is more varied, more abundant, and of better quality; personal cleanliness has been greatly improved; and homes are now roomier and designed for more air and sunlight. Safety measures in the factory, the home, and in public places have saved countless lives from premature death.[1]

10. What is the outlook for further gains in longevity?

Existing knowledge in medicine and public health will continue to be applied more widely and also more intensively. At the same time, there will undoubtedly be further advances in medical knowledge. And finally, the standard of living may be expected to keep on rising. Together, these forces will certainly reduce mortality and lengthen life. This is particularly true in those countries which have

[1] See answer to Question 21 of Chapter 7, page 99.

only recently developed medical and public health services. In the more advanced countries, however, the future gains in average length of life must, in the nature of the case, be moderate at best. The mortality in these lands is already so low in childhood and in early adult life that further decreases in death rates at these ages would add comparatively little to the average length of life. Future progress in longevity will depend largely on the magnitude of the reductions in mortality from the chronic and degenerative diseases.

11. Have we been sufficiently optimistic regarding improved longevity in the past?

A number of life tables have been constructed for the purpose of gauging the gains in longevity that might be expected if full advantage were taken of the latest advances in medical and public health development. Notwithstanding the optimistic view taken when these tables were prepared, experience showed that it did not take long before an even more favorable situation actually developed. For example, a life table of this kind prepared in 1922 showed an expectation of life at birth of 64.75 years; this was practically duplicated in a life table based upon the experience of white females in the United States during 1930–39. Another such hypothetical table constructed in 1941 had an expectation of life at birth of 70.8 years, which was excelled by the figure of 71 years experienced by white females in 1948. In other words, experience has shown that our optimistic views regarding prospects for improved longevity were generally conservative. Our past experience should make us hopeful of considerable gains in longevity in the less advanced countries of the world which are developing better medical and public health facilities for their people.

12. What is a life table?

The life table is a table of figures that shows how many, out of a group of people followed from birth, survive from one year of age to the next. From these figures is computed the expectation of life which, at birth, is the average length of life. An example of a life table is shown on page 398. The life table is generally based upon the death rates at each age of life as observed in a community during some period. In the example, the figures in column 2 show the chances of dying within the year following a birthday, according

EXCERPT FROM LIFE TABLE FOR WHITE MALES
IN THE UNITED STATES: 1949-51*

Year of Age	Rate of Mortality per 1,000 — Number Dying between Ages x and x + 1 among 1,000 Living at Age x	Of 100,000 Born Alive		Complete Expectation of Life or Average Future Lifetime; Average Number of Years Lived after Age x per Person Surviving to Exact Age x
		Number Surviving to Exact Age x	Number Dying between Age x and x + 1	
x	$1{,}000q_x$	l_x	d_x	$\overset{\circ}{e}_x$
0	30.69	100,000	3,069	66.31
1	2.12	96,931	205	67.41
2	1.38	96,726	134	66.55
3	1.06	96,592	102	65.64
4	0.90	96,490	87	64.71
—	—	—	—	—
—	—	—	—	—
—	—	—	—	—
19	1.53	95,250	146	50.45
20	1.62	95,104	154	49.52
21	1.69	94,950	161	48.60
22	1.74	94,789	165	47.68
23	1.76	94,624	166	46.77
24	1.74	94,458	164	45.85
25	1.71	94,294	161	44.93
26	1.68	94,133	158	44.00
—	—	—	—	—
—	—	—	—	—
—	—	—	—	—
103	443.12	24	19	1.67
104	460.14	14	11	1.59
105	477.09	7	5	1.53
106	494.03	4	3	1.46
107	511.00	2	2	1.40
108	528.10	1	1	1.34

* Last year for which detailed life tables are available by race and sex.

to the experience observed among white males in the United States during 1949–51.

The usual life table starts with a group of 100,000 persons at birth. The example shows their chance of death in the first year of life to be 30.69 per 1,000. Therefore, among the 100,000 births we start with, there will be 3,069 deaths in the first year of life, and 96,931 will be left to reach their first birthday.

In the year of age after their first birthday, the chances of death are 2.12 per 1,000 according to the example. The number of deaths within the years among the 96,931 survivors who reached age one is then

$$96,931 \times \frac{212}{1,000} = 205$$

With this number of deaths within the year, the number surviving to their second birthday is $96,931 - 205 = 96,726$. Continuing with this procedure, it is a simple matter to arrive at the numbers surviving to successive ages.

13. What is meant by "expectation of life"?

The expectation of life is the average number of years remaining, per person, among a group of some stated age, assuming that they will thereafter experience the mortality rates of the life table. The expectation of life, therefore, shows the average remaining years on the assumption that the mortality rates of the life table will remain unchanged in the future.

14. How is the expectation of life measured?

The life table on page 398 will be used as an example. We start with the reasonable assumption that, on an average, one-half year of life is lived by each person in the age of his death. This means that, of the 95,104 of the life table who attain age 20, there were 154 who died after ½ year of life in that age, 161 who died 1½ years after reaching age 20 years, 165 who died 2½ years after reaching age 20 years, and so on. Thus, the total years of life lived by the 95,104 after entering age 20 and until the last is accounted for by death comes to $154 \times 1\frac{1}{2} + 161 \times 1\frac{1}{2} + 165 \times 2\frac{1}{2} +$ etc. $= 4,709,746$ years of life. The average number of years of life lived after age 20 is then
$$4,709,746 \div 95,104 = 49.52 \text{ years.}$$
In like manner, it is possible to compute the average number of years remaining after any other age. Computed from birth, the figure yields the average length of life.

15. Is the average age at death a good measure of the longevity in a community?

The average age at death in a community is influenced strongly by the age composition of its population. In a new community, to which only the relatively young have migrated, the average age at death will necessarily be low. On the other hand, in an older community from which the young have migrated, the aged will form a larger proportion of the total population and so the average age at death will tend to be high. To measure the longevity in a community correctly, it is necessary to prepare a life table from death rates according to age; the answer is provided by the average length of life, or the expectation of life at birth, in this table.

16. Who prepared the first life table?

The earliest table on record is credited to the Roman Praetorian Prefect Ulpianus who lived in the middle of the third century A.D. Just how the table was drawn up or whether it actually gave expectations of life or annuity values is uncertain. In 1693, the English astronomer Edmund Halley published a life table based solely on birth and death records for Breslau. The average length of life indicated by Halley's table was 33.5 years. The first life table which took into account both the number of deaths and the population exposed to risk of death was computed by Milne from records for two parishes in Carlisle, England, covering 1779 to 1787.

17. Have life tables been prepared for species other than human?

Life tables have been prepared for several species of insects, birds, and mammals. They have also been used to find the average length of life of automobiles and such physical equipment as electric light bulbs, telegraph poles, and railroad ties.

18. What is the age at which a person may expect to live just as long again?

The 1960 life table for white males in the general population of the United States shows that between age 35 and 36 there is, on an average, another 35 years of life remaining. For white females, this age is between 38 and 39 years, for nonwhite males between 33 and 34 years, and for nonwhite females between 35 and 36 years. This halfway station in life, when the expectation of life is equal to the attained age, is somewhat variable, but much less so than the average length of life. With this halfway point at about 35 years, the average person may expect, according to averages, to live to age 70, which happens to be the oft-quoted Biblical "three score and ten." No doubt it is this figure that Dante had in mind in the opening lines of his Divine Comedy, where he refers to himself as halfway on the road of life. Writing this, supposedly in 1300, he was then 35 years old.

19. How have the chances of reaching school age, maturity, and old age increased since 1900?

At the beginning of the century only about 87.5 percent of the babies born alive lived to their first birthday; today about 97.5 percent do so. Under conditions of 60 years ago, about 81 percent would survive to enter school at the age of 6, while under present

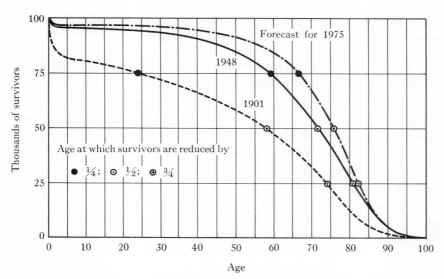

Chart 20. Survivors from birth to successive ages, according to life tables for the United States, 1901, 1948, and forecast for 1975 on the basis of "low" mortality.

conditions the figure is close to 97 percent. Similarly, the proportion who would reach the voting age of 21 has risen from 77 to nearly 96 percent. The proportion who would live to the usual retirement age of 65 years has gone up from 41 to over 70 percent. The chances of living to ages 95 or 100 have not increased measurably. (See Chart 20.)

20. How do the gains in expectation of life compare at different ages?

Most of the gain in expectation of life has been made under age 50 for white males and under age 60 for white females. For the colored, these gains extend into ages 10 years higher. The situation among white males may be cited as an example. At age 60, the figure for 1960, namely 15.9 years, is only 1.5 years greater than that for

1900–1902. On the other hand, at age 50, there is a rise of 2.33 years so far this century. At age 20, the increase amounts to about 8 years, but at birth it comes to practically 19 years. These differences by age reflect the great progress made in reducing mortality from the infectious conditions, which took their greatest toll among children and young adults. However, it is noteworthy that there have also been some gains at the higher ages, even though they are small. The gains in later life are necessarily small because there has been little progress in controlling the diseases of old age.

21. How does the longevity of men compare with that of women and which has had the more rapid rise?

Not only do women have a greater expectation of life than men at all ages, but their gains in longevity have also been greater. As a result, their advantage over men has been growing. In 1900, the expectation of life at birth of white females was nearly three years more than that of white males, but in 1960 it was close to seven years greater.

However, the difference in expectation of life between females and males declines at the later ages. While white girl babies have an expectation of life today almost seven years greater than white boy babies, at the age of 60 white women have an expectation only about four years greater than white men.

22. How does the longevity of the white and colored populations compare?

Although the longevity record of the colored is appreciably below that of the white population, the difference has steadily decreased. In 1960, the expectation of life at birth of colored males was 61.1 years, about six and one-third years less than that of white males; for colored females it was 66.3, or close to eight years less than that of white females. About three decades earlier, in 1929–31, the corresponding differences were 11½ and 13⅙ years, respectively. While the average length of life of whites in this country has risen 9⅕ years since 1930, that of colored persons has gone up 15½ years. Nevertheless, the longevity of the colored today still lags about two decades behind that of the white population.

There is an interesting quirk in the longevity record for the colored after age 60. Probably because of many misstatements as to age, the computed figures for expectation of life for the colored at the higher ages are somewhat higher than for the whites; it is doubtful that this is actually the case.

23. How is the composition of our population being changed by the rise in longevity?

Every rise in longevity results in a higher average age of the population and an increasing proportion of older persons. Combined with a falling birth rate, the rise in longevity brings about an accelerated aging of the population.[2] The greater extension of the average length of life of women than of men will bring our population an increasing excess of females over males, particularly at the later ages. The immigration of large numbers of young men was once a factor in keeping the proportion of the aged at a low level, but this is no longer the case. With the more rapid gain in longevity of the colored and the reduction in immigration, which was mostly white, the proportion of our nonwhite population is also increasing.

24. How do the foreign-born and native populations compare in longevity?

At the beginning of the century the longevity of the foreign-born was decidedly less than that of the native population. At age 20, for example, foreign-born men in this country had an expectation of life two and one-half years less than native white men, and foreign-born women had three years less than native white women. By 1930, the differences were cut to about one year, and by 1940 they had just about disappeared.

25. How does the industrial population compare with the average of the country in longevity?

The best indication of the longevity of the industrial population is the experience of the millions of industrial policyholders of the Metropolitan Life Insurance Company. In 1911–12, these policyholders had an expectation of life at birth of 46.6 years, about 6.5 years less than that of the country as a whole. Since then, the average length of life of this industrial group has risen much faster than that of the general population, and by 1960 it was 70.5 years, a little higher than that of the country as a whole. The elimination of the gap in longevity between the industrial and the general population reflects the rapid rise in the standard of living of the working people.

[2] See answers to Questions 6 and 8 of Chapter 15, pages 226 and 227.

26. Is the average length of life longer in rural areas than in cities?

Between large cities—those of 100,000 persons or more—and smaller urban centers there is little difference in longevity, according to the figures for 1939, the latest available. Rural areas, however, do show up considerably better than cities of any size. The expectation of life at birth for white males living in the country was two and one-half years greater than for those in cities; for white females in the country, it was one and one-quarter years greater than for those in cities.

27. Which states have the best record for average length of life?

According to the latest life tables for states (1949–51), the six leading states were South Dakota, Nebraska, Minnesota, Iowa, Kansas, and North Dakota. They lie in the West North Central section of the nation and are for the most part agricultural in character. Each of these states had, in the period 1949–51, an expectation of life at birth of about 68 years for white males and between 73 and 74 years for white females. In contrast to South Dakota and Nebraska, the top states, where the expectation of life at birth for white males was 68.4 and 68.2 years, respectively, Arizona and Nevada had corresponding figures of only 63.3 and 62.8 years. Nebraska was the top state for longevity of white females with a figure of 74.0; at the bottom of the list was New Mexico with 69.1 years.

Most of the industrial states have longevity records somewhat better than the average for the country. The states of the South generally fall below the nation's average.

Not all factors which influence the longevity ranking of the states can be isolated. The states near the top of the list enjoy a relatively high standard of living. They also have a high level of public health administration and accessible medical and hospital facilities of high quality. On the other hand, Nevada and New Mexico at the other end of the list have large Spanish-speaking populations on a lower standard of living.

28. Is it possible to calculate the expectation of life of the single, married, widowed, or divorced?

The expectation of life can be computed only for a group whose identity remains essentially unchanged during its lifetime. Thus, there is no difficulty in computing the expectation of life for native white females, since they will necessarily be so classified at all times.

However, the case is much different for single females, particularly at the young ages. Most of them will eventually marry and, as a group, experience the mortality of the married. Futhermore, many of the married will later become either widowed or divorced, and so fall into a category with still another mortality experience.[3]

29. Do college athletes and college graduates in general live longer than other persons?

A study of men graduating from college from 1870 to 1905, showed that their expectation of life at the age of 22 was five years above that of white males of the same age in the general population. The record of college athletes was little different from that of other college graduates, but honor men had a two-year advantage over other college graduates in expectation of life at age 22. College attendance is so much more common today than 50 to 80 years ago that the differences between the college and noncollege groups have probably been greatly reduced. But the same general ranking may still persist, with college honor men living the longest on the average, and college athletes and other graduates doing better than those not attending college.

30. How does the longevity of clergymen, teachers, physicians, and lawyers compare with that of the general public?

Clergymen, teachers, and lawyers are favored with a low mortality and, therefore, a longevity better than average. In a survey in England and Wales, it was observed that at the age of 25 clergymen had an expectation of life five years greater than that of the general male population of the same age. Physicians, on the other hand, have had little advantage in longevity. Records of American doctors showed that at age 25 the expectation of life for male physicians was the same as for the general male population, and women physicians aged 25 had only a very small advantage over women generally. Physicians had a mortality below average from infectious diseases and surgical difficulties, but a higher mortality from the degenerative conditions. Apparently, the advantages of medical knowledge and of a good social standing that doctors enjoy are not sufficient to offset the toll taken by the strenuous labors usual in their profession.[4]

[3] See answer to Question 16 of Chapter 7, page 98.
[4] See answer to Question 26 of Chapter 18, page 284.

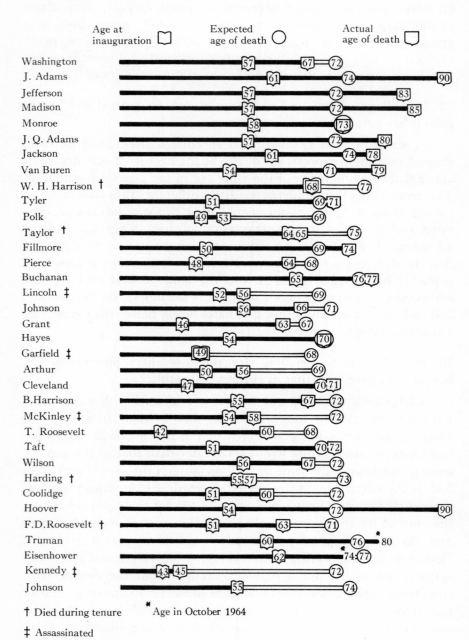

Chart 21. Longevity of Presidents of the United States. Expected years of life after inauguration compared with the years actually lived.

31. Has there been any change in the longevity of Presidents of the United States?

The Presidents who were inaugurated before 1850 outlived the expectation of life they had at the time of taking office by an average of 2.9 years. Those inaugurated between 1850 and 1900 failed to reach their expectation of life by about 2.9 years on the average. Those who have served during the present century have averaged 11 years less than was to be expected when they took office. Outstanding exceptions are ex-Presidents Herbert Hoover, Harry S. Truman, and Dwight D. Eisenhower. It is significant that since the beginning of the century two Presidents, McKinley and Kennedy, lost their lives through assassination, and two other Presidents, Harding and Franklin Delano Roosevelt, died while in office. It would appear then that the increasing burdens of office and the very hazards incidental to the Presidency are now taking a greater toll from our chief executives. (See Chart 21.)

32. Is longevity inherited?

There have been a number of studies indicating that longevity may be affected by constitutional inheritance. Environment, however, has a greater influence on length of life than inheritance. The gains in average length of life as a result of the improvements in the standard of living and the advances in the medical sciences have come to about 21 years since 1900. On the other hand, the studies on the inheritance of longevity show only a relatively small difference between those with long-lived parents and other groups. In other words, the extraneous factors in length of life greatly outweigh the influence of heredity.

33. How does the expectation of life of insurance policyholders compare with that of the general population?

The latest available data from the files of the Metropolitan Life Insurance Company indicate that at age 20 male policyholders of ordinary insurance had an expectation of life about two and one-half years more than white males in the general population of the United States. At the same time, the industrial policyholders (those insured for smaller amounts with weekly or monthly premiums) now have an expectation of life at birth half a year better than the comparable figure for the general population.

34. Why are there differences between the longevity of life insurance policyholders and that of the general public?

Anyone who buys life insurance must pass either a medical examination by a doctor or a physical inspection by an insurance agent. The purpose of these is to weed out persons for whom the chances of early death are exceptionally high. Life insurance policyholders, therefore, are a select group in regard to health, and consequently also in regard to mortality. In addition, those who buy insurance for relatively large amounts and pay premiums on an annual or semi-annual basis are likely to be professional or business persons. They have an advantage in longevity because of their better economic standing. Even those who buy their insurance for relatively small amounts have, as we have seen in the preceding question, significant advantages. They have enjoyed marked improvements in their standard of living in recent decades and this is reflected in their improved longevity.

35. Do persons with annuities live longer on the average than those who have life insurance?

Annuitants are distinguished from those who buy life insurance by several basic factors. A person who buys an annuity expects to live a long while. The man in obviously poor health would hardly make such a purchase. On the other hand, the purchaser of life insurance is interested in protecting his family against the possibility of his untimely death. If he believed he did not have long to live, he would probably be even more eager to buy insurance. Although there is unquestionably some overlapping between the two groups, the longevity experience of annuitants is generally and materially above that of insured persons.

36. What is a "generation" life table?

The usual life table, which has been referred to in the previous questions, is based on the experience of a community over a short period, seldom more than a decade; it is really a cross-section or snapshot table.[5] Such a table obviously introduces an unreal assumption, namely, that the mortality conditions of a given period are continued for the lifetime of a generation. A "generation" life table, on the other hand, is one which is based on the experience of babies

[5] See answer to Question 12 of this chapter, pages 397 and 398.

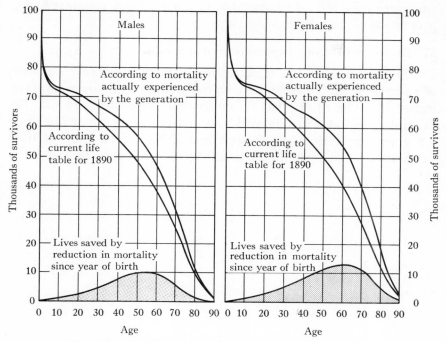

Chart 22. Survivors to successive ages, out of 100,000 born alive in Massachusetts in 1890, according to mortality: (a) actually experienced by the generation, and (b) prevailing in the year of birth.

born in the same year and followed by counting survivors at each birthday until the last has died. This type of life table takes account of the changing mortality conditions that a group of persons actually meets over the years. Unfortunately, the records are not always available from which to compute a generation table. It would require more than a century of accurate data to follow a large group of individuals born during the same year until the death of the last survivor. However, it is possible to approximate a generation table from mortality data by an indirect method. Chart 22 shows, in the upper curves, the survivorship of the generation born in 1890 in Massachusetts. The lower curves show the survivorship predicted from a snapshot life table based on mortality conditions prevailing in 1890. The difference between the two sets of curves is shown in the shaded areas at the bottom and represents the lives saved because of the improvement in health conditions and mortality since 1890. This saving amounts to one-fifth of the men living at age 60 and a slightly higher proportion of the women at that age.

37. Do we outlive our expectation of life?

Since the usual life table reflects only the mortality situation of a single period and does not take into account the future improvements, it is safe to say that we outlive our expectation of life. For example, men born in 1890 will have an average length of life about 4.2 years longer than the expectation of life at the time of their birth; for women born in 1890 it will be about 5.8 years longer.

Chapter 25

———————————

Some Effects
of War

1. How many civilian lives were lost in World War II?

The loss of life among civilians in European countries has been conservatively estimated at 20 million. Anything like accurate data are lacking for Eastern and Central Europe, which were chiefly affected. Russian losses have been put at anywhere from five to seven million. Estimates for Poland exceed four and one-half million, and for Yugoslavia nearly one and one-half million. The greater part of civilian loss of life was due to high mortality in overrun areas and among workers, particularly Russians and Poles, sent to Germany. The civilian losses include about six million Jews exterminated by the Germans. Deaths due directly to air bombings and military operations are a relatively minor part of the total, perhaps no greater than two million. In China, also, the number of civilian deaths in

411

World War II was large, but no reliable figures are available. Several millions died in India and Southeast Asia due to wartime shortages of rice and to inadequacy of malaria control. In Japan, 400,000 to 500,000 deaths of civilians have been attributed to the war. A large part of this toll resulted from bombings of Japanese industrial centers. Small losses of civilian life were sustained in the Middle East and in North Africa.

2. How many lives were lost in combat among the armed forces in World War II?

The combat losses of all World War II belligerents have been placed at about 10,000,000. Axis losses, estimated conservatively at 5,200,000, were appreciably greater than those of the Allies, whose battle toll was about 4,500,000. These figures exclude deaths among prisoners of war from Eastern Europe who were put into Germany's labor forces, and deaths among Germans who fell into Russian hands. Germany's military losses, estimated at 3,250,000, were the heaviest of any country in the war. Japan's losses were about 1,500,000. The estimate of Italian combat losses is 150,000 to 200,000, and for Germany's other satellites about 225,000. Russian losses, by far the heaviest among the Allied nations, were estimated to have been about 3,000,000, or two-thirds of the total Allied losses in combat. The countries of the British Empire had battle losses of from 375,000 to 400,000, about three-fourths of them from Great Britain. The United States lost nearly 300,000 men on all fronts in World War II. Battle deaths of our other European Allies are estimated at nearly 450,000, excluding deaths incurred by the underground forces. French losses, including those of the Free French are officially estimated at 167,000. Poland's losses amounted to 125,000, including the deaths among Poles fighting with the Allies after the collapse of their country. Yugoslavia's military death toll was 75,000 and Greek losses about 50,000. China's military deaths after Pearl Harbor are conservatively estimated at 250,000.

3. How did the combat losses of World War II compare with those of World War I?

The total battle toll in World War II was appreciably greater than that in World War I. Death losses in the earlier conflict are not accurately known, but most of the estimates are of the order of

8,000,000. This is 2,000,000 less than the estimated number of 10,000,000 for World War II.

The comparative toll of the two World Wars differs greatly for most of the major belligerents. In some cases it is difficult to make accurate comparisons because the national territories were not identical in the two wars. American losses in World War II were about six times as high as in 1917–18. Both German and Russian losses in World War II were higher than in the earlier conflict. If allowance is made for differences resulting from boundary changes after World War I, the German figure is about 50 percent higher and the Russian figure twice as large in the last war as in World War I. Japan presents the most striking contrast, her losses in World War I amounting only to a few hundred, compared with 1,500,000 in the last war. British Empire losses in World War II were less than half those in the earlier conflict because of the radically different nature of the European phase of the two World Wars. French losses in the recent war were only about one-eighth those sustained in 1914–18, and Italy's about one-third those in the earlier war.

4. How many men served in the armed forces of the various belligerents in World War II?

Altogether 93,000,000 men and women served in the armed forces of the belligerent nations in World War II. The Allied nations mobilized more than 62,000,000, as against a total of over 30,000,000 for the Axis countries. Of the Allies, Russian mobilization was the largest—22,000,000. The United States was next with 14,000,000. The British Empire called 12,000,000 into service, over half of which were furnished by the United Kingdom. On the Axis side, Germany mobilized 17,000,000 and Japan 7 to 8 million. In relation to the total population, the number mobilized by Russia and England was 13 percent; by the United States, 11 percent; Germany, including Austria, 21 percent; and Japan, 11 percent.

5. What were the losses in World War II in relation to the size of the armed forces and to the male population?

The total battle losses of all belligerents in World War II were about one-tenth of the total number mobilized for war service. The Allied losses were about 7.5 percent of the total; Axis losses came to about 17 percent or proportionately twice as heavy as for the Allies. The battle losses of the major belligerent nations, in relation to the size of their armed forces, were: on the Allied side, United States, 2 percent; Russia, 14 percent; British Empire, as a whole, 3 percent; and the United Kingdom, separately, 4 percent; on the Axis side, both Germany and Japan lost nearly one-fifth of their fighting forces.

In relation to the male population at the main productive ages, 15 to 64, Germany's losses were greatest. Based upon the prewar population of Germany and Austria, battle losses were more than one-eighth of all males in this age group. Our losses were 0.6 percent of the corresponding population; the United Kingdom, about 2 percent; Russia, about 6 percent; and Japan, about 7 percent.

6. How were military deaths distributed according to age?

Military deaths in wartime are heavily concentrated at the young adult ages. In the armed forces of the United States, about 95 percent of the deaths occurred among men under age 35. About half of all the deaths were among men between 20 and 24, and about one-fourth at ages 25 to 29. The average age at death was 25, but the peak numbers were at ages 21 and 22. Those killed in action were on the average 24 years old.

7. What were our combat losses in World War II?

There were 297,000 men killed in action or died of wounds in all the armed forces of the United States. This figure includes men who died while prisoners of war. Army and Air Force fatalities were 239,000, or about 80 percent of the total. Of the remainder, 37,000 were Navy personnel, 20,000 Marines, and approximately 600 Coast Guardsmen.

8. What were the principal types of fatal combat injuries in World War II?

The types of combat fatalities varied greatly according to the place of action, and differed for the Army and Navy. Army statistics based upon the wounded men admitted to hospitals show that high explosive shells were responsible for more fatalities than any other agent in the European fighting, and that gunshot wounds accounted for most of the remainder. In the jungle fighting in the Pacific areas, gunshot wounds were the most frequent cause of combat fatalities. In the Navy, losses were particularly heavy from drowning and from burns.

9. How does the number wounded in World War II compare with earlier wars?

The total number of American fighting men wounded in World War II was about 700,000. This figure excludes those killed in action, but includes those who died subsequently. Army wounded accounted for nearly 85 percent of the total, the Marine Corps for 9 percent, and the Navy and Coast Guard for 6 percent.

The number of World War II wounded in all the services was nearly three times as high as the World War I total of about 235,000. Army wounded in World War II were more than 2.5 times the figure for World War I; for the Marines, 6 times as high; and for the Navy, more than 100 times as high. In fact, for the Navy and Marine Corps combined, the casualties in World War II were greater than in all our previous wars.

10. How did the fatality rate among our wounded in World War II compare with that in World War I?

The fatality rate among Army wounded in World War II was 4.4 percent, until then the lowest in history for any army in the world, and little more than half the rate of 8.3 percent in our Army during World War I. For the Navy and Marines the contrast is even greater, with a fatality rate of 2.9 percent in World War II, compared with 12 percent in World War I. Among the United States forces in the Korean fighting in 1950–51, the fatality rate was only 2 percent.

11. How do deaths from disease and injury among the armed forces compare with the combat deaths in our wars?

In World War II, deaths from disease up to the end of 1945 totaled approximately 20,000, and deaths from noncombat injuries approximately 75,000, or a total of about 95,000 noncombat deaths. Thus, combat deaths exceeded those from disease and injury by more than three to one. For the Army this ratio is about 3.5 to 1, and for the Navy a little more than 2 to 1.

The ratio of combat to noncombat deaths in our armed forces in World War II contrasts greatly with our experience in earlier wars. Whereas in World War II this ratio was about 3 to 1, the number of deaths in the two broad categories were about equal in World War I. In all earlier wars combat deaths were only a fraction of those due to injury and disease. In the Spanish American War, noncombat deaths were approximately 13 times those in combat, in the Civil War more than twice as many, and in the Mexican War, seven times as many.

12. What were the prinicpal types of fatal noncombat injuries in World War II?

Air transport accidents accounted for nearly one-half of all fatal noncombat injuries from Pearl Harbor to the end of 1945. The next largest category was motor vehicle accidents, including training accidents in tanks, which were responsible for about one-sixth of the total. Water transport accidents and drownings accounted for about one-tenth of the fatal noncombat injuries, and accidents involving the use of firearms for about 7 percent.

Aviation accidents took a higher toll in the Army than in the Navy. About half the accidental deaths among Army and Air Force personnel were due to this cause, as compared with about 40 percent in the Navy and its auxiliary forces.

13. How many men were prisoners of war?

The total number of men taken prisoner in World War II may never be accurately known, but for all the belligerents it may have exceeded 15,000,000, not counting those involved in the final surrender of the armed forces of Germany, Japan, and their satellites. The Western Allies captured more than 4,500,000 enemy troops, all but about 50,000 of them in the European and Mediterranean fighting, and disarmed several million more when the Axis countries surrendered. The total captured by the Russians, which included large numbers of Hungarian and Romanian troops, was probably of the order of 4,000,000 to 5,000,000.

Germany and her satellites suffered the greatest number of prisoner of war casualties, the losses being especially high in the fighting in Russia and in the final campaigns in Western Europe. Several hundred thousand Italians were Allied prisoners of war at one time.

The Germans took about five million prisoners. Not far from 1,500,000 Frenchmen were held as prisoners of war from 1940 until near the end of the war.

About 115,000 American soldiers and sailors were captured by the enemy, nearly 100,000 of them by the Germans. Of the British and Commonwealth forces, more than 300,000 were captured, the majority being men from the United Kingdom who were taken prisoner by the Germans.

14. How good was the health record of our armed forces during World War II?

The health record of our armed forces during World War II was remarkably good. The death rate from disease was the lowest in our military history, and in fact, lower than among men of the same ages in the civilian population. The leading causes of death from disease showed no substantial difference from those found in a civilian group of like age distribution, namely, diseases of the cardiovascular-renal system, tuberculosis, influenza and pneumonia, and cancer. Diseases which showed a significant excess mortality among service personnel were malaria, dysentery, beriberi, and scrub typhus. This is not surprising in view of the large numbers of men exposed to the hazards of war in tropical areas.

The chief nonfatal diseases were also similar in order of frequency to those which occurred among civilians, e.g., respiratory disorders, gastrointestinal upsets, and the like. The only major diseases occurring with unusual frequency in the armed forces were malaria, hepatitis, rheumatic fever, venereal diseases, and some of the communicable diseases common in childhood. In the Pacific and in the Asiatic theaters of the war, malaria was the leading cause of disability for a time. In one period of active combat there, it resulted in more than twice as many noneffectives as battle casualties.

15. How did the mortality from disease among the armed forces differ in the two World Wars?

The chief difference was with respect to influenza and its complications, which was by far the leading cause of death in World War I. Altogether, of the approximately 50,000 deaths from disease in World War I, about two-thirds were accounted for by influenza and its complications, especially streptococcal pneumonia and emphysema. In contrast, no serious epidemic of this type occurred in World War II. Communicable diseases accounted for a high proportion of the total morbidity and mortality from disease in World War I. In fact, measles was the second leading cause of death from disease in 1917–18.

16. What were the chief medical advances in World War II?

Wartime needs stimulated the search for new drugs which would be effective against infectious organisms. This led to the use of the sulfa drugs on a wide scale and to speeding up the development of penicillin. The success with penicillin gave great impetus to research in antibiotics with the result that during and since the war many new products have been discovered and brought into use, notably streptomycin, aureomycin, chloromycetin, and terramycin. Other major advances, many of them representing results of wartime research, were made in the use of blood and blood derivatives. New knowledge was gained as to the most effective methods of treating shock due to blood loss. Another important fruit of this work is gamma globulin, which is now used widely in the prevention or modification of measles and scarlet fever and other conditions.

In the field of preventive medicine, the most important new developments were an effective vaccine against typhus and active immunization against tetanus. The latter is now in wide general use, particularly in childhood immunization. Wartime provided large-scale demonstrations of the control of diseases transmitted by insects. Area spraying of DDT by airplanes to control typhus, malaria, and other diseases, and the general development of chemicals effective against insects and rodents have provided new public health measures against a wide variety of diseases.

There were many gains in the field of psychiatry, the development of group methods of treatment being perhaps of greatest importance. Research in aviation medicine was important in the development of high altitude flying. Medical studies based upon atomic research have opened vast new fields in the investigation of disease and disease processes.

17. What new medical problems were met in World War II?

The chief new medical problems faced by our armed forces in World War II revolved around the protection of our fighting men against tropical diseases in the Pacific areas, North Africa, and the Middle East. The foremost problem was malaria control, and this was made the more acute because the major source of supply of quinine was cut off by the Japanese conquest of the East Indies. This difficulty was finally overcome by a combination of antimalarial measures—the spraying of places where the disease-bearing mosquitos breed, and the use of new antimalarial drugs which had to be developed and manufactured on a large scale.

Typhus also was a potential threat to our soldiers. This disease proved to be controllable by the simple measure of delousing native populations and our servicemen with DDT and the vaccination of soldiers again epidemic typhus. Other types of typhus or rickettsial diseases were encountered in the Pacific areas against which the chief measures were protective clothing. The threat of yellow fever among our men stationed in some tropical countries was met by development of an effective vaccine.

18. What was the venereal disease record in our armed forces during World War II?

The Army and the Navy, working closely with civilian leaders, accomplished a great deal in controlling venereal disease. As a result, the average rate for all such diseases, from Pearl Harbor to the end of military operations in 1945, was less than one-half the figure for World War I. For syphilis, which accounts for a minor part of the total, the record was even better. Thus, in the Army the admission rate for all venereal diseases from 1942 to 1945 was about 43 per 1,000 per year, against 95 in World War I. The admission rate for syphilis was 6 in the last war, compared with 17 in 1917–18. The figures for the Navy were lower than for the Army. The use of penicillin worked a revolution in the treatment of the venereal diseases in World War II.

19. What is the size of our veteran population of various wars?

The number of veterans living as of mid-1962 was approximately 22,275,000. Of the total, 15,126,000 were officially classified as veterans of World War II, and more than 2,455,000 of World War I. About five and one-half million were veterans of the Korean conflict, of whom over one million also saw service in World War II. The remaining veterans (148,000) are the survivors of all other wars, and of the regular establishment.

20. How much is being paid out to veterans in compensation payments because of war connected disability, and how many are receiving them?

Over three million American veterans are receiving compensation payments for service connected disability and pensions; these payments exceed $3,650,000,000 a year. World War II veterans, who account for over two million of the total, are receiving nearly $2,000,000,000 a year. The remainder consists almost entirely of payments to World War I veterans. The great majority have disabilities of relatively limited extent.

The foregoing figures relate to June 30, 1962. They keep changing because of deaths of veterans and redetermination of eligibility for compensation. The number receiving disability is on the decline, but the amounts are not because of the liberalization of benefits to some classes of veterans.

In addition to the amounts paid to living veterans, substantial sums are paid to dependents of deceased veterans. Such payments are being made in behalf of more than one million deceased veterans who were killed or died as a result of war service. The payments to these dependents as of mid-1962 were over one billion dollars.

21. What military casualties were sustained in the war in Korea?

American casualties numbered 136,913. This count includes 33,-629 killed in action and 103,284 wounded. Our losses in Korea exceed those in all our previous wars except the Civil War and the two World Wars. Reported battle losses of the South Korean forces were about 165,000, including 21,625 dead. Those of the other United Nations countries have been small. Communist losses have been estimated at nearly 1,250,000.

22. What was the loss of life in the merchant marine of the various belligerents in World War II?

Losses of life among merchant seamen in World War II exceeded 50,000 for the Western Allies and the neutral countries of Western Europe. Figures for Russia, Germany, and Italy are not known, but they are probably relatively small. Russia's allies furnished most of the ships in which supplies were sent to that country.

Nearly 6,150 members of the U.S. Merchant Marine were reported killed or missing in World War II. This is nearly nine times the death toll in World War I. As in World War I, British losses were by far the heaviest, totaling over 35,400 men or about two and one-half times that for World War I. The figures include seamen of other nationalities serving on British ships. The Japanese losses of about 27,000 seamen in World War II were second only to those of the British.

23. What was the loss of life from bombing among civilians in various countries during World War II?

The civilian death toll from bombing in World War II will never be accurately known, but probably reached 1,200,000 and perhaps 1,500,000. At least two-thirds of the victims were nationals of the Axis countries. About one-half million German civilians were bombing victims, according to the careful estimates made by the United States Strategic Bombing Survey. The Japanese toll, estimated by the survey, was 360,000 to 375,000. About one-third of this total was accounted for by the two atomic bombs dropped upon Nagasaki and Hiroshima. England's civilian deaths from air bombing exceeded 60,000, and those of France were reported to be 54,000. Civilian deaths from air raids in Eastern and Southern Europe are estimated to exceed 100,000, about half of which were sustained by the Poles. The Russian losses are unknown, but probably were severer than those sustained by the English.

24. What were the major types of injury resulting from atomic bombings of Japan and what aftereffects were suffered by the victims?

Burns accounted for more than 50 percent of the fatal casualties from the atomic bomb. Most of these fatal burns resulted from fires caused by the bomb but many resulted from thermal radiation due to the intense heat it generated. The remaining fatalities were in large measure due to blast injuries, either directly from the force of the explosion or indirectly as a result of the collapse of buildings. Thus, in general, the principal causes of fatal injuries from the atomic bomb were no different in character from those caused by conventional bombs.

The types of casualties peculiar to the atomic bomb were those due to nuclear radiation. The immediate prognosis was related to the degree of exposure. Such fatalities represented 15 to 20 percent of the total number. Death in these cases was for the most part delayed—from hours to weeks after the bombing.

The long-term aftereffects of nuclear radiation among the survivors are not all known. Radiation exercised an important influence on gene mutation on those exposed and on their offspring.

25. What was the health record of the United States during World War II?

The health of the American people was maintained at an extraordinarily high level during the war. The country was free from any severe epidemic during the entire war period. Moreover, intensive efforts were made to use our medical resources efficiently, and the food rationing program and other measures helped to bring improvement in the general nutrition of the population. The use of new medical discoveries and particularly the availability of new drugs also helped in the control of disease. As a result, the death rate, exclusive of mortality from enemy action, declined during the war. The rate in the entire period 1941 to 1945 was about 15 percent less than in the preceding five-year period. Mortality was lower in every age group, with reductions particularly large at the childhood ages. New low death rates were recorded during the war for tuberculosis, respiratory diseases, and childhood diseases, and for infant and maternal mortality.

The situation in World War II was very different from that in World War I, the closing year of which was marked by an influenza epidemic of great severity, causing an increase of nearly 30 percent in the over-all death rate in 1918 as compared with 1917.

26. What was the course of the death rate in European countries during the war?

Wartime mortality in Europe varied widely from country to country. England's record, like our own, was exceptionally good, except in 1940 when there was a severe influenza epidemic. England developed a very high degree of efficiency in her health services during the war and successfully overcame the health problems incident to the large scale evacuation of metropolitan areas, the air bombing of cities, shortages of food, and the accelerated production of war materials. The health of the German people was at first maintained at a high level, largely because the country had prepared for war and seized the food and other resources of occupied countries. But when the tide of war turned against her, there was a rapid deterioration in health conditions in that country. Death rates elsewhere in continental Europe rose during the war. Except for Denmark, the rise was particularly marked in countries occupied by the Germans. Unfortunately, reliable figures are not available for most of the countries, and none at all for Eastern Europe. Compared with the prewar figures, the death rate in France in 1944 showed an increase of 30 percent; that of The Netherlands in 1945, an increase of 75 percent; and that of Belgium in 1944, an increase of 20 percent. In many countries there was a sharp increase in the mortality from tuberculosis and in infant mortality.

27. What major outbreaks of disease developed during both World Wars?

The situation with regard to epidemic diseases was much better in World War II than in World War I. In the earlier conflict there were large scale outbreaks of typhus fever in Eastern Europe, but this disease was kept under good control, even in most parts of Eastern Europe during the last war. The great epidemic of influenza in 1918 engulfed all the European continent as well as other regions. The total loss of life throughout the world resulting from that epidemic is estimated to exceed 20,000,000.[1]

Although influenza struck parts of Europe in two of the war years, it was not very severe, and the number of deaths was relatively small. Perhaps the worst outbreak of epidemic disease in Europe in World War II was a severe and fatal form of diphtheria. Altogether about 2,000,000 people in Western Europe were struck by this disease, and the number of deaths was estimated at about 250,000. The greatest death toll from disease indirectly related to the war was that from malaria in India and Southeastern Asia. With the major source of supplies of quinine cut off, the disease raged uncontrolled in many areas, and deaths from malaria increased by more than a million a year over the peacetime level.

28. What in general has been the effect of war on pandemic disease?

Pandemic diseases frequently have been associated with wars, in some cases occurring during the war period and in others immediately following. Up to modern times the disease responsible for pandemics following wars often could not be identified, but plague and typhus are believed to have been the chief offenders. In the fifteenth century, syphilis also took on the proportions of a pandemic in many parts of Europe. Typhus fever was one of the causes of the collapse of Napoleon's army in his invasion of Russia. The returning soldiers caused widespread and devastating outbreaks of the disease, particularly in Germany. As a result of the outbreak of typhus that swept Serbia in 1914, the Austrian army stopped active military operations for about six months, and this circumstance may have been a factor in the ultimate outcome of the first World War.

Perhaps the most striking modern example of war-borne disease is the great influenza pandemic of 1918–19, which swept over a great

[1] See answer to Question 24 of Chapter 11, page 166.

part of the world. Otherwise, the most serious pandemics resulting from the war were those which swept Eastern Europe, and especially Russia, during World War I and the revolution. In Russia alone it is estimated that 20 to 25 million persons fell ill with typhus, and 3 million died. The incidence of cholera and typhus was high, and syphilis was rampant. Altogether, possibly 8 to 10 million persons died in Russia from pandemic diseases between 1916 and 1923.

In comparison with World War I, the incidence of pandemic disease in World War II was light and for the most part affected relatively circumscribed areas.

29. Are the death rates from accidents, suicide, and homicide affected by war?

The major effects of war on the accident rate in this country resulted from the expansion of the production and the entry of inexperienced workers into factories. In World War II, however, this was offset by a drastic reduction in the mortality from motor vehicle accidents as a result of restrictions on driving. In countries which were subject to blackouts during the war, there was an increase in accidents due to this cause.

Suicide rates are profoundly affected by war. It has been the experience in all countries that the rate from this cause is markedly reduced during wartime, largely because people are less occupied with their own personal problems. Another factor is the improved economic conditions resulting from the expanded production of military goods. Homicide likewise declines in wartime, but generally the fluctuations are not as great as for suicide.

30. How was the marriage rate in the United States affected by World War II?

Generally, the marriage rate rises within the early period of war, declines during its course, increases sharply in the immediate postwar years, and then reverts more or less to its prewar level. The marriage rate started to climb in June, 1940, after the fall of France and the subsequent discussion of conscription. The upswing gained momentum after the attack on Pearl Harbor as thousands hastened into marriage in the hope of escaping induction, or in anticipation of entering the armed forces and of serving abroad. As a result, the rate reached a new peak of 13.1 marriages per 1,000 population in 1942; only three years prior, in 1939, it was 10.7 per 1,000. With the entry of increasing numbers of young men into military service and the shipment of thousands overseas, the marriage rate fell off during 1943, 1944, and the early months of 1945. Then came V-E Day early in May, and V-J Day a few months later, followed shortly thereafter by the start of large-scale demobilization. Each of these events brought an immediate upsweep in the marriage rate, carrying it to its highest level in our history. The peak rate of 16.2 per 1,000 in 1946 resulted mainly from the backlog of delayed marriages among young men who preferred to wait until the war was over, and also from the special appeal of marriage to men who had long been separated from the opposite sex and the comforts of home. In part, too, it was related to the war and postwar boom in divorce, inasmuch as many of the divorces were shortly followed by remarriage. (See Chart 2 on page 39.)

31. What was the wartime trend of marriage in other countries?

The marriage rate in Germany rose sharply in 1939 but then fell even more rapidly in 1940. A further decline occurred in the middle war years. The marriage rate in England showed a large increase in 1939 and again in 1940. Although the rate fell in the middle war years, only in 1943 and 1944 was it below the pre-1939 level. The postwar rise was relatively small. The rate in both France and Belgium declined sharply in 1940, soon recovered, but then fell again during the period of active military operations there in 1944–45. Both countries showed a sharp postwar increase in marriages.

32. What was the effect of the two World Wars on the birth rate in the United States?

Countries involved in war have generally experienced a fall in the birth rate during the war period, and a rise after the close of hostilities. However, there have been striking variations from this pattern which have been introduced by such factors as the duration and intensity of the conflict.

The birth rate of the United States was barely affected by World War I, in which it participated for only one and one-half years— from April 1917 to November 1918. There was a decline in the rate for 1919, but this was followed by a high point in 1921. World War II presented a different picture. In the short period from 1940 to 1943, the birth rate in the United States rose by 18 percent. Two factors contributed to this rise, namely, war-induced prosperity and the sharp upswing in marriages in anticipation of active service in the armed forces. In the next two years, 1944 and 1945, the birth rate declined with the large transfer of men overseas. After the end of the war, with the release of men to civilian life, there was a resurgence in the birth rate (after allowance for unrecorded births) to a level of 27.0 per 1,000 in 1947, the highest since 1921.

33. What effect has war had on the birth rate in other countries?

In all the belligerent countries of Europe, birth rates showed a sharp decline during World War I. The severity of the decline was in almost direct proportion to the degree to which normal life was disrupted in the various countries, being least in England. For the entire period of World War I, birth deficits for the various countries have been estimated as follows: 599,000 for England, 1,686,000 for France, 311,000 for Belgium, 1,426,000 for Italy, and 3,158,000 for Germany. In all the countries of Central and Western Europe there was a sharp but temporary recovery in the birth rate after the war.

While the general course of the birth rate in Europe during World War II was similar, there were striking variations due to the differing train of events in the two wars. In England, where most of the men remained within the country for the greater part of World War II, the birth rate declined slightly in the early years. The rate then increased so sharply that from 1942 forward it was above the prewar level; in 1944 it was actually at the highest point since the early 1920's. The birth rate in Germany fell in the early war years; in the late war years, the reduction was very sharp, but there was recovery afterward.

The French birth rate, which was extremely low before the war, showed a moderate decrease in the early war years, but thereafter rose above the prewar level. The postwar level has been higher than at any time in a generation. Italy's birth rate fell continuously during the war period.

34. What was the effect of the World Wars on the population of the belligerents?

Lack of accurate data since World War II and the continued unsettlement of great parts of the world have made it difficult to measure over-all population losses due to the war, but they were exceptionally heavy in Eastern Europe. Poland's net loss, for example, was approximately 9,000,000, and Yugoslavia's in the neighborhood of 1,000,000. France suffered a population loss of approximately 1,500,000. Losses for Russia and Germany are of unknown extent. Russia's loss was perhaps as large as Poland's, the major part being due to the high mortality in the large area of Western Russia that was overrun by the Germans. It is likely that Germany suffered a net loss of population, but of moderate extent.

The population of many countries declined in World War I also. For France, deaths, including military losses, exceeded births by approximately 2,800,000, or about 7 percent of her 1914 population. For Germany this loss was about 1,400,000, or 2 percent of her 1914 population; and for Italy, about 1,200,000, or 3.5 percent of her prewar population. Russia's losses were large, but difficult to estimate. If the entire period covering World War I and the revolution is taken, the net loss of population was probably in excess of 10,000,000.

35. What have been the major migratory movements during and since World War II in Europe?

How many people in Europe were uprooted during World War II will never be known accurately, but a published estimate of 30 million does not appear unreasonable. The greatest migratory movement resulted from Germany's forced importation of possibly 10 million workers to man her factories and farms, and to build her western defenses. The most tragic of these forced population movements was the uprooting and later extermination of the major part of the Jewish population of Europe. Another major population movement resulted from the shift of millions of Russian factory workers eastward to areas safe from German attack.

Extensive movements of Europe's population occurred early in the war as the result of the arranged exchanges of population. On the basis of Germany's agreements with Russia, Italy, and Romania, more than 500,000 Germans moved from the Tyrol, the Soviet occupied areas of Poland, and Romania. Another 400,000 Germans were shifted to the part of Poland which Germany took over in 1939. The settlement imposed by Germany on Poland brought the deportation of many Polish citizens from their homes. When the German armies approached the Volga region, Russia moved 400,000 persons of German ethnic origin living in that area. After Yugoslavia's liberation, approximately 100,000 Germans were forced out of that country. Elsewhere in Europe, agreements between Finland and Russia involved the resettlement of nearly a million persons, and an even greater number of persons were involved in the various exchanges of population between countries in Southeastern Europe.

Extensive postwar shifts of population, chiefly of Germans from border states, resulted from agreements among the Allies at the war's end. Altogether, postwar migration, apart from the repatriation of displaced persons, is estimated to exceed 10,000,000.

Most of the wartime displaced persons were returned to their homes; others settled elsewhere. The new State of Israel now has approximately two million inhabitants, a large part of whom have come to the country from Europe since 1939. The United States, Canada, Great Britain, Argentina, and Brazil have been the chief places of settlement of displaced persons who did not want to be repatriated. The United States has accepted over 400,000 such people up to July 1959. In addition, the country has admitted 271,517 refugees between 1954 and 1962.

36. What major wartime shifts took place in the population of the United States?

Demands for war production caused a considerable internal migration in this country. The chief sources of these migrants were the rural areas in the Middle West and South, but there was also a sizable migration from cities in various parts of the country to the main centers of war production. The West Coast states, whose population increased more than 50 percent in the war decade, received the largest number of migrants. Other areas which showed large population gains during the war were the Southwest, particularly Texas, and the industrial belt in the Middle West. Most of this wartime migration has been permanent.

37. How many children were orphaned in both World Wars?

For World War I it is estimated that the total number of orphans was of the order of nine million. Of these, about two million were in Poland, one and one-half million in Germany, nearly one million in France, and one-half million in Italy. The actual number of war orphans must have been considerably larger if those with parents killed in postwar disturbances are included. The number in Russia was huge, and as late as 1928 the surviving "wild" children of Russia were estimated at nine million.

No reliable estimate of World War II orphans has appeared, but it is likely that their number is of the same order as World War I.

For the United States, about 120,000 children were orphaned by the death of the father in service during World War II.

38. What was the trend of juvenile delinquency during World War II?

Selected figures on police arrests and on cases disposed of by juvenile courts showed a sharp rise during the war, but there was a relatively quick reversion toward prewar levels in 1946 and 1947.

The wartime increase in juvenile delinquency was greater for girls than for boys. This difference was due in large part to the significant increase in the number of late teen-age girls arrested or referred to juvenile courts for sex delinquency. For both boys and girls the rise in delinquency may be attributed chiefly to wartime disruption of home and family life by the absence of the breadwinner, or by the employment of mothers. Difficulties arose, too, because many teen-age boys and girls were earning more money than they knew how to use wisely. Recent figures show a decrease in juvenile delinquency, the first such decline since 1948.

39. How much has World War II already cost this country?

Estimates of the cost of World War II to this country vary according to the basis used. A conservative estimate would be approximately $500,000,000,000. This figure covers direct war costs, including the excess of military expenditures over prewar figures, war shipping, emergency housing construction, the increased amount of interest paid on the national debt, and the costs of veterans' benefits up to the present. If to this huge estimate we added the amounts spent to rehabilitate Europe through the Economic Cooperation Administration, and the costs involved in the occupation of Japan and in its economic rehabilitation, we would drive this figure closer to $600,000,000,000.

The over-all estimate does not include the cost of the "cold war," nor the amount spent since the end of the war on the manufacture of atomic bombs and the development of new atomic and other weapons. It likewise does not include the capitalized money value of the men killed or disabled in service, nor the loss of civilian production.

Selected References

NOTE: Many sources were consulted in the preparation of this book. However, the fields covered are so extensive that to list all such references would result in a bibliography of excessive length and questionable value. Fortunately, there are already excellent lists of authoritative works to which the serious student can refer. All readers, however, should become acquainted with the sources of information provided by governmental agencies, the national voluntary health associations, and interested private organizations through their periodic and occasional publications. These are listed below. While this bibliography makes no pretense at completeness, it does cover the principal subjects treated in the volume.

OFFICIAL PUBLICATIONS OF THE UNITED STATES GOVERNMENT

U.S. Department of Commerce, Bureau of the Census, Washington, D.C. 20025
   18th Census of Population, 1960
   Current Population Reports. Several series are published at various times.

Various Reports from 1950 and 1960 Census of Population
Statistical Abstract of the United States, published annually
Historical Statistics of the United States, Colonial Times to 1957

U.S. Department of Health, Education, and Welfare, Washington, D.C. 20025
Indicators, published monthly
Trends, published as an annual supplement to monthly *Indicators*
New Directions, Background Papers on Current and Emerging Issues, published annually

PUBLIC HEALTH SERVICE
Vital Statistics of the United States, (Mortality—Natality—Marriage—Divorce), published annually
Vital and Health Statistics, special reports published at irregular intervals
Current Mortality Analysis, published monthly
Monthly Vital Statistics Bulletin
Health Statistics from the National Health Survey, several series of special reports based on data from the National Health Surveys, published at irregular intervals
Facts of Life and Death, selected statistics on the nation's health and people (formerly *Health and Vital Statistics for the United States*), published annually
United States Life Tables
Mortality by Occupation and Industry, United States, 1950
Cancer Rates and Risks, 1964
End Results and Mortality Trends in Cancer, 1961
Handbook of Heart Terms, 1964
Tuberculosis in 1963, An Overview
Arden House Conference on Tuberculosis, 1959

SOCIAL SECURITY ADMINISTRATION
Social Security Bulletin, published monthly

WELFARE ADMINISTRATION
Welfare Review, published monthly
Converging Social Trends, Emerging Social Problems, 1964

U.S. Department of Justice, Washington, D.C. 20025
Uniform Crime Reports for the United States, published annually

U.S. Department of Labor, Bureau of Labor Statistics, Washington, D.C. 20025
Monthly Labor Review
Work Injuries in the United States, published annually
Consumer Expenditures and Income, 1960–61

U.S. Veterans Administration, Washington, D.C. 20025
Administrator of Veterans' Affairs, Annual Reports

OTHER OFFICIAL PUBLICATIONS

United Nations, New York, New York
DEPARTMENT OF ECONOMIC AND SOCIAL AFFAIRS
Demographic Yearbook

Statistical Yearbook
Monthly Bulletin of Statistics
WORLD HEALTH ORGANIZATION, PALAIS DES NATIONS, Geneva, Switzerland
Epidemiological and Vital Statistics Report, published annually

United Kingdom, England and Wales, General Register Office, Somerset House, London, England
Occupational Mortality, Registrar General's Decennial Supplement, 1951

OTHER SOURCES OF PUBLISHED REPORTS

American Cancer Society, Inc., 219 East 42 Street, New York, New York 10017
Cancer, published monthly
Report on the Research Program, 1963

American Diabetes Association, Inc., 18 East 48 Street, New York, New York 10017
Proceedings, published annually
Diabetes Abstracts, published quarterly

American Heart Association, Inc., 44 East 23 Street, New York, New York 10010
Cardiovascular Diseases in the U.S., Facts and Figures, 1964
Modern Concepts of Cardiovascular Disease, published monthly

American Hospital Association, 840 North Lake Shore Drive, Chicago, Illinois 60611
Journal of the American Hospital Association, Guide Issue, August, 1963

American Medical Association, 535 North Dearborn Street, Chicago, Illinois 60610
Distribution of Physicians in the United States, 1963
Consumer Expenditures for Medical Care, 1956–61
Medical Education in the United States, 1962–63
Journal of the American Medical Association, published weekly

American Nurses Association, Inc., 10 Columbus Circle, New York, New York 10019
Facts About Nursing, published annually

American Public Health Association, 1790 Broadway, New York, New York 10019
Journal of the American Public Health Association, published monthly

American Rheumatism Association, 10 Columbus Circle, New York, New York 10019
Rheumatism Review, published biennially
Primer on the Rheumatic Diseases, 1959

American Statistical Association, 810 18 Street, N.W., Washington, D.C. 20009
Journal of the American Statistical Association, published quarterly

Health Information Foundation, University of Chicago, Chicago, Illinois 60637
Progress in Health Services, published bimonthly

Health Insurance Institute, 277 Park Avenue, New York, New York 10017
   Source Book of Health Insurance Data, published annually

Institute of Life Insurance, 277 Park Avenue, New York, New York 10017
   Life Insurance Fact Book, published annually

Metropolitan Life Insurance Company, 1 Madison Avenue, New York, New York 10010
   Statistical Bulletin, published monthly

Milbank Memorial Fund, 40 Wall Street, New York, New York 10005
   Milbank Memorial Quarterly

National Association for Mental Health, Inc., 10 Columbus Circle, New York, New York 10019
   Mental Hygiene, published quarterly
   Fifteen Indices: An Aid in Reviewing State and Local Mental Health and Hospital Programs

National Health Education Committe, Inc., 405 Lexington Avenue, New York, New York 10017
   Facts on the Major Killing and Crippling Diseases in the United States Today, 1964

National Institute of Demographic Studies, Paris, France
   Population, published quarterly

National Safety Council, 425 North Michigan Avenue, Chicago, Illinois 60611
   Accident Facts, published annually

National Tuberculosis Association, 1790 Broadway, New York, New York 10019
   American Review of Respiratory Diseases, published monthly

Population Association of America, Princeton, New Jersey
   Population Index, published quarterly

Population Investigation Committee, London School of Economics, London, England
   Population Studies, A Journal of Demography

Population Reference Bureau, Washington, D.C.
   Population Bulletin, published monthly

Society of Actuaries, 208 South LaSalle Street, Chicago, Illinois 60604
   Build and Blood Pressure Study, 1959

Index

Marital status *(Continued)*
 various countries, 42
Marks, Herbert, x
Marriage, 32–47
 age, 41–45, 67
 bigamous, 45
 business conditions, 38
 centers, 36
 chances of, 32, 38, 44
 childless, 19, 22, 68
 civil ceremony, 37
 color, 41
 common-law, 34, 37, 41
 dissolution, 61–76
 divorce, chances of, 61, 67
 duration before divorce, 67
 early, 42
 economic conditions, 38
 education, 38
 farmers, 37
 foreign-born war brides, 6, 40
 Gretna Greens, 36
 inter-racial, 41
 interval before birth of first
  child, 34
 laws, 35, 36, 45
 leap year, 33
 length of life of married couples,
  51
 licenses, 37
 mixed, 41
 number, 33
 number of children, 22
 occupation, 37
 premarital examinations, 35, 386
 religious ceremony, 37
 remarriages, 44
 rural areas, 37
 seasonal incidence, 33

Marriage *(Continued)*
 servicemen marrying overseas, 6,
  40
 social-economic status, 38
 trend, 32, 33, 38, 39
 United States compared with
  other countries, 34, 35, 42
 urban areas, 37
 war, 38, 39, 424
Massachusetts, Department of Public Health, 239, 369, 389
Maternal mortality, 30, 31, 105
Maternity
 hazards of, 30, 155, 182, 196
 health programs, 78, 389
Measles, 217
Median age of population, United
  States, 11
Medical care
 expenditures, 55, 57, 84, 85
 factor in improving mortality,
  99, 104
 insurance, 86, 90
 public health program, 45, 384,
  386, 389
Medical schools, 89
Medical science, effect on mortality
  reductions, 99–104, 302, 395,
  418
Men
 age
  at birth of children, 17, 18
  at marriage, 41–43, 45
  at which family responsibility
   is highest, 55
 body measurements, 360, 361
 chances of remarriage, 45
 income by occupation, 281
 length of reproductive period,
  17

Rural areas (*Continued*)
  divorce, 63
  families
    disruption, 52, 53
    - size, 50
  homicide, 270
  length of life, 404
  lightning, accidental death from, 255
  marriage rates, 37
  medical care, expenditures, 85
  mortality, 97
  motor vehicle accidents, 250
  pneumonia and influenza, 165
  public health administration, 377
  rheumatic fever, 193
  suicide, 263
  tuberculosis, 118
Russia, length of life, 393

Sabin, Dr. Albert, 218
Salk, Dr. Jonas, 218
Saranac Lake Sanatorium, 370
Sardinia, antimosquito campaign, 108
Scarlet fever, 218
Schistosomiasis, 346
Schizophrenia, 316, 324, 325
School
  absences, 81, 216
  accidents in, 255
  child health activities, 223
  children, age, 13
  enrollment, 13
  high, graduates, 13
  mentally handicapped children, 331
  years of, 13, 14
Sclerosis, multiple, 349
Scotland, length of life, 393

Senile psychoses, 316, 326
Separation, marital, 73–74
Sex ratio
  births, 18–25
  mortality, 95
  population
    age, 11, 229
    color, 11
Shattuck, Lemuel, 369
Shock, Dr. Nathan W., vii
Sickness, 77–91
  age incidence, 80, 233
  care, 77–91
    agencies, 78
  cases, 79, 81, 233
  causes, 82
  definition, 78
  disability, 79–81, 233
  drugs used, 83
  expenditures for medical care, 57, 84–86
  frequency, 80–82
  hospital care, 81, 83–85
  insurance for medical care, 86, 90
  medical care, 81, 83–85
    Veterans Administration, 84
  rate, 79
  school time lost from, 81, 216
  season, 79
  sex incidence, 80
  special services used, 83
  time lost, 81, 251, 286, 287
Silicosis, 284
Sleeping sickness, 344
Smallpox
  epidemics, United States, 342
  incidence throughout world, 342
  New York City, 382
  outbreaks, 342, 382